QUIET COURAGE

The True Story of a French World War II
War Bride and her American Soldier

Joy Ng

LifePath Press

D1410153

CONTENTS

DEDICATION

For Jimmy, my partner in the journey.
You gave me courage to spread my wings.

*If I take the wings of the morning,
and dwell in the uttermost parts of the sea;
even there shall thy hand lead me,
and thy right hand shall hold me.*
Psalm 139: 9, 10

ACKNOWLEDGMENTS

I am profoundly grateful to the people who supported and encouraged me in the production of this book. Suzanne told me her story and gave me permission to share it with the world. Melanie Dobson ignited the process with her book *Chateau of Secrets*. Leslie Leyland Fields challenged me to go bigger and taught me how to write a book. Marianne Kujawa contributed parts of her remarkable story. Suzanne's sister Nicole Kerlau and her brother Marc Chédotal, as well as Suzanne's children, shared their memories.

My sister, Heidi Payne, read, re-read, asked questions, made suggestions, and encouraged me every step of the way. Sean Griffin and Margot Starbuck lent their editing skills. Sarah Brazel, Leanne Ng, Suzanne Jensen, Alison Jensen, Rick Vinal, and Sonja Healey provided invaluable suggestions. Jeannine Leader prayed for me.

Most of all, I am thankful for my husband Jimmy. He wisely melted into the background while his mother and I talked for hours on end. He patiently drove me around France, Germany, and parts of the United States while helping me research Suzanne's story. He responded to countless versions of every chapter, picked up the slack around our home, solved numerous computer technology issues, and, most of all, he is my best friend and biggest cheerleader.

Suzanne Ng and Joy Ng

At Suzanne's kitchen table in 2019

PREFACE

The Story Unfolds

*When an old man dies, a library burns to the ground...
But if you can take something from your internal collection and share it—with one person or with the larger
world, on the page or in a story told—it takes on a life of its
own.*

—Old African Proverb and
Susan Orlean, *The Library Book*

T he Greatest Generation is a term coined by news anchor
Tom Brokaw to describe the men and women of the
United States and Western Europe who experienced the
Great Depression and World War II. Members of this generation
are often characterized by personal responsibility, humility, a
strong work ethic, thrift, faithful commitment, and silence.

Most of them rarely talked about their life experiences. This is
the story of one French girl from that generation.

Suzanne Ng became my mother-in-law when I married her
oldest son Jimmy in 1973. I called her Mom. Not only was she
my mother-in-law, but she was also one of my dearest friends.
She embodied all the characteristics of the Greatest Generation.
In addition, she was kind and generous, thoughtful and insight-
ful. At the age of 95, her memory was keen and she had unique
perspective because of the history she had lived.

We moved from Alaska to Washington State in 2014 to spend
more time with Mom. She and I enjoyed shopping together, tast-
ing samples at Costco, and going for rides with our chauffeur,
AKA my husband, Jimmy. Our best times were spent sharing our
lives and talking together. We loved to sit and chat with a cup of
tea in the cozy, immaculate kitchen of her manufactured home.

Like most people of her generation, Mom rarely spoke about

her life experiences. She did not share details about growing up in France, living through World War II, or becoming a war bride. One day, however, Mom began to tell me her stories, and she allowed me to put those stories on paper.

Our daughter, Sarah, asked me to read a book her college professor had written. *Chateau of Secrets*, by Melanie Dobson, became the catalyst for Mom to share her memories with me. It is historical fiction set in France during World War II. I read it aloud to Mom. We talked about how the story related to Mom's experiences during that time period in France. Then, one day, Mom showed me some old photo albums, and she told me about the people and places captured in those pictures.

One story led to another as the amazing, beautiful, and sometimes poignant story of her life unfolded for me. Sometimes her eyes shone as she told me about the happy times with Dad. Sometimes she giggled as she related their love story. Sometimes I could see in her the shy young French girl coming to America. Sometimes she had nightmares after sharing her stories of the occupation years.

I am sorry it was hard for Mom to tell her story, but it is important we know. This is part of our heritage. It is what made Mom and Dad who they were. In turn, it has had a profound impact on us, her children. Their legacy is also a small piece of the history of the world. Perhaps we will all be stronger, wiser, kinder, and more appreciative by understanding and remembering her story.

Often, when I stopped to see Mom, she had a story waiting for me. Usually, it was something she had been pondering during the night. When Mom reminisced, I took notes. Then, I went home and carefully recorded the stories. I always brought what I had written back to Mom, read it to her, and confirmed the account was accurate. She made corrections, added details, or was reminded of an entirely new story. The only thing she balked at in this narrative is when I wrote, "Bing was cute, and Suzanne was beautiful."

She said to me, "I didn't say that."

I replied, "I know you didn't. I said that. I have seen your pictures and you were, indeed, very beautiful." So, I left those words in my book.

MAP

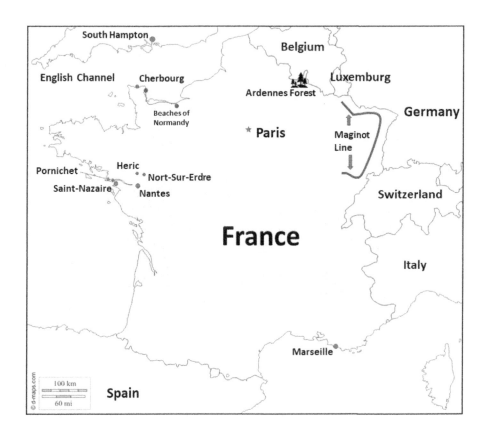

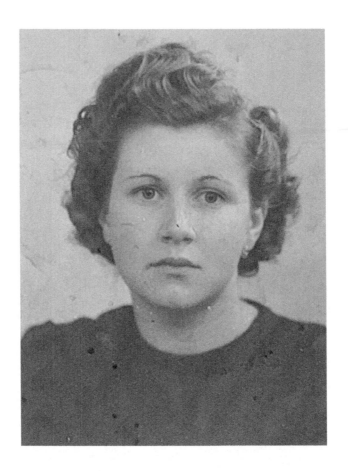

Suzanne Chédotal, 1944

1 HUSHED RUMORS

Freedom is not bought cheaply.
It has a cost; it imposes a burden.
—Ronald Reagan

June 6, 1944 began as any other workday for nineteen-year-old Suzanne Chédotal. Her meager breakfast consisted of bread spread with applesauce she had saved from the night before. She washed at the basin in her small rented room and dressed in the same patched clothes she wore day after day. The social life of the quiet French girl consisted mostly of her interaction with colleagues at the post office where she worked. Occasionally, she took the train home to visit her family on weekends. Her days were filled with work and finding food; there was little time for anything else.

Suzanne walked the one-quarter mile to work. Her steps quickened as she passed the ruins of her war-torn city. Charred walls, broken windows, and piles of stones mixed with concrete pieces bore witness to what once had been happy homes, thriving businesses, or architectural masterpieces. There was dust everywhere. Watching the ongoing destruction of the beautiful city grieved Suzanne. Even the historic Basilique Saint Nicolas near her place of employment was severely damaged. One-third of the magnificent neo-gothic church had been reduced to rubble; many of its beautiful stained-glass windows were broken. The tall center bell tower and some of the spires remained intact, stubbornly pointing toward heaven.

Suzanne enjoyed her job at the Banque Postal in the heart of Nantes, France. The large post office building processed the mail for the city, and it also functioned as the area bank. Suzanne's assignment, along with 39 other bookkeepers in a large room

9

on the third floor, was to process checks. They worked in teams of two, each pair sharing a desk. Suzanne calculated the tax on each transaction, entered the information into the individual's account, and kept track of the money coming in and going out.

It was interesting to work with the typewriter and adding machine; not many people had access to those modern machines in German-occupied France. The large, heavy adding machine sat on Suzanne's desk. It performed calculations through a clockwork-type mechanism. Suzanne pressed keys to enter the numbers to be added or subtracted and, then, pulled the crank handle on the side of the machine. The running total appeared on a narrow roll of paper, like a cash register tape.

The big room was a busy, noisy place with the constant tap, tap, tap of many typewriters, all in use at the same time. At the end of the day, Suzanne always had a long paper tape documenting the many transactions she had processed that day. Her work was sent to the fourth floor for auditing. If the day's total was as much as one *centime* (cent) off, the bookkeeper had to find the error. Suzanne rarely had any mistakes. Sometimes she helped her teammates find what they had done wrong. She was smart and diligent; she had earned the respect of both her supervisor and her co-workers.

That morning, Suzanne arrived at her place of employment early. She hung her jacket on the back of her chair and kept her purse close by. She wanted to be able to grab them quickly and take them with her when the air raid sirens wailed. The bombing of Nantes was awful. It was the Americans who were attacking her city. The bombs were intended to harm the Germans and the infrastructure they were using, but civilians often bore the brunt of the attacks. The French people wanted to be liberated, but they hated the bombing. Sometimes they even cursed the American bombers.

The convent where Suzanne had been living was destroyed by an errant bomb. She knew the people who were buried alive in the rubble that day. She had heard them crying. The memory haunted Suzanne.

The Americans were in England. Suzanne knew they were planning an offensive; rumors spread quietly despite the Nazi ban on communication with the free world. "How long will the bombing continue?" she wondered.

Suzanne settled into her desk and concentrated on the accounts in front of her. Time passed quickly when she was engrossed in her work. Suddenly, she was interrupted by the familiar sound of the warning sirens. Aircraft were approaching. There would be more bombing. She snatched her jacket and purse. Along with her co-workers, Suzanne rushed down two flights of concrete stairs. Clackety, clack, clack, clack. The sound of the wooden soles of their shoes echoed in the stairwell. On the street below, she joined hundreds of other pedestrians hurrying to the nearby, unfinished train tunnel. It would provide safety and shelter when the bombs fell. People came running from all directions. Clackety, clack, clack, clack, again, as the crowd rushed down the cement steps to the hard-packed sand at the entrance of the tunnel.

Inside the crowded tunnel, Suzanne shivered in the dark, damp, cool, air. The musty, earthy smell of wet sand was pervasive. Usually, while they waited in the shelter of the tunnel, they could hear the ominous sounds of bombs exploding in the distance. Today, they heard no explosions. All around her was a rumble of incomprehensible chatter mixed with hushed whispers, "The Americans have landed." No one spoke openly for fear of German retaliation.

The crowd waited impatiently in the tunnel for several hours until the all-clear signal was given. Suzanne was melancholy and thoughtful as she walked back to her office. "Where did the bombs fall today?" she wondered.

Weeks passed and Suzanne heard only vague rumors about the progress the Americans were making as they swept through Brittany. She did not know what was happening and she did not know what to expect. The Nazi occupiers continued to control Nantes. Though there were frequent air raid warnings, no more bombs fell on Nantes. Suzanne waited and wondered.

It was more than two months after the Allies landed in Normandy before an American vanguard entered Nantes and the Germans abandoned the city. The Germans left much destruction in their wake. They resolved to leave nothing the Allied Forces could use as they fought to liberate France; they burned, disabled, or destroyed as much infrastructure and supplies as possible.

Suzanne continued working at the post office. Hope grew as peace settled on the city and the restrictions imposed by the Nazis ceased to be a way of life. Suzanne knew, however, that there was much work to be done before her country would be free. Hitler had not yet surrendered; some parts of France were still under German control. It would take years for France to recover from the pain and destruction of the war. Many buildings in Nantes had been reduced to rubble. Train tracks, roads, and bridges were out. The shelves in the stores were empty. Friends and relatives did not know the fate of those who had disappeared or been taken by the Germans. Would they return home? French citizens were unaccustomed to speaking openly about their hopes and fears; they did not adjust quickly to their restored freedoms. Life was not going back to normal any time soon, but, at least in her corner of France, the war seemed to be over.

2   UNEXPECTED ENCOUNTER

That was a memorable day to me,
for it made great changes in me.
But it is the same with any life.
Imagine one selected day struck out of it,
and think how different its course would have been...
but for the formation of the first link
on one memorable day.
—Charles Dickens, *Great Expectations*

Shortly after Christmas of 1944, Suzanne developed a sore spot at the corner of the fingernail on her left middle finger; it was just a hangnail, really, but it became infected and painful. After years of a poor diet and the difficult conditions of the war, her immune system was not strong enough to fight the infection. She was unable to operate her typewriter or adding machine, so Suzanne's supervisor agreed to give her some time off to rest and heal. She decided to take advantage of this opportunity to visit her maternal grandmother and her Aunt Juliette and Uncle Alexandre in Héric. (She called them Tante and Tonton, which simply mean aunt and uncle in French.) It would be good to spend time with people she loved and trusted.

Suzanne packed a small bag and walked to the station. While she waited for the train, she looked across the street at the unkempt botanical garden. The long trenches, which had been dug across the gardens to provide refuge for citizens during air raids, still scarred the landscape. One day, she hoped, flowers would bloom again in the garden and lovers would walk hand in hand on its well-groomed paths. For now, she was thankful the threat of an air raid was past. She would not have to crouch in those trenches, watching bombs fall from the sky. Suzanne was happy to leave the scars of the city behind for a few days.

The train took Suzanne to Nort-Sur-Erdre. After a visit at home with her parents and her younger brothers and sisters, Suzanne rode her bicycle eight miles to the little town of Héric. Her heart warmed as she approached her aunt's house, which also contained the *boucherie* (butcher shop) they owned. This neighborhood held good memories for Suzanne; she had lived on this street when she was a little girl. She opened the front door without knocking and greeted each of the occupants with three kisses, as French people do—left cheek, right cheek, left cheek. How glad she was to be with her grandmother, Tante and Tonton, and her dear friend Therese. She had rarely been able to visit them during the past two years. She had missed them, and they had much to talk about.

They sat around the table in the comfortable kitchen adjacent to the butcher shop, enjoyed a simple meal together, and talked about the events of the past few months. They were thankful the Allied troops had liberated most of Brittany. They knew very few details of the war effort as the Americans and the British troops, joined by the French Resistance, continued to push the Germans back. They believed the Germans would be defeated.

There were so many things Suzanne hadn't known about during the occupation years. For example, in a secret room just above where she now sat, Tante had hidden Therese's husband, Barik. He had been captured and held as a prisoner of war by the Germans until he escaped and made his way home. It was unsafe for him to stay in his own house, so Tante made a place for him in the little attic room behind the maid's quarters. They put a wardrobe over the door leading to the hiding place; no one could tell it was there. The only other entrance was a door which opened to the outside; it was way up high and hidden by thick vines. He lived there, undetected by the Germans, for two years. Not even any of their neighbors knew he was there. (No one mentioned the affair he had with the maid. It was better to forgive and move on. Suzanne, however, never quite forgave

Barik for cheating on Therese, nor for taking advantage of the vulnerable young maid.)

They talked about Suzanne's siblings. Albert was 14 when the war engulfed France. He kept a low profile during the occupation years. Suzanne had not seen him at all in the past two years. Whatever he had been doing was secret. They were all worried about him. Conscription was mandatory for young French men when they turned 18; Albert's 18th birthday had come and gone. They wondered where he was, and they hoped he was safe.

Tante asked Suzanne about her sore finger. Suzanne explained the problem, and Tante examined it carefully. It was terribly swollen; thick yellow pus oozed from around her fingernail. Tante lamented that they did not have proper medical supplies. She soaked some bread in hot milk, applied it to the infected area, and wrapped clean rags around Suzanne's finger. It was the best they could do.

Tonton told Suzanne about the contingent of American soldiers camping at the *Chateau de Blain,* the castle not far from Héric. They felt safe with the Americans keeping close watch on the pocket of Germans who were holding out just 30 miles away at the U-boat base in Saint-Nazaire; 28,000 Nazi soldiers remained there in a highly fortified complex, completely enclosed by huge concrete bunkers. The Americans patrolled behind Héric's Catholic church, just two blocks from the *boucherie.* Sometimes the Americans interacted with the German soldiers who were also on patrol; they talked and exchanged things like cigarettes and coffee. They believed the war was almost over, and they hoped there would not be a battle for Saint-Nazaire.

Tante cautioned Suzanne about the American soldiers who came to town in the evenings to visit the pool room, the bars, and the cafés. They liked to hang out where the girls were. There was one particular American, however, who didn't visit the bars. He came, instead, to the butcher shop almost every evening to buy a small piece of steak. He didn't drink or smoke, and he wasn't interested in the kind of girls who frequented the bars. He liked steak better. He was gregarious, and he had a friendly smile. He didn't speak French, but they always managed to communicate when he came to their *boucherie*. Tante and Tonton looked forward to his daily visits.

They teased that maybe he would come that evening. "You should meet him, Suzanne," suggested Tante. "He is so cute!"

Suzanne blushed. She was not looking for a boyfriend, and certainly not an American boyfriend. It was so pleasant to eat dinner together, to laugh, and to talk freely of the future without the oppression of the German occupation.

Tante and Tonton talked about their *boucherie*. French people still had ration coupons to manage the supply and demand of meat, as well as many other products. There was more meat available for French residents than when the Germans were in charge, but it was still in short supply. It would take a long time for the ravaged farms to be able produce enough food to meet the needs of the population.

Tonton was able to go out to the countryside to purchase some cattle and pigs. He was pleased his butcher shop had fresh beef for sale. Tante was once again able to sell pâté, pork sausage, and smoked ham. She made those delicious French favorites in the covered carport behind the butcher shop. She carefully tended the smoker at the back corner of the carport to maintain the proper temperature and amount of smoke for the ham and sausages. She baked the pâté in the brick, wood-fired oven at the back of Therese's bakery, just three doors up the street. Therese used the oven for baking bread in the mornings, but it was available for Tante to use in the afternoons.

The little bell jingled softly as the front door of the butcher shop opened. Tante and Tonton got up from the table and hurried to greet the customer they had been expecting. It was the young American soldier they had told Suzanne about.

Private First Class Bing Ng entered the little shop. A large storefront window next to the door looked out onto the main street. It let the soft evening light fill the immaculate shop. The smell of raw beef and the aroma from the smoker behind the shop mingled in an appetizing way. In the back right-hand corner of the shop, a large walk-in ice box held a fresh quarter of beef, hanging from the ceiling. Tonton refilled the ice box with fresh ice every day to keep the precious meat cool.

Tonton already knew what cut of beef Bing wanted. He tied his big white apron over the black and white checked pants and white top he was wearing. The men talked pleasantly while Tonton carried the large quarter of beef to the big butcher block cutting table in front of the window. They communicated quite well, even without a common language; smiles and gestures are the same in every language and the Army had issued Bing a small English-French phrase book.

Tonton sharpened his gleaming stainless-steel knife on a gray sharpening stone. He carefully cut and trimmed a tender, marbled, piece of fresh steak. He weighed it on the balance scale at the side of the table, wrapped it in white butcher paper, and handed it to Bing.

Bing turned to face the other side of the shop where Tante stood behind the cash register. He took a minute to appreciate the delicacies in the glass enclosed case which displayed pâté, sausage, and smoked meats. Tante entered the purchase price in the cash register, smiled at Bing, hesitated, and then called out in a cheery voice, "Suzanne, will you please bring me some change?"

Suzanne put down the dish she was carrying and retrieved the cash from its hiding place. She entered the shop through the side door which connected the *boucherie* to the living quarters. Tante greeted Suzanne with an impish grin and introduced her to the young soldier. Suzanne blushed as she shyly acknowledged the introduction. He was indeed cute. His soft Asian features accentuated his warm smile. He looked sharp in his olive drab army uniform and garrison cap. He appeared to be very young.

Bing noticed Suzanne's finger was wrapped in a rag. He let her know he would like to look at it. She hesitantly gave him her hand. He carefully unwrapped the rag from around her finger and examined the injury. She could see the concern on his face.

He motioned that she should wait there; he would be right back. Then, he hurried out the door.

Tante couldn't help teasing Suzanne, "Suzanne, bring me some change. There is a cute American here!" Suzanne protested, but she was clearly interested in this kind soldier.

Bing hurried back to the Army encampment. He was a cook and an aide for the American Army Medic Group; he had access to their medical supplies. He returned in less time than Suzanne had expected. He must have run the whole way.

Suzanne met him at the door. She hadn't had a new dress or new shoes in a very long time, but her slim figure was attractive in the clean, pressed, patched clothes. She looked beautiful with her soft brown hair framing her flushed face. She was usually shy, but this friendly American set her at ease.

Tante invited Bing into the family kitchen. They sat at the table while he tended to Suzanne's finger. She winced as he cleaned her wound. He applied sulpha cream from a small tube and gently dressed it with a clean, white bandage, all the while tenderly speaking words she did not know, but clearly understood. She would keep it dry and he would return the next day to change the bandage.

They spent the rest of the evening together, laughing and communicating. It was so pleasant to be with her family and friends... and with Bing. When Bing finally left to return to the encampment, there was a lilt in his step that hadn't been there before. Suzanne hummed softly as she got ready for bed and closed the shutter on the guestroom's window.

Suzanne awoke early the next morning. She could hear the activity in the street, so she knew it was morning, even though the thick wooden shutters kept the morning light out of the tiny bedroom. She snuggled under the soft, down-filled duvet for a little longer, pondering the events of the evening before. Who was that handsome soldier? She chided herself for her interest in the young American. She knew so little about him, yet the memory of the pleasant evening and the kind soldier made her heart skip a beat. He had so tenderly cared for her injured finger. She had felt comfortable with Bing. She smiled, hoping he would return that evening.

Bing did, indeed, return that evening, and the next, and the next. Each time he came he tended to Suzanne's sore finger, applying more sulfa cream and changing the bandage. The pain eased, the infection decreased, and the wound began to heal.

Suzanne spent the days visiting with friends and relatives and helping as much as she could, despite her bandaged finger. She strolled along the narrow streets of the town she knew so well. She kept track of the time announced by the old church bell tower as she anticipated Bing's arrival at the end of the day. One afternoon, Suzanne was surprised to see Bing driving a 16-wheel truck through the narrow streets of the town. She could hardly believe her eyes! He was so cute and so young; he looked like a little kid driving that big truck.

Héric had only three main streets. The two-story brick and stucco houses stood adjacent to each other in straight lines. They had attic spaces, steep tile roofs, and windows with shutters that could be closed against the noise of the street, the cold of the winter, or the light of the long summer days. Businesses occupied most of the first-floor rooms facing the narrow street; the families lived above or adjacent to their shops. The love story of Suzanne's own parents, Alphonse and Laurence Chédotal, had unfolded in this setting.

3   SUZANNE'S HERITAGE

No one has yet explained how war prevents war.
Nor has anyone been able to explain away the fact that
war begets conditions that beget further war.
—General Dwight D. Eisenhower

Alphonse waited on the street in front of the *mairie* (town hall) for the arrival of his bride. He kept his eyes trained in the direction Laurence would come from her home, just a few blocks away. When he saw her walking confidently toward him, his face lit up.

Laurence is a French feminine name, pronounced
with the accent on the second syllable.

She was beautiful in her white, ankle-length gown with layer upon layer of soft ruffles. Her long, delicate veil touched the ground. Matching white shoes and stockings completed the fashionable wedding outfit. Laurence quickened her pace when she saw her groom. He was always so handsome, even when he wasn't dressed in the three-piece suit and bow tie he wore on their wedding day.

Together, Alphonse and Laurence climbed the front steps of the town hall where the legal wedding ceremony would take place. They exchanged vows, signed their names in the official leather-bound Book of Marriages, and became Monsieur and Madame Alphonse Chédotal. They received their *Livre de Famille* (Family Book); it documented their marriage and would one day record the births of their children.

Then, the newlyweds walked hand-in-hand to the big stone church in the center of Héric for the religious service that followed the civil ceremony. Their union was blessed by the local

Catholic priest. Church bells rang out the happy news as family and friends wished the young couple well.

Alphonse and Laurence Chédotal

Suzanne's parents were married on August 28, 1923 in her mother's hometown. Laurence had lived most of her life in Héric. Alphonse was from Saint-Nazaire, 30 miles to the west.

Saint-Nazaire sits on the north bank of the Loire River Estuary near the Atlantic Ocean. During the last half of the 19th century, the construction of railroads and the growth of its seaport caused the small French fishing village to grow from just 800 inhabitants to 30,000 people. It became home to great shipyards. Many transatlantic voyages commenced at the Port of Saint-Nazaire. Rivers and canals in the low, flat land connected Saint-Nazaire with the rest of the country.

Alphonse Chédotal was born in 1899 in Saint-Nazaire. His mother died when he was very young, leaving Alphonse and his father all alone. Eventually, his father, Joseph Chédotal, remarried. His stepmother, Alexandrine, was always kind to Alphonse. She had no other children. The Chédotal family was poor, but they were happy.

Alphonse was smart and hardworking, with an infectious personality. He seemed to light up a room when he entered. He was invited to live with the family of a teacher who gave him the opportunity to attend high school and trade school. Alphonse gratefully accepted the generous offer; his family could not afford to pay for the lodging or the tuition. Alphonse was captivated by the latest technology and he eagerly grasped new ideas. He was innovative and visionary; he also enjoyed working with his hands and creating new things. He became one of the first electricians in Western France.

The Great War began in 1914 when Alphonse was 15. It lasted for almost five years. The Allied Powers, including France, Russia, Britain, and the United States, stood against the Central Powers which consisted of Germany, Austria-Hungary, Bulgaria, and the Ottoman Empire. Germany wanted power, prestige, and more land for her expanding population.

In Europe, most of the fighting happened on two fronts. The Western Front was a line from Belgium to Switzerland, from which Germany sought to invade France. On the Eastern Front, Germany pressed into Russia. World War I, as it came to be called, reached into other parts of the world, as well. It involved each power's colonial empire, spreading the conflict to Africa and across the globe. French Indochina (what is now Vietnam) was under French protectorate. France sought to use Indochina's natural resources and manpower to help fight the war.

For the first time in history, airplanes, submarines, tanks, chemical weapons, and radio communications were used in warfare. Bigger, more powerful guns and bombs were employed. Never before had there been a war of such great scope and magnitude; it was one of the deadliest wars in history. The conflict directly caused approximately 21 million military and civilian deaths. In addition, the movement of large numbers of troops around the globe contributed to the Spanish flu pandemic which caused 50 million additional deaths worldwide. More military personnel died from the flu than were killed in combat.

The Great War profoundly impacted Alphonse's hometown. The Allied Forces chose Saint-Nazaire as one of their most important entry harbors into Western Europe. More than 30,000 American troops were stationed in Saint-Nazaire from 1917-1919. The troops lived side-by-side with French people, sharing their cultures and their lives. No battles were fought in this area, but Saint-Nazaire was key to the support of the war effort on the Western Front.

Like all other able-bodied French men, Alphonse was obliged to serve in the French military for at least three years. He joined the French Navy when he turned 18 and was sent to defend France's interest in French Indochina. He survived the sinking of his ship in the Suez Canal. He was able to save just one of his personal possessions when he abandoned ship—his fountain pen. He kept the pen as a reminder of his experience.

It was believed the Great War would be the war to end all wars. An armistice to stop the fighting was signed at the eleventh hour, on the eleventh day, of the eleventh month of 1918. (This date became known as Armistice Day and is still celebrated in the United States as Veterans Day.) The armistice was followed in 1919 by the Treaty of Versailles which officially ended the war. The peace was shaky, however. The Allies wanted to punish Germany. Germany was unhappy with the way she was treated; she was blamed for the war and forced to pay large reparations. Troops from both sides returned to their homes around the world and resumed their lives, but Germany's resentment festered.

After WWI, Alphonse was hired by the electric company in Héric. It was a rewarding job at that time and in that place. Cutting-edge electric power was becoming available and affordable for the general population. Alphonse was a pioneer in the new field; he connected many homes to the grid, bringing electric lights and modern conveniences to his neighbors.

One of the first electrical appliances used in French homes was the electric iron. No more did busy homemakers have to repeatedly heat their irons on the stove or fill them with hot coals. Those new irons were finicky, though. Many women brought their irons to Alphonse for repair; it seemed he could fix anything. He relished the new electric appliances, and he could envision the great potential of electrical energy.

While working in Héric, a lovely local girl caught his eye. Laurence Harrouet was the oldest daughter of a prominent family in the town. Her parents sent her to an exclusive finishing school in Nantes, the largest city in the area. She returned to her hometown as a well-educated, accomplished, fashionable young woman. She was the most beautiful girl in town; everyone said so. She was also very talented. She could paint, draw, and make music. She seemed a little classier than most of the other inhabitants of this little country town. Alphonse was also more educated than most of the people in Héric. Alphonse and Laurence were drawn to each, not only by the intellectual bond they shared, but also by their love of music. Laurence played the mandolin and Alphonse played the banjo. They loved playing duets together.

After their wedding, the young couple made their home in the tight-knit community of Laurence's family. Their daughter, Suzanne Pierrette Jaqueline Chédotal, was born on October 20, 1924 in Héric, France. Suzanne was the first of seven children born to Laurence and Alphonse. Albert, Raymond, Lucette, Nicole, Bernard, and Marc would arrive over a span of the next 20 years.

4   FORMATIVE YEARS

During the formative years, a child's character and most important individual traits and ways are being formed. Children absorb what they see at home as a sponge. Learning is happening at an unimaginable pace and with intensity that won't be repeated at any other point in their life.

—Elena Verigo

Church bells called parishioners to Sunday services as six-year-old Suzanne, holding tightly to her younger brother's hand, hurried across the narrow street in front of their house. The children stopped to peer through the window of their grandfather's *boucherie* (butcher shop) before Suzanne tugged at the heavy front door. On most Sunday mornings, Suzanne took Albert to see their grandfather at the butcher shop. He would give them just enough money to buy a piece of candy.

A little bell jingled when the children entered the shop. Their grandfather appeared at the open door of the walk-in icebox. "Bonjour, Grandpère!" Suzanne and Albert exclaimed in unison. Their grandfather smiled broadly. He exchanged the customary three kisses with each of the children. Then, as they expected, he reached into his pocket and handed them a few centimes. "Merci, merci," responded the two happy children.

Suzanne and Albert ran to the candy store next to the church. Suzanne examined all the possibilities before choosing an orange *sucette* (lollipop). She liked to carefully consider her options, but she always chose an orange *sucette*. Albert was more adventurous in his selections.

Suzanne spent her formative years, in the heart of Héric. She knew most of the inhabitants of her little town. The people who lived on her street were relatives or close friends. They shared their daily activities. Suzanne was a quiet, pleasant, well-behaved little girl who was welcome in her neighbors' homes and shops. She was well-liked, and she often skipped from one house to another.

The first seven years of a child's life are known as the formative years because so much of the child's growth and development takes place during this time. These years are crucial for physical, intellectual, and social-emotional development. The years Suzanne spent in Héric laid the foundation for the woman she would become.

The front doors of the houses and shops opened right onto the street. Many people set chairs just outside their front doors. There was no need for a porch; they sat in those chairs, watched the activity in the street, and visited with friends. A few people owned cars or trucks; those vehicles shared the paved street with pedestrians, bicycles, motorcycles, and horse-drawn buggies and wagons.

At the corner of the block where Suzanne lived with her family was a bicycle and motorcycle repair shop. It belonged to Suzanne's parents. Suzanne's father was busy working as an electrician, so they hired a mechanic to run the shop. A Michelin Man hung over the door of the repair shop. Like Suzanne, the Michelin Man character was born in France. Its comical white body was made of bloated rubber tires stacked on top of each other. Suzanne often looked at the little man with wonderment.

*Suzanne with her parents and siblings
in front of their home*

Adjacent to the repair shop was the billiard room and café Suzanne's mother ran. She served coffee and soft drinks, but no food. A delivery man brought wooden cases of glass-bottled drinks to the café every week. They did not have enough money to buy those wonderful soft drinks for themselves. Sometimes, the delivery man gave Suzanne and her little brothers a bottle to share. It was so delicious and such a treat. Ice was also delivered to the café each week. It kept the bottled beverages cool, but they did not serve ice in the glasses.

Behind the café was Suzanne's family's kitchen. The kitchen also served as the dining room and gathering place for the family. Though the kitchen had a window facing the courtyard behind the house, there was a storage shed just outside the window. It blocked most of the light which could have come through the window. Consequently, the kitchen was very dark. There was no running water in the house. They carried water in buckets from the pump in the courtyard. Upstairs were two bedrooms and the bathroom. They had no refrigerator; they kept food cool in the dark, old, creepy basement.

At mealtimes, Maman (Mom) set Suzanne's little brothers,

Albert and Raymond, on the lowest step of the staircase leading to the second floor. She sat on a chair facing them and fed them in turn from the same bowl. Sometimes she gave Suzanne a taste, as well. There was no fancy store-bought baby food in those days. Her mother mixed bread with water or made a white sauce with flour, milk, and sugar to feed to the little ones.

Albert was sedate and rarely got into mischief, but he was not a happy little boy. They called him "Yeng-yeng," imitating the sound he made when he so frequently whined or complained. On the other hand, Raymond always had a twinkle in his eyes; he was happy and active. He couldn't sit still, and he got into everything. Raymond had a little bicycle. It had no peddles, but he could sit on it and use his feet to make it go very fast.

Beside Suzanne's house was the home of her Great Aunt Modeste and Uncle Pierre Sezestre. (Uncle Pierre was Suzanne's godfather and he is the reason one of her middle names is Pierrette.) They were one of the few families at that time and place who owned a truck. During the week, Uncle Pierre collected butter and eggs from the farms surrounding Héric. On Fridays, they drove the truck to Saint-Nazaire to sell the eggs and butter at a big covered market.

French people typically have two or more given names. Traditionally, first names come from the Roman Catholic Calendar of Saints. Second or third names often honor a godparent.

Next to their house was a covered alley leading into the courtyard behind the houses. The courtyard took up the entire interior of the block. It contained the little building where Suzanne's mother kept supplies for the café, the carport where Aunt Modeste and Uncle Pierre kept their truck, and a storage building for the products they collected from the farms. There was also a sawmill at the back of the alley. On the other side of the alley, a tailor shop and a little store which sold chickens and rabbits completed that side of the block.

Across the street lived Suzanne's grandmother and grandfather. Adjacent to her grandparents' house was a very old stone building with thick walls and tiny windows. It must have been hundreds of years old. It was used just for storage, but it added a bit of historical charm to the neighborhood.

Her grandparents had a cow. They let the cow graze in a pasture about a quarter mile from the house. Suzanne was sometimes tasked with bringing the cow home to be milked. She always took a stick with her, but she never needed it. The gentle cow walked obediently beside her on the street all the way home.

On the other side of her grandparents' house was the *boucherie*. Tante and Tonton lived beside and above the butcher shop. Their daughter, Dede, was younger than Suzanne, and she was a *fille unique* (only child). Aunt Juliette was busy working in the *boucherie*, so they took in a young girl named Rene to help. Rene was from a very poor family. Although they were kind to Rene, they never treated her like family. She took care of Dede, and she helped with the butchering and the housework.

Before Suzanne was born, her grandparents ran the butcher shop together. When their son, Alexandre, was old enough, he took over Grandmère's place in the *boucherie*. He and Grandpère wore the typical French butcher's uniform when they worked —black and white checked pants, a white coat, and a big white apron. When Alexandre married Juliette, she began making pork pâté, sausages, and smoked hams to sell.

Suzanne often popped into the butcher shop. It was a happy, friendly place. (She could not have imagined the life-changing encounter which would transpire within those walls more than a decade in the future.)

Uncle Alexandre had an exceptionally beautiful, well-trained horse which he used for harness racing. The horse pulled a two-wheeled cart, called a sulky, and raced at a specific gait. Uncle Alexandre took pride in his horse. They won many races together. Suzanne liked to look at the beautiful horse. She never rode a horse, however, nor did she ever ride in the sulky.

Next to the butcher shop was a small general store. Beyond the general store was a café, and then a bakery. The bakery belonged to close family friends, Therese and Beric Fraud and their baby daughter, Michelle. Therese and Suzanne, despite their age difference, were kindred spirits. Their friendship began when Suzanne was just a little girl and it strengthened as Suzanne grew older.

The bakery was a busy place. French bread has a well-deserved reputation for quality, taste, and texture. Its chewy crust and tender interior are hard to replicate. French people rarely make bread themselves at home; they leave that task to the professionals. A representative from each of the households in town visited the *boulangerie* (bakery) daily to purchase fresh loaves of bread or baguettes. Customers walked or rode their bikes to the little shop. They bought just enough bread for the day's meals and the next morning's breakfast. They would come again the following day for fresh bread. Suzanne watched people leave the bakery with a long baguette tucked under an arm, standing on end in a woven shopping basket, or tied to the back of a bicycle. The crusty, golden-brown bread was not wrapped in paper or plastic.

Suzanne loved to visit Therese at the bakery. The delicious smell of freshly baked bread spilled out onto the street. A little bell jingled when Suzanne opened the big front door. Inside was a counter with a cash register. Loaves of bread were piled on shelves beside the counter. There were long loaves and round loaves. Baguettes stood on end behind the counter. On weekends, Therese baked brioche. She made them with yeast, butter, and eggs. They were light and puffy, big and delicious. Of all the wonderful breads Therese made, the brioche were Suzanne's favorites.

Therese made the bread in the kitchen behind the shop. On the back wall was a brick oven. The oven opened into the kitchen, but there was also access to the oven from the courtyard outside. Therese could feed wood into the brick oven without bringing the wood inside the building.

A spring fair was held on the streets of Héric every year. Farmers came to town to sell their animals. It was an exciting time, and Suzanne eagerly anticipated the annual event. In front of the shops and houses on Suzanne's block, the farmers set up pens for little piglets. It was so much fun to watch the baby pigs wriggle and squeal. Suzanne loved to pet them. Cattle were displayed further down the street. Other farmers came from all over the area to dicker over prices and buy the pigs and cattle.

The year Suzanne was seven, Therese asked if she would like to take a tray filled with brioche and sell them at the fair. Suzanne was delighted with the idea; she wanted to be trusted with important tasks. Though she was a quiet, reserved little girl, she went bravely up and down the street selling the brioche for 25 *centimes* each. She did not have to work very hard to convince the farmers and spectators to buy the tempting brioche. When the tray was empty, Suzanne went back to the bakery to give Therese the money and refill the tray. Suzanne was proud to be helping Therese.

At the end of the block where Suzanne lived, the street widened into the *Place de la Republique*, an open area with a pond. This public space belonged to the town. Suzanne's second cousin (Pierre and Modeste's son) lived across from the *Place de la Republique* with his wife and their three small children.

Saint Nicolas Catholic Church was the center piece of the town. It was located just around the block from Suzanne's house. Suzanne could not see the steeple of the old stone church from her front door, but its bells ordered their days. They struck the time every hour. The bells also signaled weddings and deaths. The bell was rung three times for the death of a woman or three times three times for the death of a man. Then, the bells tolled one stroke for each year of the deceased's life. Maman listened attentively when the bells tolled, and she carefully counted each sound. Often, she could tell by the bells who had died.

Suzanne's parents rarely went to church, but Suzanne sometimes attended Sunday services with her grandparents. Their family had a pew near the front of the sanctuary. Suzanne didn't enjoy the services because they were in Latin, which she didn't understand.

It was the fashion for little girls to have white scarves made of rabbit fur to wear around their necks. Sometimes the furs had a tail on one end and a head on the other end, with fake eyes. Suzanne liked to wear hers; she ran her fingers over the soft fur, as if it was a kitten.

Suzanne walked the few blocks to and from the town's one-room schoolhouse by herself. She delighted in stopping at the saddlery she passed on her way home. The comfortable smell of leather filled the shop, and the owner was always kind to her.

A bus made regular stops in Héric, but the town had no train station. A shuttle traveled eight miles from Héric to the bigger town of Nort-Sur-Erdre every morning and every evening. It connected the two towns and gave the residents of Héric access to the train station at Nort-Sur-Erdre.

One fall day, Suzanne's Great Aunt Marie invited Suzanne to go with her to the country. They would help her cousins butcher a pig. Together, they took the shuttle to Nort-Sur-Erdre and walked far out into the country; it was a long walk for a little girl. They stayed four days. Suzanne slept with her cousin in a feather and wool tick bed on the floor. It was soft and warm, but it had no support at all.

Suzanne didn't like when they killed the pig; the pig screamed! After that, the work was fun. Other relatives gathered from the surrounding area to help. There was much to be done. They made sausage and ham, mousse, and *pâté de campagne*. (*Pâté de campagne is a* coarse grind of lean and fatty pork with spices and a little liver. The humble, yet delicious, dish makes good use of trimmings. It is often served with French bread as the first course of a meal.) They used every part of the pig. It was a pleasant family reunion; they were happy, working hard together. When the work was completed, her cousin gave Suzanne and her aunt a ride home in a horse-drawn carriage.

One day, an unfamiliar farm truck drove to the front of Suzanne's house. Suzanne watched wide-eyed as a farmer and her father's co-worker opened the back of the truck. There, on an old mattress in the bed of the truck, slept her father. He did not awaken when they carried him into the house and up the stairs. All that day, and the next day, and the day after that, her father did not wake up. Adults spoke in hushed tones and told the children to be quiet. Suzanne learned her father had been working on electrical wires high up at the top of a pole when he had fallen to the ground. He remained unconscious for two weeks. Her mother tenderly cared for him until he awoke and regained his strength. He was never quite the same, however. He became angry easily and he sometimes lost his temper.

The Chédotal family lived happily in Héric until Suzanne's father got a promotion; he was put in charge of the electric company in Nort-Sur-Erdre. It was time for the family to begin a new chapter in a new town.

5 THE NEW HOUSE

A house is made with walls and beams;
a home is built with love and dreams.
—Ralph Waldo Emerson

The Chédotal family moved to Nort-Sur-Erdre in 1931, just as the Great Depression began to affect France. The town was so named because it sits on the River Erdre, about 23 miles north of Nantes. The Nantes-Brest Canal, with its locks, bridges, and towpaths, intersects the Erdre River at Nort-Sur-Erdre. It was surrounded by small family farms. Nort-Sur-Erdre had a train station and a bus stop, making it easy to get from this small community to the big city of Nantes and beyond. Nort, as the family often called the town, had a population of close to 4,000 people. Though Nort was bigger than Héric, it was also a tight-knit community.

Suzanne's father bought a long, narrow lot at 18 Rue des Brosses, a few blocks from the town center. A train track ran along the back edge of the property. The town's main street bordered the front of the lot. Across the street was a row of small, single-story houses which had been built 100 years before.

Alphonse had a lovely, modern house built for the family. He hired an architect to design the house with many of his own ideas incorporated into the plan. The family rented a little house nearby for almost two years while the new house was being built. They enjoyed walking to the lot and watching the new house take shape.

Soon after moving into the rented house, Suzanne's mother became very sick with kidney trouble. She was able to get out of bed just to go lay on the chaise in the kitchen/living area. Suzanne was only seven, but, with her mother's directions, she was able to accomplish most of the household tasks by herself. She peeled potatoes and added the ingredients to make stew.

Suzanne was happy to help. She liked to be entrusted with responsibility by her parents, and she tried to do her best. She felt grown-up as she swept the floor and watched over her brothers.

Raymond continued to be a challenge. Though he was a good-natured, happy little boy, he frequently got into mischief. Suzanne had to watch him very closely. He brought his little bike with him when the family moved to Nort. Raymond loved to ride his bike as fast as he could down a steep hill near the house. One day, as he was barreling down the hill, he encountered a farmer with a herd of cows crossing the road. Raymond was unable to stop before running into the cows. He was hurt, but not badly enough to keep him from continuing to race down that hill.

That year, Christmas was special for Suzanne. Maman was feeling better, so the whole family walked together to the town hall for the annual Christmas play, performed by the town's school children. There was excitement in the air. A beautiful Christmas tree graced the hall. The town residents sang Christmas carols together, cheered for the performance, and greeted each other, "Joyeux Noel!"

After the play, Suzanne's family returned to their home for dinner. Though they never decorated their own house for Christmas, they always had a special Christmas dinner. Suzanne's father went out into the country to buy a goose. Her mother stuffed it with chestnut dressing. Suzanne did not like the strong taste and smell of the greasy goose meat, but the special dinner was fun. They had mashed potatoes and vegetables. For dessert, her mother made orange slices and pineapple pieces soaked in kirsch, a clear, colorless brandy made from cherries.

After dinner, the children prepared for the arrival of *Père Noel* (Father Christmas), the French version of Santa Claus. They placed their shoes by the fireplace and filled them with carrots and treats for Père Noel's donkey, *Gui*. (Gui is the French word for mistletoe.) In the morning, Suzanne and her siblings would find an orange and some candy in their shoes.

The Chédotal children rarely got any other Christmas presents. That year, however, Suzanne received a gift. She was the only one of the children to get a real Christmas present. Her parents wanted to reward her for her hard work and sweet attitude when helping while Maman was sick. Suzanne's hand shook as she opened the package and found a beautifully decorated wooden pencil box. A crane was painted on its smoothly sanded top. Suzanne cherished the special gift and she kept it always. She studied the crane and learned to copy the picture. (Suzanne continued to enjoy drawing cranes. At the age of 95, she had a picture of cranes hanging in her living room. It evoked happy childhood memories.)

Finally, the new two-story house was ready to move into. Though the house incorporated many characteristics typical of French architecture, it also had some unique features that no other French houses in the area had at that time. For example, their new home was the first house in town to have indoor plumbing. Suzanne's father was delighted to have the opportunity to put into practice some of the innovations he had been dreaming about.

The exterior was made of brick and stucco with a steep slate roof and a tall front gable. The front door, with its round window, opened onto a porch with a hipped roof. The windows had metal shutters which were closed at night, as if putting the house to sleep. The house sat very close to the street with a fence defining the narrow front yard. Suzanne's mother planted flowers in front of the house.

The front door opened into a large hallway. (Even though there was a nice front entryway, family always entered the house through the back door to the kitchen.) To the left of the front entryway, was the family dining room, with a big table and a cozy fireplace. A radio sat on the mantle of the fireplace. The kitchen was behind the dining room. On the other side of the front hall was a parlor with a formal dining set. The parlor was used just for special occasions. At the end of the hall behind the parlor were the bathroom and the master bedroom.

A staircase began in the center hallway and led to the second floor. There was a big landing at the halfway point. The wooden steps were nicely polished, clean, shiny, and slippery. The children slid down the stairs on their bellies, headfirst on pillows. They were usually reprimanded for sliding down the steps, but they did it anyway; it was so much fun.

At the top of the stairs was a common area with a banister lining the stairwell. Suzanne could look over the banister at the stairs coming up from the first floor. All the upstairs doorways opened into the common area. There were two bedrooms; one for the girls and one for the boys. Between the two rooms was a large walk-in closet with rods for hanging clothes; most French houses had no closets, only wardrobes in which to keep the clothes. There was also a door into a windowless, slanted-ceiling storage room. The big trunks Suzanne's father got when he was in the Navy were kept there.

Raymond and Albert shared the boys' room. In the girls' room, Suzanne shared a bed with the newest addition to the family, Lucette. (Her nickname was Lulu.) Lulu was little when she started sleeping with Suzanne. Suzanne wanted to cuddle the darling baby girl, but Lulu did not like to cuddle. She complained fiercely at Suzanne's attempts to be affectionate with her.

The new house had many modern conveniences. It had electric lights, an electric stove, an electric refrigerator, and electric heaters. There was a well in the basement of the house. It had a thick, heavy, concrete top, so none of the children could fall into it. Suzanne's father installed an electric pump; it brought water to the kitchen and the bathroom. In the bathroom there was running water to the sink, the bidet, and the bathtub.

At first, they had only cold running water. They heated water for their baths on the stove. Suzanne's father soon developed a hot water heater for the bathroom. He hung a barrel on the wall above the tub. Then, he installed an electric heating element inside the barrel. It was luxurious to have hot running water for their baths.

There was no toilet in the house; an outhouse stood at the back of the lot near the chicken coop. They used newspapers for toilet paper. At night, they could use a chamber pot or a hygienic bucket with a tight-fitting lid so they wouldn't have to go outside in the dark or the cold to the outhouse. In the morning, Suzanne's mother emptied the hygienic bucket and the chamber pots into the outhouse and cleaned them well.

The basement of the new house was not at all creepy like their basement in Héric had been. It was new and clean and all concrete. In addition to the well, it held big barrels of wine, which they purchased from an area farmer. Spigots at the bottom of the barrels made it easy to fill the family's wine bottles. Also, stored in that cool, dry basement on built-in shelves were bottles of cider and special wines, potatoes, carrots, and baskets of apples. The apples stayed fresh and crisp all the way until Easter.

One day a week was set aside for doing laundry. Behind the house, not far from the kitchen door, was an unattached laundry room. The floor and walls were concrete. The laundry room was very clean and well-designed. On one side was a fire pit with a grate that held a large tub. On Mondays, Suzanne's mother built a wood fire in the fire pit, filled the tub with water, added soap, and boiled her laundry. The adjacent wall held a low counter with another tub. This tub she filled with cold water. She took the clothes, one at a time, out of the boiling water, scrubbed them on a washboard, rinsed them in the cold water, and wrung them by hand. It was hard work to wring the water out of the clothes; Maman had strong hands and wrists. She hung the clothes to dry on a line outside. It ran from the washroom to the chicken coop at the back of the lot. There were also clothes lines inside the washroom for rainy days.

There was plenty of room for a big garden between the washroom and the chicken coop. Suzanne's father did not know anything about gardening when they moved into their new house, but he was eager to learn. There were two other houses in the neighborhood when Suzanne's family moved to Nort. Alphonse quickly developed a close friendship with his neighbors, Monsieur Robin and Monsieur Dugue. They were happy to teach him how to grow a garden. He loved his garden and he quickly became a master gardener. He was able to raise most of the food for his growing family to eat. He developed a creative watering system for the garden. He built a tall pylon and secured a cistern to the top of the pylon. He pumped enough water from the well in the house to fill the cistern. Then, he attached pipes and hoses to the cistern and used the stored water and gravity to irrigate his garden.

Papa loved his garden, and Suzanne liked helping him with the crops. There were potatoes, onions, turnips, carrots, cabbages, rhubarb, berries, tomatoes, and herbs in the garden.

Often, when Maman was cooking dinner, she sent Suzanne to the garden to fetch a *bouquet garni*. Suzanne carefully chose the fragrant herbs. She usually included parsley, thyme, and bay leaves. She tied the herbs together tightly with a string and dropped them into the stew or soup Maman was cooking.

The property had grape vines and lovely, productive trees. A large walnut tree gave the family nuts. Apple, peach, cherry, and plum trees provided them with all the fruit they needed. Maman made apple sauce and preserves. She canned peaches, and plums.

Suzanne's family raised rabbits for meat and chickens for eggs. One of Suzanne's daily chores was gathering the eggs. Early each morning, Suzanne or one of her brothers walked a quarter mile to a farm to get milk. They carried the milk home in a covered aluminum milk pail. The cover fit very tightly so the delicious, fresh milk did not spill.

A lady in a horse-drawn buggy came by their house at 11:00 each morning selling freshly baked bread. She was the spinster sister of the local baker. The children watched for her to come and ran out to get some bread. They chose a fresh baguette or a two-pound loaf. The lady kept track of how much money they owed in an unusual way. She had a ring with sticks on it, one stick for each customer. She used a knife to make notches in the sticks, indicating how much her customers owed for each purchase. At the end of the month, she added up the number of notches, and her customers paid her for all the bread they had taken that month.

Wagons also came by each week selling fruit, vegetables, and fish. The fish wagon came on Fridays. They could buy mussels, sardines, oysters, or other inexpensive seafood. It was traditional to eat fish on Fridays; Catholic people did not eat meat on Fridays in those days.

Suzanne's family always had plenty to eat. They ate simple, but delicious food in the traditional French way. For breakfast they had hot chocolate or rich, dark coffee in a bowl and toast made of left-over bread from the day before. They liked to dunk their bread in the coffee. Suppers usually consisted of vegetable soup and bread.

The biggest meal of the day was at noon. Shops closed. Children came home from school. Workers took a two-hour break. There were three courses for dinner, starting with pâté and fresh bread, followed by the main course of meat, potatoes and vegetables. Dessert was often fruit and sometimes pudding or jam.

For special occasions, Suzanne's mother made Eggs in Snow. She beat egg whites and cooked them in hot milk until they were hard like meringue. Then, she removed the meringue, strained the milk, and made it into *Crème Anglaise*, a kind of vanilla pudding. She served the pudding with the meringue on top. (Suzanne's mother never made cakes or cookies.)

The whole family gathered around the table in the big dining room of the new house for meals. They savored the tastes and textures and beauty of the food. They took their time. Eating together was a great pleasure.

Suzanne lived in the beautiful house with the people she loved. She had everything she needed. She was content.

The Chédotal Family's Home

6 MIDDLE CHILDHOOD

The Swing

by Robert Louis Stevenson

How do you like to go up in a swing,
Up in the air so blue?
Oh, I do think it the pleasantest thing
Ever a child can do!

Up in the air and over the wall,
Till I can see so wide,
Rivers and trees and cattle and all
Over the countryside –

Till I look down on the garden green,
Down on the roof so brown –
Up in the air I go flying again,
Up in the air and down!

Suzanne bit her lower lip in concentration as she worked with her crochet hook and yarn. She sat in her mother's red and gold *fauteuil Voltaire* (upholstered armchair). The comfortable chair had a high back and open arms. Her mother usually sat is this chair when she worked on her knitting projects in the evenings. It was conveniently located in the corner of the dining room by the window. An electric lamp on the high wooden side-table cast a yellow glow on Suzanne's project. She completed a few stitches, scrutinized her work, unraveled the yarn, and began again. She enjoyed designing and creating clothes for her doll.

Suzanne treasured her only doll. The nameless, celluloid doll was 18 inches long; she had no hair, and her eyes did not open or close like some of the more expensive dolls. When she first came to live with Suzanne, she did not have any clothes. Suzanne collected bits of yarn left over from the knitting projects of her relatives. She tied all those pieces of scrap yarn together, and she learned to crochet. She figured out how to do most of the stitches herself by trial and error, making unique outfits for her doll. Her first project was a cape. She played with the doll and the cape for a while. Then, she unraveled the yarn, rolled it back into a ball, and made a new project with the same yarn. She reused the yarn, over, and over again, making new and even more intricate creations each time.

Suzanne had a happy childhood. She was often content to entertain herself. She attended school, helped around the house, and played with her younger siblings. The maritime climate made for mild, wet winters and warm, dry summers; it was pleasant weather for children to be outdoors. Sometimes they played in the river on the other side of town where the water was shallow, and it was safe for children to play.

There were no other children in their neighborhood. Suzanne had friends at school, but the Chédotal children never invited other children over to play at their house. They rarely went to the homes of people who were not relatives. They had no paper or crayons to play with, and they had only a few toys. Suzanne played dominos, checkers, and pick-up sticks with Albert and Raymond.

On Friday mornings, Suzanne walked the few blocks with her mother and siblings to the outdoor market. The market in Nort-Sur-Erdre didn't sell food, but there were always interesting things to see. There were displays of clothes and baskets, hats and shoes, linens and dishes. They always saw friends and neighbors at the market. It was a weekly social event for the little town. The Chédotal family rarely bought anything at the market; they just enjoyed going to look. Suzanne's family usually took the train to Nantes when they needed to buy clothes. There was a small *épicerie* (grocery store) in town where they could purchase necessary supplies.

Only the doctor in Nort-Sur-Erdre had a car at that time. Although her grandparents in Héric had a horse and buggy, her father never owned a horse. Suzanne's mother had a bicycle, and her father had a motorcycle. The family used the train or the shuttle for transportation.

Often, Suzanne and her little brothers took the shuttle by themselves to Héric to visit their maternal grandparents. It was safe for children to travel alone; the shuttle driver knew their family. He dropped the children off right in front of their house so they wouldn't have to walk the half-mile home from the regular stop at the train station. One day, when the shuttle driver brought them home, he told Suzanne's parents her little brother, Raymond, had broken the shuttle's window crank handle. Raymond had a reputation for getting into mischief, but Suzanne knew he had not broken the handle. The shuttle driver insisted, and Suzanne's father paid for the broken handle. Suzanne had a very keen sense of right and wrong; she was greatly bothered by the injustice of the situation.

Suzanne's father was gregarious and fun-loving, and he enjoyed making friends. As he installed electrical service for the houses in the town and the farms in the surrounding area, he befriended his customers. He was beloved. While most people were called by formal names, Suzanne's father was always called Chédo. They knew he could fix anything. If someone commented to a neighbor that they had a broken electrical appliance, they would simply reply, "Bring it to Chédo." He enjoyed an especially close relationship with his two closest neighbors. The three men played cards together in the evenings.

Chédo played an active role in the local volunteer fire department. One day, an article highlighting his work with the fire department appeared on the front page of the local newspaper.

Singing was one of Chédo's greatest pleasures. His rich baritone voice could often be heard belting out a familiar tune from a musical or an opera. He knew them all. His favorites were *Toreador* and songs from the *Merry Widow*. He was often asked to sing at community gatherings and weddings. He was, indeed, the life of every party.

Chédo was also a jokester. When he retrofitted existing homes with electrical wiring, he had to run the wires along the surface of the interior walls. To camouflage and protect the exposed wires, Chédo ran the two wires in grooves made in a long, narrow board. He attached the board to the wall and covered the wires and grooves with a smaller, flat piece of board. The boards were painted to match the color of the walls. Chédo's finish work was meticulous, and the covered wires were hardly noticeable. Working inside the homes gave Chédo an opportunity to play his tricks.

He had a small metal device that, when dropped, sounded exactly like glass shattering. He waited until the owner was out of sight. Then, he dropped the metal device, quickly returned it to his pocket, and continued with his work. When the homeowner heard the sound of shattering glass, she ran to see what had happened. Chédo feigned ignorance, as the lady of the house searched for what she thought Chédo had broken.

He also had a piece of soft plastic that looked like fresh cat poop. Chédo laid it in the corner of the room and called for the housewife to come quickly to clean up the mess he had found. The surprised and embarrassed woman hurried to get her cleaning supplies. Chédo delighted in seeing the shock and surprise on their faces, and, eventually, they shared a good laugh.

On the other hand, Suzanne's mother was very formal. She routinely had coffee at four o'clock in the afternoon with her next-door neighbors, but she never developed a close relationship with them. French people typically address each other formally unless they are very close friends. Though Laurence saw these women almost every day, she never progressed beyond calling them Madame Dugue and Madame Robin. She did not share her hopes and dreams with her friends, nor did she show her feelings. She was well-educated and seemed a little bit classier than the other women in town. She was a neighborhood leader, carrying out the instructions of the doctor if a neighbor was sick and bringing food to those who needed help. However, she kept people emotionally at arm's length.

Maman loved her children. She rarely said the words, but she was kind, and she took good care of them. She made their meals and cleaned their house. She bought them nice clothes. Suzanne was proud of her mother's proper speech, the elegant way she carried herself, and the way the neighbors respected her. Suzanne knew she was loved by her mother, but she did not feel connected to her. She did not read to Suzanne, nor play with her, nor hold her hand when they went walking. Neither did she teach her how to sew, crochet, or play the mandolin. The Chédotal family did not talk about their feelings, only about the events of the day. Suzanne did not know her mother's thoughts, but she did know her mother loved her.

Suzanne often visited her father's stepmother in Saint-Nazaire. She had always been very kind to Alphonse. Even after his father died and his stepmother remarried, she loved Alphonse's children and treated them like they were her very own grandchildren. They always called her Grandmère-Nazaire. She demonstrated her love for Suzanne in a different way than Suzanne's mother did. Suzanne loved to run into her open arms and hear her say, "Ah, ma petite mignonne!" (Ah, my little cutie.) Grandmère-Nazaire praised her crochet projects and spent time with her. Grandmère-Nazaire was not elegant and well-educated like her mother, but she loved Suzanne with all her sweet, uncomplicated heart.

7   THE PRIDE OF FRANCE

*She was the most beautiful object built by man
during the twentieth century.*
—Richard Rene Silvin

Eight-year-old Suzanne did not have to be awakened on this particular Friday morning. She lay quietly in the dark waiting for her aunt to stir. The day before, Suzanne had taken the shuttle from her home in Nort-Sur-Erdre to her aunt's house in Héric. She looked forward with excitement to the plans for the weekend. She was going to attend the launching of the SS Normandie.

Suzanne heard her aunt open the back door. She was up and dressed in a flash. She hurried to the courtyard behind the house. "Good morning, Suzanne!" called Aunt Modeste cheerfully. "Ça va?" (How's it going?)

"Ça va bien," replied Suzanne. (It is going well.)

Suzanne helped Aunt Modeste and Uncle Pierre take butter and eggs from the storage shed in the courtyard and load them into the truck. Suzanne was careful not to break the precious eggs. Her uncle had spent the previous four days driving to farms in the surrounding area, collecting the farm products. Today they would sell them at the big market in Saint-Nazaire. "It is so nice to have a helping hand this early in the morning," complimented Uncle Pierre. Suzanne adored her godfather, and she held a special place in his heart.

When it was loaded, they climbed into the truck and began the 30-mile drive to Saint-Nazaire. Suzanne held her celluloid doll in her arms. She also had a bag in which she had packed her best clothes, her yarn, and her crochet hook. They passed farms on their way. The farmers were out with their lanterns, starting their early morning chores. The houses in town all had electricity by now, but most of the farms were not yet hooked up to the electrical grid.

By the time they arrived at the covered market in Saint-Nazaire, the sun was up. The market was buzzing with vendors, busily setting out their wares. Suzanne helped Aunt Modeste and Uncle Pierre unload the truck and arrange the eggs and butter on the table at their assigned spot. With everything in place, Suzanne was free to wander around the market.

The sights and smells and sounds of the market intrigued the little girl. Farmers sold brightly colored fruits and vegetables. Butchers had beef, chicken, rabbits, and ducks for sale. One butcher sold horse meat; he hung a skinned horse's head above his display. There were smoked hams, pâté, and the pungent smell of handmade sausage. Fishermen brought their morning catches—catfish, clams, mussels, oysters, sardines, shrimp, *escargot* (snails), and herring. That section of the market smelled of the sea; Suzanne was careful as she walked because the concrete floor under the seafood was wet and slippery. There were tables set with jars of golden honey and jewel-colored jam. Bakers displayed fragrant, freshly baked bread and pastries.

Suzanne stopped to watch a cook making crepes on a large, flat, circular, cast iron pan over a crackling fire. He poured the thin batter onto the center of the hot pan and spread it thin with a wooden paddle. The batter sizzled for a few seconds. He flipped the large golden-brown crepe, cooked it a little longer, and added the perfect circle to the growing pile of ready-to-sell crepes. As each crepe was purchased, it was folded and filled with the customer's choice of fresh, local fare. Butter, *sucre* (sugar), fruit, and sausage all pair well with crepes.

There were many interesting things to look at. Suzanne surveyed the hand-made baskets hanging from the ceiling and piled on tables. They came in many sizes and colors with handles to make them easy for shoppers to carry. The baskets were for sale. Every shopper brought her own basket to the market; vendors did not provide bags.

One vendor sold bathing suits for children. Suzanne remembered her bathing suit was too small for her. She had instructions from her mother to buy a new one at the market. Suzanne admired the red striped bathing suit.

Grandmère-Nazaire could not come to the market herself because she was lame. She walked with a very pronounced limp, so it was hard for her to walk very far. Her sister, Madame Peret, usually came to the market to meet Suzanne when Suzanne got a ride to Saint-Nazaire. Suzanne and Madame Peret would walk to Grandmère-Nazaire's house together.

Soon, Madame Peret found Suzanne in the crowd of shoppers. She greeted her with three kisses—left cheek, right cheek, left cheek—and told her how nice it was to have her in Saint-Nazaire. Suzanne showed her the red-striped bathing suit. She agreed it was a good choice, so Suzanne purchased it with the *francs* (French currency) her mother had given her. They said good-bye to Aunt Modest and Uncle Pierre with three more kisses all around, "Merci, merci. A bientot." (Thank you, thank you. See you soon.)

Madame Peret and Suzanne began the long walk to Grandmère-Nazaire's house. Grandmère-Nazaire lived at the edge of town. As they approached their destination, Suzanne could see the SS Normandie across the field behind the house. The enormous ocean liner had been under construction at the shipyard for two years. Every time Suzanne visited Grandmère-Nazaire, she noted the progress. She watched the ship grow bigger and bigger as new sections were added. It was almost ready for launching. The big cranes had already been taken away. The freshly painted black hull shone in the midday sun. Suzanne was invited to attend the launching of the SS Normandie with Madame Peret in just two days. Her sons, Pierre and Rene, worked at the shipyard; they were able to get tickets for their mother and Suzanne to attend the grand event. Suzanne did not know what to expect at a ship launching, but she was very excited.

Suzanne climbed the stairs that ran along the outside of Grandmère-Nazaire's house. She paused on the landing at the top to get a better look at the impressive ship. Grandmère-Nazaire was waiting for her when she opened the kitchen door. She welcomed Suzanne with three kisses and the words Suzanne loved to hear, "Ah, ma petite mignonne!"

The little upstairs apartment had just two rooms. In the kitchen, pots and pans hung on the wall. There was a table and a twin-size bed in the kitchen. The second room had a bed, a dresser, and a wardrobe. Suzanne slept in the big bed with Grandmère-Nazaire; her husband slept in the little bed in the kitchen whenever Suzanne visited.

The apartment downstairs was rented out. Madame Peret lived in the one-story house adjacent to this two-story structure. It had a thick, thatched roof which could easily be seen from the window in Grandmère-Nazaire's apartment. Grandmère-Nazaire did not like thunderstorms; she worried the lightning would catch the straw roof on fire and burn down the entire building. "One day, we had both the kitchen window and door open during a thunderstorm," Grandmère-Nazaire told Suzanne. "The storm came very close. Suddenly, lightning flashed at the same time the thunder roared. All the pots and pans, which had been hanging on the kitchen wall, fell to the floor." She paused, remembering the frightful storm. "The lightning came in through the window and went out through the door," she declared.

Suzanne, Grandmère-Nazaire, and her husband sat down at the kitchen table to enjoy dinner together. Grandmère-Nazaire had very little money, but she grew vegetables and rhubarb in her garden. She had purchased three small sardines. They each ate one sardine with potatoes, carrots, and radishes. They also had traditional fresh French bread, spread with homemade rhubarb jam. Suzanne learned to appreciate rhubarb jam at Grandmère-Nazaire's house; it was her favorite jam.

After dinner, Suzanne sat on the bed in the kitchen and worked on her most recent crochet project. She was making a new dress for her doll. Grandmère-Nazaire noticed she was doing the pineapple stitch. Suzanne was surprised the pattern already had a name; she thought she had invented the pattern herself.

Suzanne fell asleep early that night. The room was dark and quiet with the shutters closed. She slept well in the cozy bed next to Grandmère-Nazaire's warm body.

Sunday, October 29, 1932, dawned clear and crisp. It was time for the launching of the SS Normandie. Madame Peret and Suzanne walked side by side across the field to the shipyard. The SS Normandie loomed in front of them. The imposing ship appeared to grow even bigger as they approached. Its black hull was 1,029 feet long. Eventually, the upper decks, with their many portholes and windows, would be painted a gleaming white and three red smokestacks would tower above the ship. It would take two more years to complete her interior and make her ready for her maiden voyage. For now, she was huge and shiny and new. She would come to be known as one of the most beautiful ships ever designed.

A crowd of 200,000 people, dressed in their finest clothes, were on hand for the grand event. It seemed surreal; Suzanne had never before seen so many people in one place. There was noisy chatter in the crowd, and a band played above the din. A thick layer of lard was spread along the skids on which the giant ship rested. (The lard made the skids slippery and would help the ship slide into the water.) The pungent smell of the lard was not at all pleasant. The braces holding the ship in place were removed, and the lines were readied for launching. Suzanne, wide-eyed and quiet, took in every detail.

Finally, the crowd quieted. Dignitaries gave speeches. The First Lady of France was on hand to christen the ship. A bottle of champagne was attached to the rail of the ship with a long line. The First Lady threw the bottle toward the ship. It swung through the air, hit the bow, and shattered, splashing the champagne across the front of the ship. The French national anthem played as the lines holding the SS Normandie in place were released. The weight of the elegant giant on the slippery rails caused the Normandie to slide into the waters of the Loire Estuary. The enormity of the hull displaced a great amount of water and created a wave which crashed into a few hundred spectators. Fortunately, no one was injured. Suzanne would never forget that moment for as long as she lived.

◆ ◆ ◆

A Note on The History of the SS Normandie

The SS Normandie was an ocean liner built in Saint-Nazaire for the French line Compagnie Generale Transatlantique (CGT). The flagship of the CGT, she made 139 westbound transatlantic voyages from her home port of Le Havre, France to New York City. At the time, she was the largest and fastest ship afloat. She was the first ship ever built to exceed 1,000 feet in length. She could berth 1,972 passengers. Many people considered her to be the greatest of ocean liners because of her novel design and luxurious interior.

Launched in the midst of the great global depression, Normandie was the pride of France. She represented prestige and maritime power in a rivalry between France, Great Britain, Italy, and Germany.

When World War II started, Normandie found refuge in New York Harbor, along with her rivals, the Queen Mary and the Queen Elizabeth. After the bombing of Pearl Harbor, Normandie was requisitioned by the US Navy and renamed USS Lafayette. Normandie's help was needed in the war effort.

In 1942, while she was being converted to a troopship, Normandie caught fire. Workers, who were rushing to complete the conversion, neglected to take important safety precautions. Sparks from a welder accidently ignited life preservers in the first-class lounge.

The ship's modern firefighting system had been disabled during the conversion. The New York Fire Department arrived on scene in less than 15 minutes. They were horrified to learn the

French fittings on the Normandie were not compatible with their hoses. Firefighters employed fire boats on the portside and they used dockside hoses to combat the flames on the starboard side. It took five hours to extinguish the fire.

The great amount of water sprayed onto Normandie's port side from the fire boats caused her to begin listing heavily. Several open portholes submerged, and sea water poured in. Normandie capsized onto her port side and came to rest on the muddy bottom of the Hudson River at Pier 88. She was unsalvageable. It was a sad end for a grand ship.

SS Normandie

8   GROWTH AND CHANGE

When you're twelve years old,
you still have one foot in childhood;
the other is poised to enter a completely new stage of life.
Your innocent understanding of the world
moves towards something messier
and more complicated and, once it does,
you can never go back.
—Khaled Hosseini

A gentle breeze rustled the leaves of the fruit trees in the yards of the houses Suzanne passed on her way to the town center. She carefully jumped across the little streams of gray water that ran along the edge of the street to the river; the water came from the houses that had indoor plumbing. Most of the homes she passed were enclosed by handsome walls or fences. There was little traffic on the street.

It was a pleasant Saturday afternoon, her chores were finished, and Suzanne was free to entertain herself as she pleased. The heart of Nort-Sur-Erdre was a ten-minute walk from Suzanne's house. She was drawn to the vibrancy of the town center. She strolled along the sidewalk of the main street. Though she rarely bought anything, she enjoyed the endless opportunities for window shopping. She drew in the delicious fragrance of freshly baked bread as she passed the *boulangerie*. Artfully created desserts graced the window of the *patisserie* (pastry shop); the *pain au chocolat* (chocolate croissant) and the *tarte aux poires* (pear tart) were her favorites.

She passed the local butcher shop; it reminded her of happy times spent in her grandfather's *boucherie*. She admired the latest fashions in women's hats at the *boutique de modiste* (hat shop). A little shop on the corner sold newspapers and cigarettes. Friends and neighbors gathered at the cafés. The weekly market and annual visits of the circus and the carnival all took place at the Place de la Fair, an open area behind the big church.

Pausing to gaze at Saint Christophe Catholic Church, Suzanne admired the majestic neo-gothic architecture of the old structure. A group of people, dressed in their Sunday best, gathered outside the church. Suzanne lingered to catch a glimpse of a radiant bride on the arm of her new husband, walking from the town hall to the nearby church for the religious wedding service that followed the mandatory French civil ceremony. No bells announced the joyous occasion. (The top of the church bell tower had been destroyed by lightning shortly before the Chédotal family moved to Nort.) Suzanne dreamed of being a bride herself one day.

When Jimmy and I visited Nort-Sur-Erdre in 2019, I was surprised to hear church bells ringing. We discovered a sign in front of the church explaining its history. It told of the lighting strike on October 21, 1930 that destroyed the bells and shortened the bell tower by 14 meters. Renovations were finally completed in 2006. The sign declared, "The bells once again announce the joys and sorrows of the parish."

Suzanne took note of the *Tricolour*, the red, white, and blue flag of France, waving in front of the town hall. Suzanne was proud to be a French girl.

The school Suzanne attended was also located near the town center. Suzanne usually walked to and from school with her siblings. The three-room school building housed both elementary and junior high school classes. Each classroom had one teacher with about 30 students in two or three combined grades. School started promptly at eight o'clock in the morning. At 11:00, the children walked home for a two-hour lunch break. The entire family gathered around the table in the dining room to enjoy the three-course meal Suzanne's mother had ready for them. School officially ended at four o'clock in the afternoon, but Suzanne usually stayed for study hall. Her parents paid a fee so she could attend the additional study time. The study hall lasted for 90 minutes, after a 30-minute break for a snack. It was a long day, but Suzanne looked forward to being at school. She liked her teacher, Madame Mortamoosk; she was from the south of France and spoke with a strong accent. Madame Mortamoosk was also the principal of the school.

Suzanne made friends at school, and she was a good student. In fact, she was consistently at the top of her class. Her favorite subject was math. She quickly grasped new concepts, and she was very good at doing math problems in her head. She did not like creative writing assignments; she would rather write about real people and actual events than make up a story. She loved to read, but she had no books of her own. There was no library in the town. The school had a few books to lend, and, occasionally, she borrowed books from friends. Suzanne faithfully read her father's daily newspaper from front to back.

Twice a week for two years, Suzanne attended catechism classes at the church. She did not enjoy those classes. The clergy were neither friendly nor kind to the children. They became annoyed if the students did not memorize the lengthy assignments each week. Suzanne completed the required studies, and she was confirmed in the Catholic church. For her first communion, she wore a beautiful white dress with a muff and a veil; it looked like a bride's dress. The family celebrated with a festive meal. Catholic traditions were part of Suzanne's culture, but she did not embrace the Catholic faith with her heart.

Suzanne with Lulu at her First Communion

Suzanne sometimes went to see her maternal grandparents in Héric. It was easy for her to make the trip to Héric and back on the shuttle. She enjoyed connecting with her relatives and friends in the town of her birth. Suzanne developed a friendship with a girl in Héric who was about her age. Ann Marie Heraud lived in the little house where Suzanne was born and spent her formative years. They often played together when Suzanne visited her grandparents.

When Suzanne was ten, her grandfather became very sick with pneumonia. A neighbor called for the local priest to come to the house to give him last rights. Grandpère did not know he was dying at the time. The family was very unhappy that the nosy neighbor had called for the priest; they did not want Grandpère to become upset or discouraged. Grandpère kept getting worse and he did not recover. After his death, Suzanne stayed in Héric with Grandmère for two weeks. Suzanne was good company and a great support to her grandmother. She even slept in the big bed with her.

It was the custom for close family members to wear black for one year after the death of a loved one. Grandmère bought two black dresses for Suzanne. For the second year after his death, Suzanne wore gray or lilac-colored dresses.

Women and girls wore dresses at that time, even for work and play. Suzanne's shirt-waist dresses buttoned up the back and had pleats in the front. She usually wore knee socks, and her mother knit warm sweaters. A neighbor made many of their clothes. One time, the family was invited to a special wedding; both Suzanne and her mother had new dresses made for the occasion. Suzanne's dress was bright yellow. Her mother's long dress was made of shimmering red and blue taffeta; it made a rustling sound when she walked. Maman looked elegant in the fancy dress.

Women wore hats when their left their homes. Usually, a woman got a new hat every year. Felt hats could be made and remade several times. Madame Modiste, the local milliner, was very talented. She could remove a brim, add a flower, or make another change to transform an old hat into a new fashion.

Suzanne's friend, Madeline Pauvert, lived on a farm at the edge of town. She and Suzanne sometimes walked together to the pasture by the river where Madeline's father let his cows graze. The fields were divided by canals filled with water from the river. Suzanne and Madeline played in the field until it was time to bring the cows home. Then, with sticks waving, the girls guided the gentle herd of 15 cows back to the barn to be milked. They also liked to play in the corn field. It was fun to run up and down the rows and play hide and seek. Even though the corn grew higher than their heads, they could always find their way out; they simply followed the nice, straight rows to the edge of the field. The farmer was not happy about the girls playing in his cornfield.

Bastille Day commemorates the storming of the Bastille in

Paris on July 14, 1789. That event signaled the start of the French Revolution. French people celebrate July 14th as *La Fete Nationale*, the national holiday of France. Suzanne's family had a very memorable Bastille Day tradition. Her father had a boat named Sampan which he kept on the river near their house. Every year, on the 14th of July, Suzanne's mother boiled a whole cow's head (*tete de veau*) in the big washtub in the laundry room. When the head was perfectly cooked, they put it in a wheelbarrow and pushed it to the river. Two neighbor families joined Suzanne's family as they sailed the Sampan up the river to a field and had a picnic. Oh, how everyone enjoyed the boiled cow's head—the tongue, the brains, the eyes, the meat. It was so delicious! They ate every part.

Suzanne's family did not make a fuss about birthdays. French families, however, usually recognized name days. Name days are a European tradition; people who are named after a saint celebrate that saint's feast day each year. Suzanne Day is August 11. There were rarely parties or gifts in the Chédotal household. Even so, being recognized made Suzanne feel special.

One day, a man, whom Suzanne's father had befriended when he installed electricity at his farm, gave him tickets to the traveling circus. Suzanne and her father went together to the circus in the center of town. They made memories to treasure. There were elephants and tigers and clowns and acrobats. Suzanne's favorite acts were the beautiful horses doing tricks.

Sometimes her father was given tickets to the annual carnival in town. He let Suzanne go to the carnival by herself. She enjoyed watching the games and taking in the excitement of the event.

Most French families went on a vacation in August; even poor people found a way to take a holiday. Suzanne's family rented a room near the beach in Pornichet for two weeks each summer. (Pornichet is near Saint-Nazaire.) While the adults laid in the sunshine, the children played in the sand, discovered shells, or walked at the edge of the surf. At low tide, they gathered mussels on the rocks. Maman cooked the delicious, tender mussels in white wine for dinner. Suzanne's siblings swam in the waves, but Suzanne never learned to swim; she was content to play on the beach or lie in the sun. On Thursdays, they walked to the market; Pornichet had the biggest market in the area.

The family enjoyed teasing Suzanne about an incident that happened when she was just two. Her parents had rented a small vacation apartment right next to the market in Pornichet. All of a sudden, Suzanne's mother could not find her. She searched the apartment and ran out to the street, enlisting the help of everyone she saw. Finally, the toddler was spotted, wandering the market, completely naked. Suzanne blushed every time they told the story.

Suzanne was the only one of her siblings who made regular visits to Grandmère-Nazaire's house. Sometimes, in the summers when school was out, she stayed with Grandmère-Nazaire for a whole month. There were many interesting things to do in Saint-Nazaire. Suzanne cherished the days she spent with Grandmère-Nazaire, hearing her stories and helping with the garden.

Grandmère-Nazaire's nephew, Rene, and his family lived in the center of Saint-Nazaire. Suzanne sometimes walked to their home to visit. They had a one-burner propane stove sitting on the counter in the kitchen. Below the counter was a bottle of propane with a hose connecting the propane to the burner.

Rene's wife, Marionette, had her hands full with several small children. She appreciated Suzanne's willingness to run errands for her. She loaned Suzanne her bicycle and sent her to the co-operative for wine. Suzanne carried three or four empty bottles as she rode the bicycle. She had the bottles filled with wine at the cooperative and carried them back to Marionette. She balanced them as carefully as she could while she rode. She worried she would fall off the bicycle and the bottles would break, spilling the precious wine. Her fears were unfounded; she always brought the full bottles back safely.

Suzanne made friends while playing at the beach in Saint-Nazaire. She walked two miles along a dirt path from Grandmère-

Nazaire's house until she got to the big boulevard running parallel to the beach. One side of the boulevard had an open view of the Atlantic Ocean. The other side was lined with impressive mansions. They had well-groomed yards and tall iron fences with gates. Suzanne wondered what those big houses were like inside and who the people were who lived in the grand homes. She crossed the road and found her friends playing on the beach. The long sandy beach curved out to a point. The girls walked together all the way out to the point, letting the gentle waves lap at their feet as they walked and talked.

When Suzanne was 14, she completed junior high school and passed a very extensive exam. Unfortunately, she was unable to go to high school because it was expensive; her parents did not have the money to send her. Also, there was no high school in Nort, so she would have had to go to boarding school. Suzanne was disappointed she could not go to high school. She believed she could have done well. She was not sure what direction her life would take without a high school diploma.

As a graduation gift, her parents gave Suzanne her first bicycle. It was the modern style with a straight, angled center bar instead of the traditional rounded one, and it was silver instead of black. She was proud of her new bicycle and her friends admired it. It was Suzanne's transportation for many years. Sometimes she rode her bike far out into the country to visit her cousins.

Suzanne and her friends rode their bikes together or went for walks along the canal that passed through Nort-Sur-Erdre. Like the roads and railways of France, the canals were important transportation links between the cities and towns. Long, straight, flat towpaths paralleled the canal. Suzanne never tired of watching the boats move along the canal. Sometimes horses pulled the boats; the horses walked along the dirt towpaths on both sides of the canal, connected to the boats with long ropes. It was interesting to watch the boats go through the locks. The boats were not tall; they had to be able to pass under bridges. People lived on some of the boats that floated along the slowly moving water. Suzanne smiled at the laundry they hung to dry on their boats, flapping in the breeze like comical flags.

Aunt Juliette had a friend named Madame Avenard, who lived in one of the beautiful mansions on the Boulevard in Saint-Nazaire. Suzanne's friend Ann Marie sometimes went to Saint Nazaire to help Madame Avenard with the housework. One weekend, Madame Avenard invited Suzanne, Aunt Juliette, Ann Marie, and Dede for an overnight visit to her home. Madame Avenard drove to Héric to pick them up in her car. Suzanne had wondered about those big beautiful houses when she played on the beach with her friends. It was exciting for her to be invited to visit one. She was amazed at its size and grandeur. It was especially pleasant to lie in bed and listen to the surf.

A few months after Suzanne finished school, her father arranged for her to be an apprentice with the tailor in town. They made fine men's clothing. Suzanne learned quickly and she became a very good seamstress. (She did not learn to sew from her mother because her mother did not sew very much; her mother even hired a woman to come once a week to do mending.) Suzanne learned to produce quality garments—finely tailored shirts, pants, and jackets. Suzanne had worked for the tailor for about six months when another female apprentice told Suzanne about some inappropriate comments the tailor had made about Suzanne. When Suzanne told her mother about the comments—comments Suzanne didn't understand—her mother told her to go get her sewing things and come straight home. She never worked for the tailor again.

Next, Suzanne went to trade school where she learned typing, stenography, and bookkeeping skills. She took the bus to Nantes for the training three days a week. The bus departed at noon, so Suzanne made herself a quick lunch before she left. She always fried two eggs in butter and ate them with toast. Her mother encouraged her to have something different for variety, but Suzanne always wanted to eat the same thing.

Suzanne never got into trouble. She did not drink, smoke, or say bad words. (Some of her other siblings did those things, but

Suzanne did not.) She was obedient and trustworthy. Though her father was often cross with the other children, he seemed to favor Suzanne, and he was kind to her.

When Suzanne was a little girl, her mother and father had played the mandolin and banjo together. Those were happy times. At some point, they stopped making music and the mandolin and banjo found their way to the little storage room upstairs. Neither Suzanne nor any of her siblings learned to make music.

In 1939, another daughter was added to the Chédotal family. Suzanne was 15 when Nicole was born. Suzanne and Lulu continued to share a double bed; a single bed was added to the girls' room to accommodate Nicole.

Though the people of France continued with their daily routines, an uneasiness hung in the air. They were well aware of the threat Germany posed. They believed Germany had her eye on the rich French coal resources. They did not, however, understand how sinister Hitler's plan was.

9 THE ARRIVAL OF THE GERMAN ARMY

Whatever happens,
the flame of the French resistance must not be extinguished
and will not be extinguished.
—Charles De Gaulle, June 18, 1940

Suzanne was frightened. She sat at the dining room table with her parents and her siblings, Albert, Raymond, Lulu, and little Nicole. The radio on the mantle above the fireplace broadcasted somber news; the Maginot Line had been breached. German troops were sweeping toward Paris. Maman's face was white; she silently clenched her teeth. Suzanne could feel her heart pounding in her chest. She wrung her sweaty hands. "How can this be? France was so well prepared," thought Suzanne, as she tried to process the information. She wondered aloud to her father, "Will they come to Nort? What will happen to us?" He wanted to reassure his teenage daughter, but he did not have the answers to her questions. The Great War was still fresh in his memory. How could he protect his family?

All of France was in turmoil. Information campaigns were organized to prepare civilians, and gas masks were distributed. Suzanne hated the heavy, cumbersome gas masks, but she, like everyone else, took one with her everywhere she went. Dread hung heavy in the air.

Germany had been humiliated by the outcome of the Great War. Adolf Hitler seized on the anger and resentment of the German people. His charismatic charm and strong leadership helped restore their pride and nationalism. His dictatorship rebuilt the economy and established tight control of every aspect of German society.

Germany was the most densely populated area in Europe at

that time. Hitler and his Nazi Party sought to gain *lebensraum* (living space) for their "superior race." Their goal was annexation of the land from the Atlantic Ocean to the Ural Mountains in Russia. They intended to purge the world of people they deemed to be inferior. The Nazis targeted Jews as scapegoats for German problems and sought to eliminate them. They also planned to get rid of any other people they considered undesirable, including homosexuals and the mentally ill.

Twenty-one years after the end of The Great War, Nazi Germany, also known as the Third Reich, began systematically invading the surrounding countries. Not every country had the same experience. Some countries welcomed the Germans, some capitulated, and others fought with all their might.

The people of Austria were deceived. Austria was in the throes of the Great Depression, with high unemployment and poverty. They welcomed Hitler and his Nazi government based on his promises of relief and jobs. Kitty Werthmann was an 11-year-old Austrian girl in 1938. Though she and Suzanne never met, her recollections demonstrate what was happening in Austria at that time. "I cannot tell you that Hitler took Austria by tanks and guns," she mused. She went on to explain that the Austrians voted him in by a landslide—98 percent of the vote. They were led to believe everyone in Germany was happy; they wanted that same way of life in Austria. After the election, they danced in the streets for three days. The new government opened big field kitchens, and everyone was fed. Then, Germany began to methodically take over every aspect of Austrian life, and the people of Austria realized the truth. "The change to totalitarian government came slowly," remembered Ms. Werthmann. "If it had happened overnight, my countrymen would have fought to the last breath."

Most European countries, however, did not welcome the Germans. The German forces seized one country after another with their fast-moving *blitzkrieg* (lightning) attacks. Czechoslovakia, Poland, Denmark, Norway, Belgium, and The Netherlands all fell to Germany.

Initially, after the Great War, the French people concentrated on rebuilding their war-torn country. They erected many monuments to recognize and pay tribute to the men and women of France who had sacrificed so much to defeat Germany and secure the freedom of their country.

Then, they turned their attention to preparing to defend against the possibility of another onslaught by Germany. They built the Maginot Line, a heavily fortified, stationary line of defense along the eastern border of France. It included concrete fortifications, obstacles, and weapons installations. It ended at the Ardennes Forest to the northeast and it did not extend along the Belgium border. The French people were confident their impenetrable line of defense and the thick forest would protect them.

As the threat of a German invasion became imminent, French men were drafted to reinforce the regular French Army. The French people enthusiastically and optimistically bade farewell to the departing soldiers. They called, "Goodbye, goodbye. We'll see you again soon!" They believed the French would stop the Germans at the Maginot Line and the war would be over.

Pierre Lebacle, a young man who worked for Suzanne's father, was drafted. He came to the Chédotal house to say good-bye. Suzanne's mother stood in the warm kitchen, holding baby Nicole in her arms. Suzanne noticed how tall Pierre was. As they wished him well and said good-bye, they were sure he would be home again soon. They did not know they would never see Pierre again.

After Germany seized Belgium, the Nazi Army pivoted south and entered France, flanking the Maginot Line. The Maginot Line was completely stationary, so most of France's defenses could not intercept the German troops. They came with such speed and force that the French government quickly realized the futility of trying to defend the capital city. Attempts to resist would result in great loss of life and destruction.

Germany attacked France on May 10, 1940. Just one month after the Germans entered France, Paris was declared an open city. The French Government departed, and the German Army entered the city without a fight. Then, the German Army marched west to the coast of France, encountering little resistance as they went.

The Maginot Line became a metaphor for expensive efforts that offer a false sense of security.

Many French people fled ahead of the advancing German Army. One day, some people from near Paris came to Suzanne's house and asked her father for help. Monsieur Liebert, a successful Jewish businessman, owned a machine shop in the commune of Courbevoie, two miles from the center of the capital city. He had a piece of equipment which was very modern and valuable. It was used to make complex and precise parts for metal equipment. Monsieur Liebert wanted to keep it out of the hands of the Germans. His neighbors helped him load the machine onto a pushcart. They pushed it ahead of the advancing German Army all the way to Nort-Sur-Erdre—232 miles. When they arrived in Nort, they knocked on the door of Suzanne's house and asked if her father could help them hide it. Chédo did not have a suitable hiding place, but he knew his neighbor had a barn with hay in it. The neighbor agreed to help, so they put the machine in the back of the barn, completely covered in hay. Monsieur Liebert returned to his family in the city, leaving the precious machine hidden in Nort.

When Suzanne was 16, the Nazis came to her hometown. Her father and their neighbors piled wagons and farm equipment in the road at the fork leading into town. They hoped to block the way of the German advance. When they had finished, they stepped back to look at their work, and they realized how futile it was. They knew the Germans would roll right over the blockade with their trucks and tanks, ruining all their things and getting angry in the process. So, they removed the blockade and watched as the German soldiers entered their town. The Nazis marched right through the town, leaving a contingency of German soldiers to occupy Nort-Sur-Erdre.

The German Army advanced so quickly that they arrived in Nort and the neighboring town of Saint-Georges well ahead of their supplies. Sixteen-year-old Roger Menoret was working at their family-owned butcher shop in Saint-Georges with his father when the German soldiers entered the shop. They were so hungry that they bought the entire inventory of sausages. They ate it all, right there in the shop, without even cooking it.

Charles de Gaulle was an officer in the French Army when the war broke out. He was unwilling to accept France's surrender to Germany. He fled to England, and, with the support of Winston Churchill, became a leader of the Free French movement. On June 18, 1940, he broadcast a message across the English Channel to his countrymen. He acknowledged the dire situation of France, but he encouraged the French people. He told them they were not alone, and they would one day prevail. He concluded his message with the words, "Whatever happens, the flame of French resistance must not be extinguished and will not be extinguished."

On June 22, 1940, France surrendered to Germany. They signed an armistice which included the following seven provisions:

1. Germany directly controlled 3/5 of France, including the north, the west, and the entire Atlantic coast.

2. Vichy France Contolled the rest of France.

3. All foreign Jews living in France must surrender to Germany.

4. The French Army was disbanded, except 100,000 troops to keep domestic order.

5. One and one half million French soldiers remained prisoners of war.

6. All French soldiers must agree they would neither leave France, nor fight against Germany.

7. France must pay the occupation costs of the German Army.

The occupation of France gave the German fleet access to French port cities on the Atlantic Coast. This made it possible for their U-boats to be far more effective; they didn't need as much fuel to reach their targets, and they could operate under water for longer periods of time in the areas of conflict.

Hitler directed his Nazi officers to keep France weak and divided. Under German control, France was divided into two zones which were closed off from one another. Occupied France was made up of the northern and western parts of France, as well as the entire Atlantic coastline. It was subjected to complete German occupation and control. Vichy France in the south was allegedly independent, but the Vichy government collaborated with the Nazis. Suzanne lived within the borders of occupied France.

The French people fell into one of three categories. Some collaborated with the Germans; they were resigned to the fact that Germany controlled France and they believed going along with the Germans would make their lives easier. Some became part of the French Resistance, secretly working against the Germans. The vast majority of the French people, however, neither collaborated nor resisted. They simply tried to survive.

The occupying German troops were billeted (lodged) in French houses. They chose to live in the biggest and the nicest houses in the towns they occupied. Most of those homeowners and their families were evicted. Some French citizens, however, were forced to share their homes with German soldiers; they were required to cook and clean for them, as well. The Chédotal family was able to stay in their own home and they did not have any Germans living with them, probably because they had so many children.

The Germans requisitioned hotels, inns, summer homes, resorts, golf courses, riding stables, casinos, crops, and animals. (A requisition is an official order laying claim to the use of property or materials.) They seized control of the French economy and resources. The Nazi soldiers confiscated everything they wanted and used it for their own benefit or for the German war effort. They commandeered men to work in Germany and to serve their needs in France. The French people were required to pay for all the expenses of the occupying forces; this was done through heavy taxation.

The French people wanted to be liberated from the Germans. They hoped someone would come to help them, but they did not know if that would ever happen. Thus, began five very difficult years of German occupation for Suzanne Chédotal, her family, and her neighbors. Life went on, but it was not life as it had been.

10 OCCUPATION

There is strange comfort in knowing that
no matter what happens today,
the Sun will rise again tomorrow.
—Aaron Lauritsen
100 Days Drive: The Great North American Road Trip

T he sun rose over Nort-Sur-Erdre. It seemed inconceivable to Suzanne that the sun should ever again be as bright as it was when the French flag had waved in the breeze in front of the town hall. Now the ugly Nazi flag, with its hideous black swastika, highlighted by a white circle on a field of red, hung limply on that same pole. It symbolized everything Suzanne had come to despise.

Suzanne was awakened each morning by the sound of German soldiers marching on the street below her bedroom window. They chanted unfamiliar words as they marched with the characteristic goosestep in a highly disciplined formation. The harsh German language was so different from the soft, romantic tones of her own French tongue. The soldiers wore tall leather boots and greenish-gray uniforms. She hated that these men had invaded her town and her life and that they flaunted their presence right in front of her own home.

The Germans issued identification cards to everyone over 15 years of age. Suzanne had her own ID card with a number assigned to her. She did not smile when the picture was taken for her ID card; there was nothing to smile about. She was required to keep the card with her at all times. It proved who she was, allowed her to obtain ration cards, and gave the Germans the means of keeping track of her.

Suzanne was saddened by the changes these intruders brought to her tight-knit community. She disliked the curfew and the poverty. There were thousands of rules and regulations to control the French people. Transportation was disorganized, goods were rationed, sport fishing was banned, freedoms were restricted, and executions took place without trials.

Most of all, Suzanne hated the secrecy and lack of trust. The Nazis pitted neighbor against neighbor. They sowed seeds of doubt and distrust. Sometimes they even paid people to spy on their neighbors. No longer did friends confide in each other. Neighbors did not tell each other about their plans or their hopes or even about any meager supplies they might have hidden in their homes. They did not share information of any kind. The Nazis used pieces of information to seize supplies for themselves, to bribe French citizens, and to keep the French people from banding together against their enemy.

The Nazi soldiers might give an informant food or privileges in exchange for information. It was hard for hungry people to turn down promises of food or supplies when the Nazis offered them a way to have the much-needed items. Yes, it was understandable, if not forgivable, and it was best to just keep secrets. There was secrecy even within their own home. Suzanne's father protected his teenage daughter by concealing information. It was safer that way.

Suzanne knew how to avoid the German soldiers. She minded her own business and kept out of their way. There was always an undercurrent of fear, uncertainty, and dread. At least they no longer had to carry gas masks with them everywhere they went.

The French Resistance was made up of brave French people who secretly sought to sabotage the occupying Nazis and the collaborating French Vichy government. The Resistance also provided intelligence information to the Allies. Sometimes, French Resistance fighters ambushed or killed Nazi soldiers. The Germans retaliated by choosing random French people and shooting them. They left the dead bodies in the streets or fields as an example to the French people. One time, they rounded up 21 innocent people and killed them all. Aunt Juliette's brother was one of the people murdered in that group.

The Chédotal family was very poor during the occupation.

Suzanne's father continued working as an electrician, and he did get paid, but taxes imposed by the Germans were high and goods were scarce. Store shelves were empty. German soldiers took anything they wanted from the French people.

Neither new clothes nor supplies to make them were available for purchase. French people carefully cleaned and patched their old clothes. Suzanne was glad she had learned to sew. She was able to mend her clothes herself; she worked so carefully that her dresses hardly looked patched at all. When Suzanne needed a coat, a neighbor made one for her out of an old blue wool blanket. Her mother unraveled yarn from old sweaters and re-knitted it into garments to fit the growing children. Her father attached wooden soles to the bottoms of their shoes to make them last longer. Suzanne did not like the clackety, clack, clack, clack sound they made on the sidewalk; she did not like to be conspicuous. Mostly, she did not like the way her shoes hurt her feet. There was nothing to be done about that. There were no shoes available to buy anywhere in France.

Suzanne's mother boiled ivy leaves to make shampoo. They used and re-used everything they could. They simply managed without things they once thought were necessities. They had no medical supplies.

There was rarely any meat to eat, only bones for making soup. Meat, sugar, bread, and flour were severely rationed. French people stood in long lines for the chance to use their ration coupons. Suzanne missed having coffee for breakfast; the drink Maman made from roasted grain was a poor substitute for the rich, dark French coffee they used to enjoy. They bought the skins of cocoa beans and boiled them to make a faintly chocolate-flavored drink. They dug roots to eat. They grew vegetables in their garden. They were able to get milk from a neighbor, but there was rarely any butter to spread on their bread. The Germans told the French, "We will make you eat grass." And they almost did.

As poor as they were, Suzanne's family was better off than people who lived in the cities. City folks did not have the ability to grow their own food and there wasn't much food available to buy. Life was especially hard for the Leibert family because they were Jewish. From the very beginning of the occupation, the Germans made it clear the Jewish people were targets. New government decrees made life increasingly more difficult for French Jews. In October of 1940, the French puppet government enacted the first decree on the Jews, excluding them from public service. They had to register as Jews at their local prefecture, and all "foreign Jews" were immediately interned. In the summer of 1941, a second Jewish decree was enacted. Jews were forbidden from all industrial and commercial activities. This meant the Liebert family could no longer work; they had no way to support themselves. Jewish property and businesses were confiscated by the government. The government gave them a pittance for food.

Suzanne's father had helped Monsieur Liebert hide his precious equipment just before the arrival of the Germans in Nort; the two men shared a secret and a bond. Suzanne's father felt a responsibility to help his brave new friend. They did not have much to spare, but they gave what they could; usually they sent food they had grown in their garden. Often, it was Suzanne who packed the supplies, wrote the address on the boxes, and took them to the post office. The Liebert family depended on the supplies the Chédotal family sent to them, and they were grateful.

Tante and Tonton continued to run their butcher shop. People came in with ration coupons and purchased small amounts of meat or soup bones. (Most of the meat in the butcher shop was taken by the Germans. Though the German soldiers paid for the things they bought, they used a very unfair exchange rate and they did not need ration coupons.) Tante and Tonton had to be very careful not to give French people more meat than they had coupons for. One time, however, shortly after the war began, Suzanne developed a large cyst on her hand. It was very bothersome. Tante gave some meat to a doctor in Nantes in exchange for his services. He removed the cyst from

Suzanne's hand. It was a dangerous thing for Tante to do, but it demonstrated how much Tante loved Suzanne.

The Germans took whatever they wanted. They exploited the local farms and resources to supply their large military. One day, some German soldiers helped themselves to Suzanne's neighbor's cherry tree. The French neighbor called out, "Hey! Those are my cherries!" A German soldier shot him dead.

Alphonse was still installing new electric service; the farms in the country surrounding the town were the last properties to get electricity. Alphonse made friends with the people for whom he worked. His farmer friends sometimes gave him food to take home for his family. Occasionally, Suzanne rode miles out into the country on her bicycle to get a little butter or bread a farmer had offered to give them. She hid it under her jacket and snuck it home, hoping she would not be stopped by the Nazis. Her heart pounded, both from apprehension and exertion, while she pedaled as fast as she could.

The sun continued to rise and set over Nort. Its French citizens bravely faced each new day with determination, not only to survive, but to live. Bernard and Mark, two baby brothers, were added to the Chédotal family, one after the other.

Many of the traditions the Chédotal family had enjoyed before the war were abandoned. There were no more family vacations at the beach. No unauthorized travel by any French citizens was allowed. Their beloved beach at Pornichet had become part of the great Atlantic Wall, Germany's line of defense along the coast of continental Europe and Scandinavia. Heavily fortified concrete bunkers dotted the shoreline. Mines, barbed wire, and impediments littered the beach.

Of course, they no longer celebrated Bastille Day. Even if they had been allowed to commemorate the French Independence Day, it was futile. France was not independent. They could not fly the French flag. There was no *tete de veau* for a picnic.

The residents of Nort, however, found a way to keep some traditions alive. They hoped to provide a sense of normalcy and joy for the children. The annual school carnival was a much-loved and anticipated event. Though they had very little, they devised a plan to organize the carnival with simple games and surprises. Suddenly, while the outdoor event was in full swing, a bus drove up. German soldiers rounded up the older teenage boys and young men, put them on the bus, and drove off. Suzanne watched in horror as some of the boys jumped out of the bus windows and ran away. She assumed the kidnapped men and boys were taken to work camps in Germany.

By the end of World War II, 1.5 million people had been taken prisoner. More than 650,000 people between the ages of 18 and 50 were conscripted. Some of the men were forced to enlist in the German Army. Other people were deported to work in German factories under the hated *Service du Travail Obligatoire*, the compulsory work service. In addition, 250,000 French people had volunteered to work in Germany with the false promise of a good job and good wages. All of these, plus the missing Jews and Resistance Fighters, were referred to as "The Absent." Most of those who survived would not return home until 1945.

Even the French people who remained in France were required to work for the Germans. In addition to the vast quantity of supplies and services required by the German Army, the Nazis also made the French people build the bunkers and the defenses which made up the Atlantic Wall. The thousands of construction workers, waiters, cleaners, cooks, and laundry people who provided services for the occupying forces were paid by the local town prefectures through local tax authorities.

Some of the teenage girls in Nort, including Suzanne's good friends Georgette (CoCo), Linnea, and Erin, organized a girls' basketball team. Basketball was new to them and they didn't know the rules very well, but they had fun playing together. The team gave them purpose and a sense of belonging. Suzanne did not love playing basketball, but who could blame her? They played by the original girls' rules; Suzanne was a guard, so she did not cross the center line and she never had an opportunity to shoot the ball at the basket. Suzanne did enjoy being with the girls and she was a loyal friend; they needed her to have enough girls for a complete team, so she played. Sometimes the girls rode their bikes to nearby towns to play with other teams. One of the girls on their team was Jewish. She disappeared along with her parents who were the owners of the local grocery store. Suzanne never saw them again.

A lady named Mary LeClerc came on Fridays to do mending for Suzanne's mother. One Friday afternoon, baby Marc found a button she had dropped on the floor, put it in his mouth, and choked on it. They had just seen the football team walk by the front of their house, and the town doctor happened to be with them. Suzanne ran after them as fast as she could. She caught up with them at the football field at the edge of town. The doctor got on his bike and hurried to Suzanne's house. Suzanne's mother had been beating on Marc's back and was able to dislodge the button before the doctor arrived, but they had been very frightened.

The French people had very little unfiltered news from the outside world. They continued to get a French newspaper, but it was strictly controlled by the Vichy government and only told them what the Germans wanted them to know. German propaganda was everywhere: in the newspapers, on the radio, in posters hung around the towns. The Germans changed the beloved French slogan, "Liberty, Equality, Fraternity," to the German version, "Work, Family, Fatherland." They especially targeted the youth, intending to change the hearts and minds of the French; they wanted the people of France to become German supporters.

Radio Vichy and Radio Paris were both controlled by the Germans; they were formidable weapons of propaganda. Though it was prohibited, most French people listened to Radio London in secret during the early years of the occupation. Eventually, the Germany Army requisitioned all wireless sets. French citizens were strictly forbidden from keeping or listening to any radio. Suzanne was pretty sure her father had a hidden radio; it was the only way to find out what was going on in the outside world. She did not know her father had hidden his radio in a hollowed out electric transformer, high atop an electrical pole. He climbed the pole, pretended to be working on the equipment, and listened to the news and encouragement Radio London broadcasted from England.

Le Père Pinon was a farmer who lived two miles outside of town. He came frequently to see Suzanne's father. He came too frequently, actually, always bringing vegetables to Suzanne's family. Suzanne thought the vegetables were an excuse to talk with her father about the war. In fact, Le Père Pinon had a connection to the French Resistance. The Allies secretly dropped guns and radios to him under cover of night in pre-arranged locations. He distributed the supplies to the people of the resistance. When the Nazis eventually figured out what he was doing, both he and his wife disappeared, never to be seen again.

A 71-year-old farmer they knew was turned in. Suzanne did not know what was said about him, but both he and his housekeeper also disappeared.

The Nazis systematically raided the homes of Jews who had been arrested and taken to Germany. Most of the Jewish people in France had been wealthy. They owned very nice things. The Nazis packed their possessions in boxes, put the boxes on trains, and sent them to Germany. One evening, the local train station manager told Suzanne's father there was a train carrying such a cargo in Nort. It was to remain at the station overnight. The station manager knew the schedule of the guards. He helped Suzanne's father and some other men sneak onto the train in the darkness and take some of those boxes. It was a very dangerous thing to do. Suzanne got two dresses and a coat from the boxes. (They were a little small for her, but she wore them anyway.) There were also some lovely orange table napkins in those boxes. They did not feel like they were stealing from the Jewish people; they were intercepting items which were being sent to benefit the Germans.

Suzanne grew to be a beautiful young woman, but she was oblivious to her own beauty. In fact, she considered herself to be plain. Her humility only added to her charm. She was slender, soft-spoken, and reserved. She had a creamy complexion, a shy smile, and bright brown eyes. Things teenaged girls in other places or at other times might fret about were of no concern to Suzanne. She wasn't fussy about her clothes; she didn't need stockings or makeup.

Experimenting with different ways to style her short brown hair was fun for Suzanne. Sometimes, she used rags to make her hair curly. Before she went to bed, she wound strands of wet hair around small strips of cloth and tied the cloths in square knots to hold them in place. In the morning, she removed the rags and arranged the soft curls with a comb. It was fashionable to sew elastics together to make a headband around which the girls could tuck their hair to create a roll. Suzanne tried to imitate the trend, but she didn't think she was very successful at creating the new hair style.

Suzanne did not have a boyfriend and she was not interested in chasing boys. Some of the young women she knew became involved with German soldiers; she felt disdain for those girls. She wondered how they could stoop so low. She could not even imagine herself ever having a German friend.

11 ON HER OWN

The woman who follows the crowd
will usually go no further than the crowd.
The woman who walks alone
is likely to find herself
in places no one has ever been before.
—Albert Einstein

Suzanne walked beside her friend Ann Marie on the quiet street in front of her uncle's butcher shop. There was not much activity in the little town; most of the shops and cafés were closed. They avoided the town hall where the Nazi flag was displayed. The doors of the church were open, but they did not go in; its bells kept track of the time as the two 17-year-old girls enjoyed a rare opportunity to rendezvous and share their lives. Suzanne was visiting her grandmother in Héric. Ann Marie worked as a cook and maid in the home of a wealthy family in Nantes. She got one day off each week and had come home to Héric for the day.

The girls chatted about superficial things. Ann Marie described the large, stately house where she worked. "Why don't you come work with me, Suzanne?" Ann Marie pleaded. "It would be so nice to have you there."

Though she did not share the details with Ann Marie, Suzanne was eager to leave home and make her own way. Her father sometimes drank too much, and, when he was under the influence of alcohol, he was not very nice. Chédo was beloved in the community. No one outside the family could ever have imagined how mean he was to his wife. He was not always mean, but it was happening more and more often. When he worked on electrical issues in the homes of friends, neighbors, and even new acquaintances, he was frequently offered a drink of wine.

He knew these people were being hospitable, so he accepted their kind invitations. Often, by the time he came home for lunch or returned from work at the end of the day, he had had too much to drink. Then, he railed on his wife, using foul and abusive language. Suzanne and her siblings did their best to stay out of his way.

Germany had a firm hold on France, and there was no indication of that reality changing. Suzanne had few options. She decided it was time to strike out on her own. She hesitated only briefly before responding to Ann Marie's proposition, "Yes, I would like that."

Ann Marie promised to talk to her employers about Suzanne as soon as she got back to Nantes. The next week, Suzanne had a job working as a live-in housekeeper and nanny. The shy, naïve, country girl took her bicycle and her few patched clothes and moved to the big City of Nantes, 23 miles away from her home.

Suzanne's employers were wealthy. They bought food and some of the other things they wanted on the black market. Suzanne was given her own room on the third floor; it was the first time she ever had a room to herself. She worked six days a week. Often, she took the train home to Nort when she had a day off. Other times, however, she stayed in the city and visited her mother's friend who was a seamstress in Nantes.

Suzanne enjoyed cleaning the big, beautiful house. She was tasked with doing the cooking when Ann Marie had the day off. That was more stressful for Suzanne because she had very little experience cooking. She did have experience with children of all ages at home, so she was comfortable caring for her employers' children. They had a four-year-old boy and a baby. Next to their house was a large park. On sunny mornings, Suzanne put the baby in a carriage, took the little boy's hand, and the three of them walked to the park.

The staff was not treated like family, but Suzanne respected their privacy, and she did her best to please the people she worked for. One afternoon, when she was dusting in the living room, a picture on the other side of the room fell off the wall and broke a vase. The family heard the crash and came running. Suzanne tried to explain she hadn't touched the picture, but they did not believe her. Suzanne spent many nights crying about that incident. She was deeply hurt because her employers didn't believe her. She no longer felt comfortable in their home.

Suzanne decided to study the German language. She hoped knowing how to speak German would help her get a better job. She found a textbook and embarked on teaching herself the unfamiliar language.

After working in Nantes for a year, Suzanne spent an afternoon with her mother's seamstress friend. Suzanne mentioned she was not happy with her position. The seamstress listened carefully and had an idea. She knew the manager of the *Banque Postal* in Nantes. (The *Banque Postal* is a French bank, created as a subsidiary of *La Poste*, the national postal service.) She talked to him about Suzanne and provided a glowing recommendation. She told him Suzanne was the oldest of seven children and had proven to be a good worker, honest, and dependable. She went on to relate that Suzanne's family was very respectable, but they needed extra money because they had so many children. The banker was interested and sympathetic. Unfortunately, Suzanne was not qualified for the available position at the bank because she had not graduated from high school. He suggested Suzanne could take a test to demonstrate she had the necessary skills and knowledge. Suzanne passed the test with flying colors and was hired to be a bookkeeper.

With the new job, Suzanne also needed a new place to live. She found a room to rent in a convent near the *Gare de Nantes*, the city's main train station. Her room was tiny, with just enough space for a bed, a table, and a chair. The Benedictine nuns who lived at the convent devoted their lives to prayer and work, welcoming guests, charity, and silence. Because these nuns did not speak, Suzanne thought it was not much fun to live with them. She was naturally reserved, but she wished she could get to know her housemates. She was at a loss as to how to make that happen. Suzanne ate one conversation-less meal with the nuns every evening; their supper consisted of only noodles and buns.

Throughout the war, Nantes was a center of conflict. The French Resistance based its underground operations in Nantes. German Nazis prized Nantes for its transportation links; the large train station and port were critical to German supply lines. It was also a thriving industrial city. The Germans controlled French factories so French industry was contributing to the Nazi war effort.

In 1941, the British began night bombing raids on Nantes in an effort to loosen Germany's hold on France. Then, the Americans joined the fray. The United States attacked during daylight hours, with formations of bombers escorted by fighter planes. German controlled factories and transportation assets were all targets of the Allied bombing raids, but often civilians became "collateral damage." Air strikes were a constant threat for the people living in the city. The worst attacks occurred in September of 1943, when most of Nante's industrial facilities and portions of the city center and surrounding area were destroyed by Allied bombs.

As the city experienced more and more oppression from both the Nazi occupation and the Allied bombing, a group of French civilian volunteers banded together to form the "Passive Resistance." These compassionate, brave individuals undertook to help the people of Nantes. They established an air raid warning system to alert citizens of incoming aircraft. They dug trenches and identified other safe places to which residents could flee for protection when the bombs fell. They tried to rescue people who were buried under rubble and debris, and they buried the dead.

Suzanne's younger brother, Raymond, also found employment in Nantes. School was not an option for children past the age of 12 during the occupation. When he was only 14, Raymond moved to Nantes to apprentice in a bakery. He learned to make the bread which, even though it was rationed, was still a staple of the French diet. Raymond slept in the attic of the bakery on bags of flour. He also joined the Passive Resistance; Raymond volunteered with the detail assigned to bury the people who were killed in the bombing raids.

Suzanne was always prepared to drop everything and run when the air raid sirens wailed. Many times, she heard the warning sirens when she was at work. She ran several blocks with her co-workers and other city-dwellers to find shelter in an unfinished railroad tunnel. They waited in the tunnel until they heard the all-clear signal. The French people wanted to be liberated, but they hated the bombing. The Americans' help was both a blessing and a curse.

One evening, Suzanne returned to the convent where she lived and found it had been hit by an American bomb. The convent was located near the railroad station; surely, the transportation hub had been the intended target. She stood on the street, staring at the destruction. She could hear the nuns who were buried under the rubble crying. Nothing could be done to help them, so they died, trapped in the ruins.

Suzanne lost most of the few things she owned when the convent was destroyed. She also needed another place to live. She found temporary lodging with some nuns who ran a Catholic hospital. This order of nuns spoke, and one of the young sisters became Suzanne's good friend. Suzanne was invited to stay with that nun's parents until she could find permanent housing. She slept on the couch in their living room.

During the times when the bombing was most frequent, Suzanne went home on the weekends. She sometimes rode her bicycle the 23 miles to Nort, but, more often, she made the commute by train.

The bombing of Nantes sent many civilians fleeing to country towns and villages where bombing raids were not as likely to occur. People in the areas surrounding Nantes opened their homes to the refugees. Spare bedrooms, living room couches, and even haylofts were filled with people who needed a safe place to stay away from the horrors of the war. Many refugees came to Nort-Sur-Erdre.

In Nort, Suzanne sometimes stood outside in the darkness,

gazing at the sky. No artificial light escaped from the carefully covered windows of the houses. She watched bombs streaking through the sky in the distance over Nantes. The sight made Suzanne shiver. She didn't know where the bombs were falling. She worried about their impact on her own life.

Suzanne made the acquaintance of four boys when she commuted between Nantes and Nort. These young men fled the bombing of Nantes to find safety in her hometown. The four refugees traveled to Nantes for work, as did Suzanne. She often ran into them on the train coming and going. Suzanne joined them as they traveled; she found security as part of the little group of five friends who made the trip together.

Across the street from the train station in Nantes was a large public botanical garden. Before the war, it had been a beautiful place for residents of Nantes to enjoy. No one spent time cultivating the garden during the occupation years. Instead, it became a place of refuge for the residents when the bombs were falling. Long, deep, trenches were dug throughout the garden.

One Friday afternoon, when Suzanne was waiting for the train in Nantes, warning sirens began to wail. Everyone ran to the safest place in the area—the trenches across the street from the station in the gardens. Suzanne crouched in a deep trench, along with many other travelers from the train station and pedestrians from the nearby streets. The trenches were open to the clear blue sky. Suzanne heard the approaching planes before she saw them. She looked up at the Flying Fortresses—large American B-17 bombers. They got very close before they began dropping their deadly cargo. The bombs looked like little bags of candy falling out of the planes. Suzanne's heart raced as she watched them fall to the ground. They landed just a few blocks away. The bombs exploded with a cloud of smoke followed by a thunderous roar. The ground shook and Suzanne's ears hurt from the sound.

Suzanne's parents did not harbor refugees from Nantes. They insisted they had no room for extra people. In reality, they already had secret guests hiding in their basement. The Chédotal family had been helping the Liebert family since the early days of the occupation, hiding their valuable equipment and sending them food. New government decrees made life increasingly more difficult for French Jews. On March 27, 1942, the first French Jews left for Auschwitz on a train carrying 1,112 French men, women, and children to their death. The campaign to eliminate Jewish people from France continued to intensify. The situation for the Jews became most dire when Nazi Germany's leaders planned the "Final Solution of the Jewish Question." This was the euphemism used to refer to the complete extermination of the Jewish population.

Mr. Liebert again reached out to his new friend, Alphonse Chédotal, for help. He had an even more precious cargo than his modern machine that needed hiding—his family. Alphonse and Laurence opened their home to these Jewish refugees. They hid the Jewish couple in the basement of the family home in Nort-Sur-Erdre. Alphonse and Laurence kept the presence of their guests a secret, even from their children. On March 30, 1944, the prefect of the area issued this statement, "There are currently no more Israelites in the Departement of the Loire-Inferieure." The officials did not know that there were, indeed, still "Israelites" in the area.

The reason behind the hatred of the Jews was a mystery to Suzanne. Suzanne was not alone. Even historians offer various conflicting explanations about why people are anti-Semitic: Jews are too powerful or too lazy; too separate or a threat to "racial purity" through assimilation; pacifists or warmongers; capitalist exploiters or revolutionary communists; the "killers" of Jesus or the progenitors of Jesus; possessors of a chosen people mentality or an inferiority complex.

Anne Frank was a young Jewish girl who hid from the Nazis in the Netherlands during World War II. In her diary, she reflected, "These reasons have one thing in common—they have nothing to do with our being Jewish. One might think that we are just the victims of bad luck—always possessing the needed quality to be hated wherever we are in the world at exactly that time in history. Who has made us Jews different from all other people? Who has allowed us to suffer so terribly up until now? It is God who has made us as we are, but it will be God, too, who will raise us up again. Who knows? It might even be our religion from which the world and all peoples learn good, and for that reason and only that reason do we suffer. We can never become just Netherlanders, or just English, or representatives of any country for that matter. We will always remain Jews."

No bombs fell on Nort-Sur-Erdre during World War II, but the people of the town were constantly vigilant. The train station was a link in the German supply chain, and German soldiers occupied the town; the threat of Nort becoming a target was real.

One day, a German soldier came to the Chédotal home. Suzanne's mother was terrified. She bravely opened the door, feigned calmness, and listened politely as the Nazi soldier told her to do a better job covering the upstairs window at the back of the house. All the windows had to be covered with blankets or dark cloths to keep light from shining out into the dark night. It was important for the town to be completely dark so it couldn't be detected by bombers at night. Maman complied. She understood the Germans were watching even the sheltered back of the house. They were unaware of her secret guests. Suzanne was glad she was not at home when the soldiers came. She did not know about the Jews hiding in her parents' basement. Nevertheless, she wanted to avoid all contact with any German occupiers.

Saint-Nazaire, the home of Suzanne's beloved Grandmère-Nazaire, was a strategic port for German forces. As a result, it also endured many assaults during the war.

The Nazis used the dry dock where the SS Normandie was built as a repair facility for its large boats. The gates of the dock could be closed, allowing the lock to be drained. This made it possible to work on normally submerged parts of ships. In 1942, the British conducted Operation Chariot, an amphibious attack on the heavily defended Normandie dry dock. An obsolete destroyer, accompanied by 18 smaller craft, crossed the English

Channel and was rammed into the Normandie dock gates. The ship had been packed with delayed-action explosives which detonated later that day. There were many casualties on both sides, but the dry dock was rendered unusable until after the end of the war. As a result, large German ships had to travel long distances for repairs.

The Nazis constructed a huge U-boat base in Saint-Nazaire. The enormous reinforced concrete bunker contained two flotillas of submarines. It measured 300 meters long, 130 meters wide, and 18 meters high. In addition to housing the submarines and their dry docks, the building also included everything needed to support the 25,000 German troops who were stationed there. There were 62 workshops, 97 warehouses for spare parts, 150 offices for supplies, 92 dormitories and rooms for crew, along with kitchens, bakeries, a restaurant, a hospital, toilets, and shower rooms. The building was a town in itself. There were enough goods stockpiled within its walls to keep those German soldiers supplied for two years. The bunker protected the U-boats from Allied bombing raids throughout the war. Despite 50 separate bombing attacks, the Allies were unable to damage it. Instead, they resorted to destroying the town surrounding the base with high-altitude carpet-bombing raids.

During one of the raids, Grandmère-Nazaire's house was damaged, and she was hurt. Though she recovered from her injuries, she spent time in the hospital. She never returned to her old house. For several months, Grandmère-Nazaire lived in one of the tiny houses across the street from the Chédotal family home in Nort. She was homesick for Saint-Nazaire, however, and moved back to the area as soon as she could.

Eventually, Suzanne rented a room in a house in Nantes. It was owned by three unmarried sisters who lived in the house by themselves. The house was about one-quarter mile from where Suzanne worked. It was very clean. The floors were made of dark wood, and they were polished until they shone. Suzanne's small room had a bed, a chest, and a table with a wash bowl. A large jar of water with a spigot was Suzanne's water supply. She was unhappy about a mouse she sometimes saw in her room; she did not like the mouse. Her room had no heat; she was often cold and lonely and afraid. The window of Suzanne's room opened onto the boulevard, so she could hear the noise in the street. She noticed some Catholic priests frequented the house late at night; they always left very early in the morning. Suzanne was aware of the improprieties going on in the house. Once again, she was disappointed by the Catholic church.

Suzanne was very much on her own in Nantes in early June of 1944. She was constantly looking for food; she didn't have much money, and there wasn't much food in the stores. She stood in long lines each evening with her ration coupons, hoping to procure something for her evening meal. She had to hurry to get home before darkness fell and the curfew began. Sometimes she could purchase two little pieces of bread from a nearby bakery. She spread the bread with applesauce her mother had made and put it together like a sandwich. That was the extent of her evening meal. Life was hard, and Suzanne longed for something different.

12 LOVE BLOSSOMS

I don't know; je ne sais pas.
Maybe; peut-etre.
—Juliette Harrouet and Therese Fraud

Suzanne's perspective changed dramatically during the seven months between June of 1944 and January of 1945. She had been a lonely, hungry, frightened teenager, living under the thumb of the Nazi occupation, with little hope of rescue. Then, the Americans came.

There were still battles to be fought, but Suzanne felt the fresh breeze of hope and promise. Her teenage years were behind her. 1945 was a brand-new year. She was enjoying Bing's company.

The Liebert family had remained hidden in the basement of the Chédotal home until the Allies forced the retreat of the occupying Germans from Nort-Sur-Erdre in August of 1944. They returned to their home near Paris, taking with them the precious machine that had been hidden under the hay in the neighbor's barn. It had remained there, undetected by the Germans, throughout the war.

It was a relief to be free from the German occupation in Nantes, Nort-Sur-Erdre, and Héric. Suzanne liked seeing American soldiers on the streets of France instead of the Nazis. Saint-Nazaire, however, was still behind enemy lines. Suzanne worried about Grandmère-Nazaire. It was impossible to visit her; she was not free. Suzanne's family had not been able to communicate with her in several months. The American soldiers would stay in this part of France until every last pocket of German resistance was defeated.

The respite Suzanne experienced while visiting her relatives in Héric brought both physical and emotional healing. Soon Suzanne's finger healed, and it was time for her to go back to work in Nantes. As she prepared to leave Héric, Bing asked for her address. Suzanne could see her grandmother in the background shaking her finger and mouthing the words, "Don't you give him your address. Don't give him your address!" Suzanne gave Bing only her work address.

Suzanne rode her bike to Nort-Sur-Erdre and spent the night at home with her family. She planned to take the train to Nantes the next morning. There were American soldiers in Nort-Sur-Erdre, as well as in Héric and Nantes. American trucks frequently passed on the street in front of the Chédotal home. The American men in her hometown had black skin. Her family had never seen colored people before. Two of those young men were welcomed into the Chédotal home on a regular basis. Suzanne's brothers adored them. They were kind and friendly. They brought the children candy. Little Marc was so enthralled with them that he declared, "When I grow up, I want to be a black American."

Suzanne had met the two black American soldiers when she was at home for a weekend in the fall. One of the young men asked Suzanne to show him the garden, so she walked in the back yard with him. When they were out of sight of the back door, he tried to kiss her. Suzanne was surprised and displeased; she refused the kiss. The young man wanted to know if she wouldn't kiss him because he was black. Suzanne was greatly offended. Her refusal had nothing to do with the color of his skin. Suzanne barely knew the young man and she did not give out kisses freely. Bing did not take such liberties with her.

When she returned to Nantes, Suzanne settled once again into her normal post-war routine. She worked long hours at the Banque Postal. She was friendly with her co-workers, but there was little time before or after work for socializing. She was always happy to see her desk mate. They were work friends and it was a comfortable relationship. She did not know if she would ever see Bing again.

The residents of Nantes did not need to seek refuge in the country anymore, so Suzanne no longer traveled with the four boys she had become acquainted with on the train during the time of the bombing. She occasionally saw them on the streets of Nantes. They were always friendly, but Suzanne rarely spent much time with them. Perhaps one of them had more than a casual interest in her, but she was oblivious to that fact. She considered them friends.

One afternoon, shortly after returning to Nantes from her sojourn in Héric, Suzanne finished her work, walked down the two flights of stairs, and stepped out the front door into the cold, misty, January twilight. She could see the four boys she knew from the train waiting for her across the street. Then, to her complete surprise, she saw Bing and his friend Ralph. She had no idea how they could have gotten to Nantes, but there they were, waiting for her, as well. She looked across the street at the boys and then turned her attention to Bing. That was the last time the boys ever waited for her. They knew she had made a choice.

Suzanne did not know what to do with Bing and Ralph. She could not bring them back to her room. She had nothing to offer them to eat. She had no way to entertain them. She was flustered and uncomfortable. They walked along the streets of Nantes in the cold, wet mist. It was hard to talk to Bing with Ralph there. Bing was always patient and seemed to understand what she was trying to communicate, but, with Ralph there, Suzanne was frazzled and didn't know what to say or do. Even if they had a language in common, she wouldn't have known what to say. As they walked by the damaged Saint Nicolas Basilica, they ducked inside the big front doors. The church provided shelter from the miserable weather and a distraction from the lack of conversation.

Bing and Ralph did not stay long; they had to return to Héric. Suzanne did not have the words to ask how they planned to get back to the encampment. She thought they must be hitchhiking. French people were happy to accommodate the American soldiers who had liberated them. At least she knew Bing did want to see her again. She decided she would go to Héric as soon as possible and connect with Bing in the security of the little town and the company of her relatives.

Suzanne worked in Nantes from Monday through Friday, but she went to Héric every weekend after her unexpected encounter with Bing in Nantes. Bing and Suzanne spent those days together. Their fondness for each other deepened and their desire to spend time together grew. Tante and Therese teased Suzanne, "We never used to see you at all and now we see you all the time. You run after Bing with a bicycle."

Love is a magical feeling, and Suzanne knew she was in love with Bing. She wanted nothing more than to be with him. She could tell he was different from the other guys. He was a gentleman and he always treated her with respect. Bing could see Suzanne was different from the other girls. She never went to the military camps or the bars to hang out where the soldiers were.

Weekends in Héric were so pleasant when Suzanne and Bing were together. Mostly, they went for walks around the little town, through the *Place de la Republique*, or past the church and out into the country. Suzanne enjoyed introducing Bing to the town where she had lived as a little girl. She pointed out the store where she spent the money her grandfather gave her to buy candy, the saddlery with the delicious smell of leather, and the school where she had first learned to read. She showed him the two-story brick and stucco house where she was born 20 years before. Some things had changed, to be sure, but this neighborhood had survived the war mostly intact.

Years before, a comical little Michelin Man had hung over the door of the bicycle repair shop near her childhood home; it had enchanted her when she was a little girl, but it was gone now. The bicycle shop, along with her mother's café and pool hall had been sold. The little bicycle shop had been converted into a small apartment and rented to Tante's friend, Madame Avenard.

Madame Avenard had married a very wealthy, much older man who owned a huge mansion on the boulevard facing the beach in Saint-Nazaire. She inherited the mansion when her husband died. Shortly before the war, Suzanne was invited to spend a weekend there. She remembered fondly the stately home and the sound of the surf on the beach at night.

When the Nazis invaded Saint-Nazaire, German officers were billeted in Madame Avenard's beautiful mansion; she was forced to leave her home, so she rented the little apartment in Héric. Madame Avenard often visited her mansion in Saint-Nazaire and sometimes she was gone for a few days. It seems she became a little too friendly with the German officers who lived in her house.

When French towns were liberated, the people of the resistance punished the French citizens who had colluded with the Germans. Those who had helped the Germans, and thereby caused the deaths of French people, were executed for treason. Women who had relationships with German soldiers were charged with *collaboration horizontale*. Madame Avenard was arrested. They brought her to the *Place de la Republique* in Héric and shaved her head.

Suzanne was at home in Nort that night. Madame Avenard rode her bike to Nort. She knocked on the door of Suzanne's parents' home. Though it was the middle of the night, they invited her to come in. She was wearing a scarf on her head. When she removed the scarf, Suzanne was surprised to see she was completely bald. Suzanne's parents let her stay with them until she figured out what to do next. Now the apartment was vacant. Suzanne did not know where Madame Avenard had gone. The war had indeed brought changes to this little town and the people who lived here.

Sometimes, Suzanne and Bing sat together on the chairs that were set along the narrow street just outside the front door of Tante's house. Though Suzanne did not speak English and Bing did not speak French, they managed to share their hearts. They used gestures, and they made good use of a little French/English phrase book Bing had been issued by the Army. They found appropriate phrases and tried to say them to each other. They laughed good naturedly at their failed attempts to pronounce each other's language.

Suzanne began to learn a little bit of English. She memorized two very useful English phrases, which she paired with their French translations. She often responded to Bing's English explanations by saying, "I don't know; je ne sais pas." She sometimes answered his questions, "Maybe; peut-etre."

Soon Tante and Therese also picked up those phrases. They delighted in teasing Suzanne by saying, all in one breath in both languages, "I don't know; je ne sais pas. Maybe; peut-etre." Then, they laughed at the extent of their knowledge of English and enjoyed with Suzanne her deepening relationship with Bing.

Their weekends together always passed too quickly. On Sunday afternoons the bells of Saint Nicholas Catholic Church signaled the time for Suzanne to return to Nantes. Bing borrowed Aunt Juliette's bike so he could accompany Suzanne for half of the eight miles from Héric to Nort. (Suzanne would leave her bicycle in Nort and take the train to Nantes.) They knew the halfway point at the top of a long hill between the two towns. They said goodbye at that spot; Suzanne continued on to Nort while Bing returned to the encampment near Héric. Suzanne always went just a short distance, stopped, and turned around to see Bing watching her. They waved at each other one more time before Suzanne went on her way.

Bing kept coming to the butcher shop for a piece of steak in the evenings, even when Suzanne was not there. He often visited with Tante and Tonton and Therese and Berik. During the five-month period Bing was stationed near Héric, they developed a strong friendship; they enjoyed each other's company, and they were quick to help each other.

One evening, Bing brought Therese a bowl of cake batter. He asked her to bake it for him in the oven at her bakery. The next day, when Bing returned, Therese handed him the cake. She had baked it right in the bowl he had used to bring her the batter. Therese was an expert bread maker, but she did not know much about baking cakes.

Another time, Tante told Bing she had a tooth ache. It was very bothersome, and she didn't know what to do about it. Bing brought the dentist from his medic unit to see her. The dentist took her back to the encampment and fixed her tooth.

Bing liked these French people he had befriended, and he very much liked the girl they had introduced him to. His thoughts turned to making Suzanne a permanent part of his life, but her world was very different from his own.

13 BING'S STORY

I do solemnly swear
that I will support and defend
the Constitution of the United States
against all enemies, foreign and domestic;
that I will bear true faith and allegiance to the same;
and that I will obey the orders
of the president of the United States
and the orders of the officers appointed over me,
according to regulations
and the uniform code of military justice,
so help me God.
Oath of Enlistment, US Army

Author's note:

Bing never told his story. He didn't tell Suzanne about his experiences during the war. He never even shared with her the memories of his youth or what he knew about his heritage. At first, they had no language in common. Then, life became busy and they didn't take the time to talk about the past. When I asked my mother-in-law about Bing's history, she responded wistfully, "I wish I had asked him these questions. I don't know why I never did."

There may have been many reasons for Bing's silence. Some of his memories were painful; perhaps he did not want to relive them. Some of his experiences were highly classified; sharing the details was forbidden by the United States military. His culture and his generation also played a part in the fact that Bing did not talk about his life story with his wife, his children, or his grandchildren. Perhaps he was afraid they would not understand the complex details of his past.

My husband and I collected bits and pieces of information from family members. Mostly, they were comments Bing had made in passing over many years. We were able to obtain some of his official military service records. However, much of that information was destroyed in a devastating fire at the National Personnel Records Center in St. Louis, Missouri in 1973. We poured over photographs, notes, memorabilia, and official documents Bing had saved. We meshed the personal information we gathered with historical accounts to piece together the following account of Bing's life.

Suzanne was delighted with the information we found. It gave her a new perspective about her husband and his history. She gained a better understanding of the events which led Bing to the little butcher shop in Héric where their lives intersected. We, his children, are fascinated by his story.

◆ ◆ ◆

Bing Yee Ng was born in Guangzhou, China on March 17, 1920. He was raised by his Chinese family; his youth was steeped in Chinese culture. Though Bing's mother was also born in China, his father was born in San Francisco,

California. A child born abroad to one United States citizen parent and one alien parent is considered a United States citizen at birth. Therefore, Bing had the good fortune of being an American citizen on the day he was born.

The Ng family owned a successful import/export business. They had relatives and business connections in New York City, San Francisco, Hong Kong, and China. These contacts gave them reason to travel between the four places.

Bing first came to the United states when he was seven. He spent about a year living in New York with his family. His parents hired a teacher from Italy to introduce Bing and his brother Jimmy to the English language. Then, Bing returned to China to complete his education. He graduated from high school in Shu Shan, Canton, China in 1935.

After finishing school, Bing came back to the United States. He settled in New York City, where his parents also lived at that time. The ambitious young man took a job working for Chinese Laundries at 131-14 Liberty Avenue, Brooklyn, New York. His responsibilities included driving a pickup truck to make deliveries, accepting payments, making reports, and completing minor maintenance on the delivery truck.

In the early 1930's, there were more than 3,500 Chinese laundries in New York City. In fact, one in four ethnic Chinese men in the US worked in a laundry. Many of the Chinese immigrants had poor English-language skills and a lack of capital. These hard working, entrepreneurial individuals identified a need for laundry service in the city and developed a way to meet the need. They were then able to provide employment for newly arriving Chinese immigrants. Chinese laundries were sometimes the butt of jokes intended to demean the Chinese minority population. However, when the Great Depression hit New York City, these businesses were coveted by other people whose business endeavors could not survive in the hard economic times.

Bing loved to hang out at nearby Floyd Bennett Field. Between World War I and World War II, Floyd Bennett Field was used for general aviation. Pioneer aviators and dare devils made history there. Dozens of records were set by pilots flying to or from Bennett Field. Amelia Earhart was one of the airport's most famous aviators at that time. Bing was enthralled by the planes; he seized on an opportunity to learn to fly.

Bing worked at Chinese Laundries for almost five years, until October 1940. Then, like his father before him, Bing traveled to China to marry a girl chosen for him by his family. Bing's uncle lived in Hong Kong. With family connections there, Bing and his young bride, Ching Fung Low, began their married lives in the thriving British Colony of Hong Kong.

In 1937, Japan had begun attacking China. The Japanese invaded city after city. They were brutal, and China was not prepared to defend herself. At that time, Japan was not at war with Great Britain, so Hong Kong appeared to be safe from Japan's sinister advances.

Claire Chennault, a former American Army pilot, was recruited by China's leader, Chiang Kai-shek, and his bright, beautiful, and influential American-educated wife, Madame Chiang. Chennault was tasked with assembling a group of volunteer American pilots to help China fend off Japanese aggressions. They were officially called the American Volunteer Group (AVG). Though President Roosevelt surreptitiously supported this clandestine mission, the AVG was not openly connected to the United States military. The United States was officially neutral; any role they played in the AVG was kept secret. Most of Chenault's recruits were former military pilots who wanted to fly fighter planes and who were enticed by the promise of adventure and lucrative salaries.

Chennault was able to arrange for China to acquire 100 American-made P-40 airplanes for his pilots to fly. The Curtis P-40 Warhawk was a single-engine, single-seat, all metal fighter and ground-attack aircraft. The rugged airplane was designed to withstand ground fire. General George C. Kenney reported the P-40 could, "slug it out, absorb gunfire, and fly home."

On July 28, 1941, the first American Volunteer Group arrived in Rangoon, Burma. Burma was chosen as the location from which to base their training and operations because of its proximity to China and because it was part of the British Commonwealth. The base was run-down and poorly equipped, but the pilots trained hard under the leadership of Chennault. He inspired them. They became a highly skilled group of fighter pilots. While they waited for their opportunity to defend China, they trained, played cards or Acey-Deucey, read books, and explored the area. They painted the noses of their planes to look like sharks with huge white teeth, gaping mouths, and beady eyes.

Chennault needed support staff for the AVG. In October, he traveled around the Far East looking for "whatever American civilians happened to be available." He crossed paths with Bing Yee Ng in Hong Kong. Bing would be an asset to Chennault; he was fluent in both English and Chinese and could serve as a translator for the AVG. Bing, who loved both the United States and China, volunteered.

On December 7, 1941, the same day Pearl Harbor was attacked, Japanese forces invaded Hong Kong. They bombed and shelled the urban areas of the city. More than 4,000 civilians were killed in the Battle of Hong Kong, including Bing's young wife. Bing was only 21 when he became a widower. On Christmas Day of that year, Hong Kong surrendered to Japan. It was fortunate Bing had already left the area; all Americans remaining in Hong Kong were taken prisoner by the Japanese troops.

The AVG soon began both defensive and offensive missions.

They were uncanny in their ability to accomplish a lot with very little. Their victories inspired the American people during the early part of the United States' involvement in World War II. They gave Americans both hope and something to be proud of. The AVG was dubbed the Flying Tigers.

During Bing's attachment to the Flying Tigers, he spent time hiding in the jungles of Burma. He hunted for snakes and monkeys to eat while watching for Japanese snipers. It was necessary for the men to shake out their shirts in the morning to get rid of the scorpions. Bing contracted jungle rot; a chronic ulcerative skin lesion caused by a variety of microorganisms found in tropical climates. These infections left him with deep, pockmark scars on his legs, a lasting reminder of his jungle experiences.

By June of 1942, the United States was actively involved in the defense of China and the Flying Tigers disbanded. The toll on their bodies, their resources, and their numbers were great. Though they were in action for only seven months, they fought 50 major battles and never lost one. One of their major accomplishments was turning the Japanese back from the Burma Road, an important supply route into China. Some of the Flying Tigers, including their leader, Claire Chennault, agreed to join the Army and stay in China. Chennault was assigned the rank of General. Bing Ng traveled back to the United States where he enlisted in the United States Army.

In the weeks between his return to the United States and his induction into the Army, Bing went to San Francisco. He stayed with his uncle who owned a restaurant at 762 Clay Street. Shortly after arriving in California, Bing was arrested by American authorities because they thought he was Japanese.

The attack on Pearl Harbor caused the United States to fear Japan might invade the continental United States. With most of her Pacific fleet destroyed at Pearl Harbor, the United States was ill-prepared to fend off such an invasion. President Roosevelt confided to his wife, "We will have to take a good many defeats before we can have a victory." He feared the Japanese could make it as far as Chicago before their forces would become over-extended.

American military leaders thought Japan might have planted Japanese people in the United States ahead of the war. Their purpose would be to work covertly against the United States when Japan implemented their planned invasion. (Japan had effectively employed that strategy in the Philippines.) American authorities rounded up civilians of Japanese descent. They were held in internment camps for the duration of the United States' involvement in the war, despite lack of evidence against them. Most of the 117,000 interned Japanese civilians were American citizens. Bing was held for only a few days, until he could prove he was Chinese, not Japanese.

Bing's Army career began on July 11, 1942. His enlistment papers documented his schooling and prior employment. His past occupations were recorded as truck driver and cook. (There was no mention of the time period between October 1940 and July 1942; those years, which Bing spent in Hong Kong or supporting the Flying Tigers, were conspicuously absent.) The official records noted Bing was proficient in speaking, reading, and writing Chinese. His hobbies were listed as hunting and playing basketball. He could play the Chinese piano, also known as a Chinese Zither. The ability to play this stringed instrument was a skill, the enlistment papers suggested, which could be used for entertainment. The Army mistakenly recorded Bing's birthday as January 27, 1920.

The Army's error was never corrected to show Bing's actual birth date, March 17, 1920. Bing took great pleasure in celebrating his birthday twice each year.

Bing was assigned to the US Army 66th Infantry Division. The insignia he wore on his left uniform sleeve was a black panther's head on a circular orange background within a red border. The panther was chosen as a mascot for the 66th Infantry Division because it symbolizes the attributes of a good infantryman: ability to kill, to be aggressive, alert, stealthy, cunning, agile, and strong. Bing's job was cooking and acting as a medical aide for the 366th Medical Battalion of the 66th Infantry Division.

The Panthers came to France on December 24, 1944. They were summoned to reinforce Allied troops who were fighting at the Battle of the Bulge in Belgium, Luxembourg, and Northeast France. In mid-December of 1944, the German Army had begun a last-ditch effort to push the advancing Allied Forces back and regain control of Western Europe. They were determined; they staged a *blitzkrieg* (lightning) counter-offensive and fought with everything they had. The Allied Forces on the front lines needed help to withstand this onslaught and keep pressing toward Germany and their goal: the defeat of the Third Reich.

On Christmas Eve, 1944, the men of the 66th Infantry Division boarded two former ocean liners which had been converted to troop ships. The SS Leopold-ville took more than 2,000 men. The rest of the 66th traveled on the HMS Cheshire. They left the pier at Southampton, England, bound for Cherbourg, France. The two troop ships formed a convoy with an escort of four Royal Navy destroyers, including the HMS Brilliant. Enemy U-boats were sighted in the area, so

PRESENTING THE

Panther Division

the convoy traveled in a zig-zag pattern. This made crossing the English Channel take longer than it would have if they had traveled in a straight line, but it made it more difficult for enemy submarines to hit the ships with torpedoes. The seas were rough as the group of six Allied ships made their way 100 miles across the English Channel.

Just before six o'clock that evening, a torpedo fired from the German submarine U-486 struck the Leopoldville. Three hundred men were killed instantly. The Brilliant pulled alongside to take on survivors. The other destroyers in the convoy chased the submarine, attempting to defend against more attacks.

Many soldiers from the sinking ship jumped onto the smaller Brilliant. There was a height difference of 40 feet between the deck of the Leopoldville and the deck of the Brilliant. Many of those who jumped were severely injured. The crew rushed to bring hammocks to the deck to cushion the fall of the jumping soldiers. Some of the soldiers missed the jump completely, fell between the two ships, and were crushed as the waves caused the ships to bump against each other.

The Brilliant picked up 500 survivors. The men were instructed to spread out evenly, both above and below decks, to keep the boat from capsizing. It was very overloaded, with just inches of freeboard. The captain was afraid the ship would sink if they took on any more weight, so they headed to Cherbourg.

They hoped other ships would take on the rescue. However, when they arrived in Cherbourg, they found most of the ships in the port had been scuttled by the Germans. Also, would-be rescuers were enjoying Christmas Eve parties; they were unaware of the tragedy taking place on the sea just five miles from the safety of the harbor.

The Leopoldville sank by the stern at 8:30 p.m. Soldiers who were not quickly rescued either drowned or died of hypothermia in the 48-degree waters of the English Channel. Bing would always be haunted by the memory of so many dead bodies floating in the water. Over 800 lives were lost that evening, including 763 servicemen from the 66th Infantry Division.

After the disaster at sea, the sinking of the Leopoldville was deemed highly classified. Survivors were warned not to breathe a word of it to anyone. Even the letters they sent home were

censored. The Army was afraid news of the disaster would dis-
courage the Allied Forces who were still struggling to defeat
the Nazis; neither did they want the Germans to know so many
reinforcements had been lost. In addition, they did not want
the citizens on the home front to understand the magnitude of
the loss. Besides, it was a great embarrassment to the military.
The rescue could have been handled better; there need not have
been so much loss of life.

*Years later, when the men of the 66th Infantry Division
were discharged from the service, they were instructed
to keep the sinking of the Leopoldville secret. They were
warned they would lose their veterans benefits if they
spoke about it. It was not until 1959 that American National Archives documents about this event were declas-
sified. The men of the 66th had no way of knowing about
the declassification. British documents about the Leopoldville remained classified until 1996.*

The remnants of the decimated 66th Infantry Division
gathered in Cherbourg on Christmas Day. Tents were set up to
house the survivors. This tent city became known as "Purple
Heart Hill." The people of Cherbourg were not strangers to
death and destruction; they had just recently sustained much
damage and loss of life in the month-long, intense battle for
Cherbourg's liberation.

One of the first priorities of the Allied Forces when they came
ashore on the beaches of Normandy just six months earlier,
was to take control of the port cities and establish supply lines
for the advancing troops. They cut off the Cotentin Peninsula
to isolate Cherbourg. Then, they fought to liberate the City of
Cherbourg and its port. The task was harder than they anticipated. There was great destruction and many casualties, both
military and civilian.

The Port of Cherbourg was finally captured by a 53-man US Coast Guard special task force under the leadership of Commander Quentin Walsh, USCG. Despite heavy casualties, his small force seized the port facilities and took control of the harbor. He discovered the remaining German garrison at nearby Fort du Hornet held 52 US Army paratroopers as prisoners. Under a flag of truce, Walsh exaggerated the strength of the forces under his command and persuaded the commanding officer of the remnants of the German garrison to surrender. All told, he accepted the surrender of over 700 German soldiers. In the process, he freed 52 US paratroopers who were being held prisoner.

A Navy Press Release in 2019 announced its newest guided-missile destroyer would be named after Captain Quentin Walsh, USCG. Bing and Suzanne's son Jimmy attended the US Coast Guard Academy where he became close friends with Richard Buckingham and his parents, Albion and Dorothy Buckingham. Captain Walsh was the senior Buckingham's commanding officer when he served in the Coast Guard during World War II. Mr. Buckingham often told his children stories about the hard-nosed, inflexible, by-the-book guy who was his CO. He always concluded by telling them how Walsh subsequently caused the surrender of the last remaining German garrison at Cherbourg. Richard often wondered how much of his father's version of this story might be mythical. As an adult, he learned the story was not only true, but bigger and even more impressive than his dad's version.

Taking control of Caen, the nearby transportation center, was even harder than capturing Cherbourg. They had anticipated controlling Caen in a matter of days, but it took two months to free the city from German control. The city was utterly destroyed in the process, with a great number of civilian casualties. Both sides engaged in total war, a military conflict in which the contenders are willing to make any sacrifice in lives and other resources to obtain a complete victory.

In Brittany, the Allies met with similar difficulties while capturing the ports of Brest and St. Malo. When the Allies finally had a secure supply line, they made the decision to isolate and contain the remaining German strongholds along the Atlantic Coast. They did not want to risk the additional destruction and bloodshed it would take to liberate the rest of the port cities.

The Allied Forces left the 94th Division to guard the pockets of remaining German resistance along the coast. The rest of the Allied Forces concentrated their efforts on pushing into Germany.

After their devastating loss at sea, the remnants of the 66th Infantry Division regrouped in Cherbourg. Because they had lost a full third of their men, they were diverted from their intended destination at the Battle of the Bulge. Instead, they were sent to the rear of the lines near the occupied ports of Saint-Nazaire and L'Orient in Brittany. They relieved the 94th Division, which proceeded to the Battle of the Bulge in their place.

It is estimated that between 50,000 and 100,000 Germans were dug in along the 112-mile front in northwestern France. These pockets of Germans became the responsibility of the 66th Infantry Division.

Bing went with the Panthers who were tasked with containing the Nazis who were holding out at the heavily fortified submarine base in Saint-Nazaire. The U-boats had escaped, but the remaining German troops were determined to resist Allied advances at any cost; they were prepared to fight to the death. In addition to the 25,000 German troops stationed at the submarine base, 3,000 retreating German soldiers also found refuge there. They had enough supplies to last for two years.

The 66th Infantry Division camped near the little town of Héric. They conducted daily reconnaissance patrols and periodic artillery fire on the pockets of resistance. The artillery fire disabled a number of big German guns and sank numerous resupply boats. Their presence kept the Germans in Brittany from staging any offensive efforts.

For the medic team, this was not difficult duty because there was not much fighting. They tended to the needs of the troops and were constantly vigilant. They experienced a time of relative peace and interaction with the newly liberated French people.

Bing enjoyed getting to know the French civilians. He liked their culture and the way they welcomed him into their homes. Most of all, he liked Suzanne. She was reserved, yet warm, beautiful, yet genuine. She laughed easily and he wanted more than anything to be with her.

14 PROMISES

I wonder how I had the courage to say yes.
—Suzanne Ng, reflecting on her response to Bing's proposal

Suzanne and Bing continued to spend weekends together throughout the mild winter and into the spring of 1945. The war raged on in other parts of Europe, and the pockets of Germans in Western France continued to hold out. Bing longed to make Suzanne his wife.

Bing sat at a rickety table in the makeshift tent he shared with several other soldiers from the 366th Medical Battalion of the 66th Infantry Division. They were billeted near Héric at the Chateau de Blaine, a medieval stone castle surrounded by a mote with a bridge leading to a big wooden door. Soldiers were housed in rooms on the castle wall, in the tall stone tower, and in tents spread out over the fields surrounding the castle. The tents were made by digging trenches in the hard-packed dirt and draping tarps over the top openings.

On a plain piece of paper, Bing skillfully shaped Chinese characters. He carefully considered his words as he composed a letter to his parents, explaining his intention to marry Suzanne. His family had chosen his first wife; he had discovered Suzanne himself. He hoped they would accept Suzanne when they understood her beauty, her character, and his love for her. He addressed the envelope to his mother and father in New York City and deposited the letter in a canvas bag of outgoing mail. Then, he waited expectantly for their reply.

The disappointing answer came several weeks later. His parents wrote that he would have to choose between his family and Suzanne. This was not an empty threat. In Bing's Chinese culture, going against the parents' decree often resulted in being permanently disowned by the family unit.

Their disapproval certainly contained an element of racial prejudice. More importantly, however, young Chinese men were expected to respect their parents' role in choosing their brides. Parents arranged marriages by following the principle of matching doors and windows. A couple's compatibility was assessed by their social, economic, and political standing. "Marrying first, then falling in love" was a reality for many couples. Demonstrating respect for the parents was paramount. Bing resisted the pressure from his parents; he chose Suzanne.

The next step was to ask Suzanne's father for her hand in marriage. Bing did not have a language in common with Alphonse Chédotal. Though Therese did not share a language with Bing, either, she understood his wishes and agreed to go to Nort to speak with Suzanne's father on behalf of Bing. Monsieur Chédotal's response was not exactly what Bing had hoped for, but it was good enough. His reply to the request was, "It is Suzanne's decision; if she wants to marry a chink, I won't stop her."

The very next weekend, Suzanne met Bing in Héric. Bing borrowed a blanket from Therese. The two young lovers walked to the edge of town, crossed the street near the cemetery where Suzanne's grandfather was buried, and strolled down a tree-lined lane. Bing spread the blanket on the ground under an apple tree. They sat together with its leaves shading them from the afternoon sun. The sun filtered through the branches, highlighting Suzanne's soft brown hair. Bing took her hand in his. It was the hand he had so tenderly nursed back to health. He did not have the French words to express his intent, nor did he have the money to buy a diamond ring. Bing proposed by touching her left hand where an engagement ring should go. He looked into her eyes and she knew exactly what Bing meant. Though Suzanne had not expected

Bing to propose, she did not hesitate to say yes. She wanted nothing more than to be with this wonderful American soldier.

Suzanne's parents were not happy about the engagement. Her father tried to change her mind. He did not want Suzanne to marry an Asian man. When Alphonse served in the French Army in Indo-China, he had come to believe Asian people were backward. Suzanne's mother worried about the future for her oldest daughter; she did not want Suzanne to marry a foreigner who would take her away from France. Suzanne was not dissuaded. Eventually, her parents gave up trying to change her mind.

It took great courage for Suzanne to say yes. Marrying Bing would mean leaving everyone and everything she knew. It would mean leaving her family, her friends, and even her country. She was just a naïve country girl who had never been anywhere, but she loved and trusted Bing. She believed they would forge a life together, combining vastly different cultures, races, nationalities, languages, and experiences to become one unique family. "Sometimes life takes a turn you never expected," Suzanne mused. She was excited about this new direction.

Nazi Germany surrendered unconditionally to the Allies on May 7, 1945. Three days later, in a small café near Cordemais, France, most of the remaining German troops in northern France conceded. A representative group of French officials and a contingent of officers from the 66th Infantry Division accepted the surrender.

One more day passed before the Nazi troops in Saint-Nazaire gave up. On May 11, 1945, Saint-Nazaire became the last town in France to be liberated. In fact, Saint-Nazaire was the last town in all of Europe to be set free.

The people of France faced a long, difficult, expensive recovery process, but the war in Europe was finally over. French people danced in the streets and celebrated their restored freedom. In Europe, it was not so much the day the Germans admitted defeat, but, rather, the actual moment of liberation which marked the real end of conflict. Cities were set free, one at a time, as the Allied Forces pushed through Europe. Liberation day differed from country to country and from region to region in the same country. For Suzanne, that day was August 12, 1944, when the Germans abandoned Nantes. For her Grandmère-Nazaire, who lived less than 40 miles away from her, liberation day came nine months later—four days after Germany officially surrendered—when the Americans finally entered Saint-Nazaire.

Dancing in the Street in Héric
La Fin de la Guerre (The End of the War)

American trucks drove across the enemy lines into Saint-Nazaire. The Germans were receptive to their arrival and complied with their instructions. There were big piles of German war supplies, including binoculars and guns. American officers confiscated those items and passed them out to the United States Army troops as war souvenirs. Bing was given a pair of

German binoculars.

With the end of hostilities, the 66th Infantry Division was no longer needed in Western France. Bing kissed Suzanne good-bye, promising to return to see her as often as possible. Suzanne promised to wait. They would get married when Bing's situation in the Army was more predictable. He left with the Panthers for a new assignment in Germany.

15 MARIANNE

I never could have imagined having a German for a friend.
—Suzanne Ng to her dear friend Marianne
in the summer of 2019

Bing moved with his fellow Panthers to the area around Koblenz, Germany for occupation duty. Allied Forces were instructed to be in every nook and cranny of Germany. This was known as "blanket occupation." The objective was to control the population and stifle resistance. They acted as a security force, were charged with establishing a military government, and took control of all German affairs.

Not far from Koblenz, a little German girl named Marianne lived in the quiet, picturesque village of Idar-Oberstein.

The small community was set in the midst of the mineral-rich hills of the Hunsruck Mountains in southwest Germany. The River Nahe flowed through the town, dividing it into two distinct parts.

Idar-Oberstein was known for the jewelry it produced from the natural gemstone deposits found in the surrounding hills. Its narrow cobblestone streets were home to jewelry stores, grocery stores, cafés, hotels, and restaurants. Perched on a cliff high above the town, the ancient Oberstein Castle stood guard. A winding road led from the town, up to the castle, over the hill, and back down the other side of the mountain.

Built into a crag in the solid rock wall at the edge of town and beneath Oberstein Castle was the Church in the Rock. It was a beautiful, unique landmark. No roads led up to the church; instead, 230 steps were carved into the face of the rock. They connected the town to the ledge where a door opened into the chapel.

Marianne Trude Schilling was born on March 7, 1940, shortly after World War II had broken out. She and Suzanne experienced the war and its aftermath from different sides of the conflict. Neither of them could have imagined the friendship they would forge many years in the future.

Marianne was the only child of Otto and Gertrude Schilling. Otto was 42 when Marianne was born. He and Gertrude were delighted with the arrival of their beautiful baby girl. The little family made their home in the first-floor apartment of a house at the edge of the town. It was situated on a little path running just to the right of the steps leading up to the Church in the Rock. Marianne's father was a goldsmith. He fashioned beautiful jewelry from imported gold and from the agates found in the surrounding hills. His shop was on the town's main street, a short walk from their apartment.

Marianne's parents owned a remote cottage where they spent weekends. It could not be reached by car or wagon; they hiked up the hill on a narrow path to the cottage. They transported their supplies in a little pull cart. The cottage itself was built of stones from a nearby quarry. There was room for a garden in the clearing. Their extended family often gathered at the secluded property on Sundays. It was a sweet retreat.

When Marianne was only six weeks old, her father, like all the other able-bodied men in town, was drafted. He went away to serve in the German Army. It did not matter that they were neither members nor supporters of Hitler's Nazi Party. He had to go, so he went.

There were very few men left in the town. Marianne's uncle, her mother's oldest brother, had only one eye. He was left behind to protect the town. He lived outside Idar-Oberstein on the road leading up to the castle.

At first, Otto sent his wife occasional letters, assuring her of his well-being. When Marianne was 18 months old, he was able to make a brief visit home. The Schilling family had a photograph taken of the three of them together. Marianne gazed at the picture often during her formative years. Her mother told her about the father who loved her so much. She assured Marianne he would come home to her one day. They received a few more letters after Otto's visit home. Then the letters stopped coming. Marianne's mother hoped, but did not know, Otto was still alive.

The Schilling Family

Life was hard for Marianne and her mother during the war. They were very poor. They continued to live in the little apartment in town, making visits to the cottage on weekends to tend their garden. They were fortunate to have the garden; it provided them with food to eat. All the stores in town had closed; there was nothing to buy or sell. Everything that could be spared was sent to support the troops.

At the end of each summer during those war years, Marianne went with her mother and the other women in town to the surrounding farms to help dig potatoes. They were not paid for their labor, but they were permitted to glean the very smallest of the potatoes. The rest of the crop was sent to the front lines to feed the Nazi soldiers. The women and children also helped pick green beans, beets, and other crops as they ripened. These crops were sent to the troops, as well.

The meagre diet of the civilians consisted mostly of the potatoes they gleaned and the few things they grew in their gardens. There was no flour, nor sugar, nor meat. When a farm animal was slaughtered, the meat went to the German Army. Often, German officials took away even the live animals. Once, Marianne's uncle secretly killed a cow, butchered it, and kept the meat. He felt a responsibility to provide for the women and children of the family. He divided the meat among his hungry relatives.

Marianne's aunt had a goat. She made goat butter from the cream which rose to the top of the pure white goat milk. Marianne liked to watch her churn the cream. Slosh, slosh, slosh went the liquid as her aunt plunged the dasher up and down in the churn until chunks of butter floated in the butter milk. Marianne's mother did not like the white goat butter; she remembered too well the sweet yellow butter they used to make from cows' milk. Marianne, however, thought it was a holiday when she had goat butter to eat. There was little variety in their diet. Marianne had no idea what an orange or a banana was.

Marianne's mother cut up her own clothes to make garments for her growing daughter. Marianne had two dresses, one for church and one for every day.

Every home in Germany was required to have a picture of Adolph Hitler hanging in a prominent place in their living room. It was the law. Marianne's mother complied, even though she did not want the war and she did not like Hitler. They were subjected to all the rules, regulations, and propaganda of the Third Reich. The Gestapo made unannounced inspections of civilian homes to make sure everyone was in compliance.

Gertrude's best friend in Idar-Oberstein was Jewish. One night, without anyone knowing, the entire family disappeared. The Gestapo came in the middle of the night, with no warning, and took them away. Marianne's mother was very sad. She did not agree with Hitler's hatred of the Jews.

As the war continued, year after year, survival became more and more difficult. There were few supplies and not much food left in Germany. Everyone Marianne knew wanted the war to be over.

Bombs began falling from the sky. Some landed on the train station in Idar-Oberstein. The bridges over the river dividing the town were taken out by the bombs. When the warning sirens wailed, Marianne and her mother ran to underground bunkers which had been built in the town for shelter. Sometimes, they stayed in the bunkers for several days at a time. Once, Marianne was sick with the measles when they heard the warning sirens. Gertrude put Marianne in an old metal washtub with handles and carried her in the tub to the bomb shelter.

Finally, in May of 1945, the radio broadcasted the announcement, "The war is over." At first, they thought it was a hoax, but, finally, the German people were convinced Germany had surrendered.

The residents of Idar-Oberstein knew the Allied Forces would be coming soon, and they were frightened. They had heard these soldiers were mean. They did not know what would be expected or demanded of the civilians. They thought the soldiers would come through town, so Marianne's uncle took Marianne, her mother, her aunts, and her cousins to his house up the hill on the road to the castle. They hoped to avoid the soldiers.

It was dark and late at night when they heard a rumbling noise. Instead of coming through town as they had expected, the American soldiers came over the mountain with their tanks. They arrived at her uncle's house on their way to the town. The soldiers knocked on the door. They searched every room in the house, took a head count, and wrote down every person's name. There was only one man in the house; the rest were all women and children. Then the soldiers left. They didn't take anything. They didn't demand anything. The next day Marianne and her mother went home.

Germany was divided into four sectors. The United States, France, Great Britain, and Russia each took charge of a sector. Idar-Oberstein, on Marianne's side of the river, was occupied by United States forces. Just across the river was the French sector. They felt lucky to be in the American sector; they understood the Americans treated the German people better than the French, the Brits, or the Russians did. Life was still hard, but there were some improvements. Gertrude held onto hope that Otto would come home, even though she had heard nothing from him nor had any news about him in more than two years.

The picture of Hitler came down from the wall in their living room. Marianne and her mother, like their neighbors, were given ration books each week. The Americans brought supplies into town. The stores, which had been shuttered, were opened and took charge of distributing the goods. Residents stood in long lines to wait their turns to buy fish, sugar, or flour. When they made a purchase, they tore the corresponding stamp out of the ration book and gave it to the storekeeper.

Potatoes, beets, and kohlrabi were trucked into town and dumped in big piles in the town square below the Church in the Rock. Once, when Marianne's mother was sick, Aunt Leni took Marianne with her to the town square to get some potatoes. They stood in line for a long time. Marianne noticed a little deformed potato. She thought it looked like a doll, so she picked up the potato and put it in her pocket. On the way home, Marianne showed Aunt Leni the little potato-doll. Aunt Leni was not pleased. She made Marianne take the potato back to the town square, return it to the people in charge of distributing the potatoes, and apologize. Marianne was very ashamed and embarrassed. She brought the potato back and apologized. She determined never again to take anything that didn't belong to her.

Marianne began going to school. There had been no school during the war because there were no teachers in town. Marianne walked to school with her friends. She enjoyed the classes and she was excited to learn to read. Quakers came from America to help the children in Idar-Oberstein. Once each week, they made a meal for the students at the school. The children's favorites were hot chocolate and soft yeast rolls. Sometimes there was hot, white, navy bean soup.

Marianne and her mother were careful to observe the curfew, which was imposed by the Americans. They had to be home by 7:00 p.m. in the summer and by dark in the winter.

Marianne and her mother visited Oma, her mother's mother, every day. Oma was suffering from dementia, so it was important to check on her and make sure she had what she needed. One day, they stayed a little longer than they should have at Oma's house. Gertrude noticed it was getting dark, so they left quickly. Gertrude held Marianne's hand tightly as they began to hurry home.

They soon realized a big, tall, black man in an Army uniform was following them. They were very frightened; Gertrude picked up Marianne and ran as fast as she could. When the soldier caught up with them, he put his hand on Gertrude's shoulder and said in fluent German, "Don't be afraid. I'm not going to hurt you or your little girl." He took his wallet out of his pocket, and he showed them a picture of his wife and his three young children. Then, he gave Marianne some chewing gum. Marianne had never seen chewing gum before, nor had she ever seen a black man. This kind American soldier changed her perception of the American forces who were occupying her homeland.

Still, there was no word from Marianne's father. Gertrude persisted in holding onto hope that Otto would come home.

Marianne and her mother discovered some tiny wild strawberries growing along the path leading to their cottage. They carefully picked the delicious red berries. Gertrude made a few small jars of strawberry jam. She set aside one of the jars and said, "We will eat this jar of jam when Otto comes home."

16 PERSPECTIVE

So many died on 6th of June.
Why did America give their young for me, for us?
—Paul Golz, German POW

T he intense, all-inclusive blanket occupation of Germany was effective, but it required an exceptionally large number of personnel. It was not realistic to maintain so many forces in Germany for an extended period of time. After the initial occupation, the 66th Infantry Division moved to Salzburg, Austria to handle the POW camps in that area. They were charged with the care and dischargement of German prisoners of war.

Kitchens were set up in tents. Army jeeps picked up the prepared food from the makeshift kitchens and distributed it to the outposts and to the POW camps. The prisoners were fed two meals a day. Bing and the other cooks of the 66th Infantry Division worked tirelessly to feed both their comrades and the prisoners with their limited supplies. Most of the food they had to work with was powdered; there were powdered eggs, powdered milk, powdered potatoes, and powdered vegetables of all kinds. They sometimes had the ingredients to make cakes and occasionally there was American beer for the troops.

The men of the 66th were friendly to the prisoners, and the prisoners responded in kind. The Panthers understood most of the German soldiers had been doing what they were told. Now, they were just anxious to go home. Some of the POW's were not even German; they had been conscripted from conquered countries and forced to serve in the German Army. Some were German men who, though they did not support the Nazi regime, had no choice but to submit to the Third Reich or face dire consequences; sometimes the threats extended to harm to their families if they did not comply. Many of the German soldiers had been fighting for their homeland, but they did not understand the underlying evil of the Nazi regime. They were all products of Nazi propaganda and coercion.

Dischargement of German soldiers by the 66th Infantry Division was done as expeditiously and prudently as possible. It was necessary to discern which prisoners were still a threat and which ones should be punished for war crimes. The others were sent home as quickly as possible.

The reception the returning prisoners received when they arrived home to their German towns was not always warm. Compared to the strong, victorious Allied troops, the malnourished, defeated German soldiers were seen by some of the German population as failures. They had promoted a lost cause and were unable to provide for the needs of the German people.

Marianne Schilling's father had been compelled to fight with the German forces as they invaded Russia and pushed toward Moscow. The winter of 1941-1942 was extremely cold. The German soldiers were dying like flies. When the German offensive failed, Otto was captured and held as a prisoner of war in Russia. The Russian Army treated their German POWs badly. The prisoners ate only crepes and water and became malnourished; many succumbed to illness and some of them died.

After many months, Otto escaped from the Russian POW camp. He made his way to *Krim* (Crimea), an island in the Black Sea, where he found work on a farm. The work was hard, the living conditions were poor, and the food was barely enough to sustain him. Eventually, Otto learned Nazi Germany had surrendered to the Allied Forces. He heard the Americans treated their prisoners well, so he left the farm, went to Austria, and turned himself in to the first American soldiers he encountered. They fed him, gave him medical attention, held him for a few days, and, then, released him.

When Otto arrived in Idar-Oberstein, he was thin and tired, but happy to be in his hometown. He was anxious to see his wife and daughter. He stopped first at the home of his wife's mother. He brought a piece of bread as a gift for her. Then, he hurried to the apartment to find Gertrude and Marianne.

Shortly after Otto left Oma's house, Marianne and Gertrude came to visit Oma. They had been at Aunt Leni's house, but they wanted to check on Oma before going home. When Oma saw them, she exclaimed, "What are you doing here? Otto is coming home." Gertrude thought her mother was mistaken. Her dementia often caused her to confuse facts. Oma persisted, "He was here. See? He brought me some bread!"

Gertrude was finally convinced. She and Marianne left Oma's house and ran as fast as they could toward their own apartment. As they approached their home, they heard someone cough. It was Otto. Marianne's mother told her, "That's Dad."

Otto had a very warm welcome home. Gertrude made a pot of potatoes for dinner. Then, they opened the jar of jam she had been saving to celebrate his safe return.

Other German POWs also had positive experiences with their American captors. Paul Golz was a 19-year-old German private who was dug in near Cherbourg when the Allied Forces landed on the beaches of Normandy. Several days later, he was captured by US troops and taken to the United States aboard the Queen Mary. He was held at a POW camp in West Virginia until the end of the war. He was amazed at the good treatment he and the other prisoners received.

"On every bed there were cigarettes and chocolate, and they had prepared food in the kitchen for us," he recalled, smiling broadly. "That is where I drank my first Coca-Cola. Wow, that tasted delicious! Ice cold." They were fed well and felt as if they were treated more like guests than prisoners.

As the war came to an end, the POWs were shown footage of the newly liberated concentration camps in Germany. Golz was stunned. It was the first time he had been confronted with the atrocities committed by the Nazis.

Upon his release, Golz returned to Germany. He never visited the United States again, but he came to realize how lucky he was to have been captured by the Americans. 75 years after D-Day, Golz reflected on the anniversary. "So many died on 6th of

June. Why did America give their young for me, for us?" Golz marveled. From his perspective, America's victory freed not only the rest of Europe, but also his own country, Germany, from Nazi oppression.

17 SHIFTING GEARS

Believe me when I say
that laughter up at the front lines is a very precious thing—
precious to those grand guys
who are giving and taking
the awful business that goes on there...
There's a lump the size of Grant's Tomb in your throat
when they come up to you
and shake your hand and mumble, "Thanks."
Imagine those guys thanking me!
Look what they're doing for me. And for you.
—Bob Hope, 1944

Suzanne hurried with her morning routine. She was anxious to get to work. Maybe there would be a letter from Bing today. Bing wrote to Suzanne every week, but mail delivery was unpredictable; the letters did not arrive regularly. She waited expectantly for the mail to be delivered every day. He had been gone for six weeks; she missed him, longed for him, and worried about him.

The war in Europe was over, but the United States was still fighting in the Pacific. In contrast to the occupation years, French people regularly had news from the free world. On June 9, 1945 Japanese Premier Suzuki had announced Japan would fight to the very end rather than accept unconditional surrender. There was the possibility Bing could be sent to help with the war effort on the other side of the world.

Goods were still scarce in France, even though the Germans were no longer confiscating resources and supplies. Work and finding food still took most of Suzanne's time. She still lived in the single room she rented at the house of the three single sisters in Nantes. She still wore the same patched clothes and wooden-soled shoes. There was, however, a glow on her face and a spring in her step. She was in love.

Suzanne continued to work in the big room on the third floor of the Banque Postal in the heart of Nantes. Her job felt familiar and she enjoyed the companionship of her coworkers. She tried to concentrate on her work that morning, but she couldn't help glancing up at the door, watching for the mail to be delivered.

It was mid-morning when a courier slid an envelope onto her desk. Her heart skipped a beat. It was a letter from Bing. She could not give it her attention until the lunch break, but just having the letter sitting on her desk filled her with joy and anticipation.

Picture Bing sent to Suzanne,
taken at the school carnival in the spring of 1945

As soon as the office closed for lunch, Suzanne opened the letter. She knew Bing's handwriting. She could only read his signature and the salutation. Every letter began the same way, "My darling Suzanne." Suzanne loved those words. She ran her finger over them and pictured Bing's face. She smelled the paper and studied the unfamiliar words on the rest of the page. Then, she sought out her English-speaking colleague. Marguerite was always happy to translate Bing's love letters for Suzanne. Suzanne suspected Marguerite did not understand written English as well as she professed to, but Suzanne was fairly certain she got the gist of the letters right. This letter brought the news that Bing was coming to see her. He would meet her in Héric the following weekend. Her heart soared.

In June of 1945, the 66th Infantry Division had moved again; this move brought them to the area around Marseille on the southern coast of France. Their new mission was to staff staging areas where troops were preparing to ship out to the Pacific. Though victory had been declared in Europe, the war was still raging on the other side of the world. These battle-weary soldiers had more work to do.

General George Marshall served as Army Chief of Staff during the war. He is remembered as the organizer of victory and the architect of peace during and after the war. He stipulated that units being sent to the Pacific must contain only the troops least eligible for discharge; only those soldiers most eligible for discharge would be sent home. The rating was calculated individually for every enlisted man based on points in three categories:

1. One point for each month of overseas service since September of 1940
2. Five points for each decoration or battle star
3. Twelve points for each child under the age of 18, up to a maximum of three children

Bing did not have many points. He knew the war on the other side of the world intimately. He had already helped with the cause in Burma when he supported the Flying Tigers, though he did not accrue points for that service. The deep scars on his legs were a daily reminder of the conditions he had endured. He had no desire to go to the Pacific. Bing had lost his first wife in that war. He felt lucky to have a second chance at love with Suzanne. He missed her very much and he looked for an opportunity to go to visit her.

The soldiers who were being repositioned enjoyed a brief respite in the South of France before shipping out to reinforce American forces in the Pacific. They, as well as the support staff in Marseilles, were treated to various forms of encouragement and entertainment.

After Germany's surrender, each US Army battalion in Europe received PX supplies twice a month. (The PX or post exchange is a military sponsored store for consumer goods. It is accessible only to military identification card holders.) The items were limited; dividing the shipments between the soldiers was quite a job. The shipments included cigarettes, cigars, tobacco, candy, gum, fruit juices, writing paper, sunglasses, cards, and combs. Sometimes, there was one fountain pen, one lighter, or other miscellaneous single articles. They held drawings for the opportunity to purchase those items from their makeshift PX.

Bing purchased an inexpensive silver ring. Someday he would do better, but at least Suzanne would have a tangible symbol of his promise to make her his wife.

Finally, Bing was granted permission to travel to Héric for a long weekend. He took the train to the area and made his way to the home of Therese and Barik. Suzanne was waiting for him when he arrived.

They walked hand in hand on the quiet streets of the little town where they had first met. Bing turned onto the little lane across from the cemetery. When they were under the apple tree where Bing had asked her to marry him, he slipped the silver ring onto her finger. Her delight showed on her beautiful face.

The visit was short, but Bing would come again as soon as he could. His future in the Army was still uncertain. Bing and Suzanne would continue to wait for each other.

The 66th Infantry Division constructed eight outdoor motion picture amphitheaters where the GI's were treated to movies and USO shows. Entertainers, including Bob Hope, a popular

American celebrity, came to encourage the troops.

Hope maintained his best audiences were servicemen and women stationed far from home at military bases in the United States and abroad. Beginning in May 1941, Hope brought his variety show to military camps and war zones to entertain troops with song, dance, comedy, attractive women, and people in the news. He discovered early on that audiences appreciated jokes about their locale and local elite. The strategy worked especially well when he teased soldiers about their bases and roasted their officers. Hope believed he gained more from the experience than he gave.

Bing enjoyed the entertainment along with his fellow soldiers. He couldn't help thinking how much more enjoyable the shows would be if he could share them with Suzanne.

The surrender of Imperial Japan was announced by Japanese Emperor Hirohito on August 15, 1945. World War II was over. It had directly involved more than 100 million people from more than 30 countries. The major participants threw their entire economic, industrial, and scientific capabilities behind the war effort.

World War II was the deadliest conflict in human history, marked by more than 70 million fatalities. It included massacres, wide-spread destruction, the genocide of the Holocaust, strategic bombing, premeditated death from starvation and disease, and the only use of nuclear weapons in war. Bing and Suzanne, from their different vantage points, had a front row seat to many of those horrors.

With the cessation of hostilities in the Pacific, the 66th Infantry Division was decommissioned. 804 of their number had been killed, 268 wounded, 19 captured and seven were still missing. Many of the men of the 66th went home. The troops who did not have enough points to be discharged were sent to Germany or Austria to serve as part of the occupation forces.

Bing was transferred to Nuremberg, Germany for occupation duty. He was pleased with his new assignment. It would keep him in Europe. He wanted to be as close to Suzanne as possible.

18 AMERICANS IN GERMANY

War with Germany ends with victory.
Victory leads to peace.
Sometimes not.
—US Army Training Video

Being arrived in Nuremberg in late summer of 1945. Ninety percent of the city had been destroyed by Allied bombing. There were piles of rubble where buildings had been. Streets were blocked by debris. Many of the German people were hungry and homeless. Agricultural production was at 35% of what it had been before the war; there was little food available to feed the hungry German people. There was no government, no economy, no infrastructure. There were few German men in Nuremberg or the surrounding areas. The Nazi government had made no contingency plan for what to do if the war was lost. In their minds, losing had not been an option. The occupation forces had a big job to do. They were responsible for meeting the needs of the people and putting the country back together. Their most important task, however, was to prevent a future war.

As part of their training, American soldiers who were sent to post-war Germany were required to view the War Department Orientation Video entitled, "Your Job in Germany." The video began, "War with Germany ends with victory. Victory leads to peace. Sometimes not." The job of the American soldiers in Germany was to lay the foundation for a peace that would last forever, rather than to establish the groundwork for a future war.

The video presented an overview of German history, reviewing Germany's pattern of war, peace, war, peace, war. Germany had initiated three wars during the previous 75 years.

1. **The War of 1870**, AKA the Franco-Prussian War

Germany was the mightiest military power in Europe when she sought to expand her borders. "Blood and Iron" was their slogan. The result was a victory for Germany, the formation of the German Empire, and the annexation of the coal-rich Alsace-Lorraine territory, which had previously belonged to France. With the end of hostilities, the danger appeared to be over and Europe relaxed.

2. **World War I**

In 1914, Germany had a new fuehrer and a new slogan, "Germany Over All." Germany embarked on a mission to seize more territory and more power. With a massive effort on the part of many European countries and with the help of American forces, Germany was defeated, and The Great War was over. Germany pretended to make nice with the free world. Americans poured in their sympathy and took out their troops. An unsteady peace reigned.

3. **World War II**

Less than 20 years later, Germany had a new fuehrer with still another slogan, "Today Germany is Ours, Tomorrow the Whole World is Ours." Germany launched World War II, conquered country after country and spread her evil over Europe and beyond. It took great effort and courage, many millions of dollars, and the sacrifice of more than 70 million human lives before the Third Reich finally surrendered. The concentration camps were empty, the countries Germany had seized were once again free, the German Army had been disbanded, and the evil government was gone. The fighting had stopped. Germany appeared to be beaten.

The training video cautioned the American troops, "Don't be fooled. You are in enemy country." Many of the German people they would meet on the streets had just recently been part of the evil regime. It was impossible to know which ones were still a danger. It was inevitable that Nazi thinking, training, and trickery would still quietly exist. The American troops were warned to trust no one, especially the youth who had known no system other than the one which had poisoned their minds. "They have read no free speech. They were brought up on propaganda, trained to pick on the weak and to hate and destroy everything you stand for. They believe they are destined to be your masters. They may deny it now, but they still believe it."

American troops were forbidden to fraternize with German people. They were warned not to be friendly nor take any Germans into their confidence. They were instructed to obey local laws, to refrain from making friends, and to respect the local customs, religion, and property rights of the German people. The soldiers were told never to argue with nor ridicule the people. "Someday the Germans may be cured of their super race and world conquest disease, but it will take time and they must prove it. We stand guard. We are determined that the vicious German cycle of war, phony peace, war, phony peace, war shall once and for all time come to an end. That is your job in Germany."

The symbols of Hitler's evil regime were removed. The Nazi flags, the swastikas, and the pictures and busts of Adolph Hitler came down and were burned. The names of the roads and buildings designated in Hitler's honor were changed.

The German people needed the Americans at this time; they did not have the resources, the manpower, or the organization to provide for their basic needs. Food was the most important thing. The limited food supplies were distributed as evenly as possible using ration coupons. The allotment was only 1275 calories per person per day. Refugee camps were established. German people were organized into work teams to dig out and rebuild their war-torn country. Every scrap of building material was salvaged to be re-used.

Amid the ruins were some unexpected surprises. Art treasures were discovered hidden in an ancient bunker 78 feet beneath the center of Old Nuremberg. The artwork was accumulated by the Nazis and carefully hidden; it survived the bombing unscathed.

The morale of the US soldiers who were left behind to occupy Germany was a major concern of their leaders. United States Armed Forces Institute courses, USO shows, entertainment, and recreation programs were used to encourage the troops.

Food and supplies were flown in from the United States. Eating is one of the greatest pleasures for men and women stationed far away from home. As an Army cook, Bing did his best to prepare the dishes they knew and loved. He had a knack for making food taste good; he could improvise without a recipe, using whatever supplies were available to make delicious meals.

General Marshal served as President Harry Truman's Secretary of State after World War II. His wisdom and leadership were instrumental in the success of the post-war peace. Among other things, he realized the importance of the occupying soldiers having the feeling of independence which Americans crave. He proposed each regiment be given trucks, rations, and a gasoline allowance to use for military vacation tours. Small groups could take turns with the vehicles and go anywhere they pleased, except into the Soviet Zone.

Bing made use of vacation tours to visit Suzanne. Rarely did more than a month pass before he found a way to go back to see her. His visits were brief. He always stayed with Therese and Berik in Héric.

Bing and Suzanne cherished the days they spent together. They were very much in love. They both had high moral standards; sleeping together before they were married was not an acceptable option for Bing and Suzanne. They had known each other for nine months. Saying good-bye when Bing left was becoming more and more difficult.

It looked like Bing would be stationed in Nuremberg for a couple of years. Dependents were permitted to join their soldiers. This was a good time to get married.

19 WAR BRIDE

First came love. Then came marriage.
Then came life in a strange new land,
and farewell to everything familiar.
Most GI war brides
wouldn't have traded it for the world.
—Brenda J. Wilt

The greens of spring and summer had changed to the yellows and golds of autumn by the time Bing came to make Suzanne his bride. She was waiting at the station in Nort-Sur-Erdre when his train arrived in early October of 1945. Scanning the windows of the passenger cars, Suzanne searched for *son cheri* (her darling). One by one, she watched each passenger descend the steps of the train. She caught a glimpse of the characteristic color of his olive drab Army uniform before his face appeared in the doorway. When their eyes met, Suzanne's heart soared. Then, she was in his arms.

Bing had arranged to take ten days of leave from his Army duties so they could be married and have time for a honeymoon. Arranging for their wedding proved to be more difficult than either of them had expected. There were no United States military chaplains in the area, so Bing approached the local Catholic priest and asked for his help. The priest refused. Bing was surprised; he professed to be Catholic. Perhaps the priest did not want to have anything to do with the wedding because Bing was an American. Maybe it was because he was of Chinese descent. Perhaps he did not believe Bing was "Catholic enough." Maybe it was because Bing didn't have a language in common with either the priest or his own intended bride. In any case, the priest refused to help the young couple, and Bing harbored a grudge against the Catholic Church because of it. For Suzanne, it was one more disappointment in a long list of disappointments by the church. She never again considered herself to be Catholic.

Next, Bing and Suzanne went to the town hall in Nort-Sur-Erdre to inquire of the officials there. Unlike the customs in the United States, all official marriage ceremonies in France take place in the town hall; they are conducted by the mayor or his representative. Usually, a church wedding follows the civil ceremony, but the blessing of the church is not mandatory. Suzanne and Bing did not need a church wedding to be legally married. The officials at the town hall in Nort did not speak English. They refused to perform the civil ceremony because Bing did not speak French. Suzanne and Bing were met with the same response at the town hall in Nantes.

What could the young couple do? They decided to take the train together to Paris. They would enlist the help of the staff at the Red Cross office in the capital city.

The Red Cross played in important role in the lives of soldiers and sailors both during and after World War II. More than 100,000 nurses recruited by the American Red Cross served in military hospitals at home and overseas. The Red Cross blood donor project collected more than 13 million units of blood for American servicemen. Red Cross employees and volunteers provided emergency message services. Twenty-seven million Red Cross packages were distributed to American and Allied prisoners of war. Red Cross staff and volunteers assisted in rest and recreation areas in the field and at military hospitals and transportation centers. They were a tremendous resource for American servicemen stationed abroad. If they could not provide a service, they often knew where the need could be met.

Suzanne and Bing took the bus from Nort to Nantes; there, they boarded a morning train bound for *Gare Montparnasse*, the capital city's main train station. The journey was long and slow; it took more than seven hours to travel the 230 miles from Nantes to Paris. The train was dilapidated with broken windows, worn seats, and few amenities; it still bore the scars of the recently concluded war. It was crowded; for most of the trip Suzanne and Bing had to stand in the aisle or sit on their suitcases.

Bridges were out and tracks had been bombed; it was necessary for the train to make detours or to pass very slowly on patched tracks. Sometimes the train moved so slowly that it would have been faster to get off the train and walk beside it.

Suzanne was enthralled by the many castles she saw as they traveled through the Loire River Valley. They were perched on hills along the wide, meandering Loire River. There were fortified castles dating all the way back to medieval times, as well as huge, stunning castles, built during the Renaissance, 500 years later. Each ancient *chateau* (castle) had a story of its own. Suzanne wondered what secrets they knew about the people who had lived within their walls—loves and losses, conquests and defeats, friends and enemies. She had studied about the castles in her history classes at school; she had read tales about the lords and ladies, peasants and surfs, knights and nobility who spent their lives in or around these amazing structures. To Suzanne, they seemed magical. No princess, however, could have been more in love with her prince than Suzanne was with Bing.

Each major town they passed had a church with a tall steeple in its center. Some of the towns showed the scars of the war; others had been spared. The damage seemed almost random. Around the little villages were golden-brown fields bordered with hedges.

It was fall and the harvest was complete. Farms had not yet recovered from the war years. Much of the livestock had been killed; the Germans had exploited and decimated the herds. Often, children and farm wives had struggled to keep up with the farm work in the absence of their men and without necessary farm supplies. There was, however, the promise of a new crop next year and hope for a yield sufficient to feed the people of France.

There was no food to buy on the train. Bing and Suzanne had taken no provisions with them. Suzanne didn't mind. It was exciting to be embarking on a new life together. She was happy just to be with Bing, to hold his hand, and to feel his strong arm around her.

When they arrived in Paris, they made their way directly to the Red Cross office. The Red Cross workers were kind and helpful. However, Bing and Suzanne learned they needed witnesses for their wedding. The witnesses could not be strangers.

The only people Suzanne knew who lived near Paris were the Lieberts. Suzanne remembered their address; she had often addressed the care packages her family sent to this Jewish family during the war.

Suzanne and Bing found their way across Paris by metro to Courbevoie. Courbevoie is a community located two miles northeast of the center of Paris. Suzanne, the inexperienced country girl, figured out how to navigate around the city. Despite being introverted, she did most of the talking with the various officials. Though these tasks pushed her out of her comfort zone, Bing was by her side. It was better for her to take the lead because she spoke the local language.

Bing and Suzanne exited the metro station. They walked hand in hand along the Seine River to the address Suzanne remembered, 86 Quai du Marechal Joffre. A large warehouse building stood just across the street that ran along the river. There appeared to be living quarters above the warehouse. Suzanne stood outside with Bing and called out, "Monsieur, Madame Liebert! It is Suzanne Chédotal." The Leiberts were delighted to see Suzanne. They were more than happy to help the young couple.

Together, the four adults walked several blocks to the town hall at the city center. When they inquired about getting married, they were told Suzanne needed notarized permission from her parents because she was two weeks shy of her 21st birthday. Suzanne and Bing had to make the long trip back to Nort to secure the necessary documents.

They boarded a late-night train and arrived in Nort the next morning. It took most of the day to accomplish the paperwork. They went to a lawyer's office to get the right documents. They carefully filled out the forms and returned to the lawyer's office with Suzanne's parents to have the papers notarized. (Though they were not pleased about the marriage, Suzanne's parents chose not to stand in the way of Suzanne's decision.) With the documents in hand, Suzanne and Bing again boarded a night train; this time, it was bound for Paris.

When they arrived once again in Courbevoie, they had not slept in more than two days. They were very tired, but they were determined.

Monsieur and Madame Liebert accompanied Suzanne and Bing to the *hotel de ville* (town hall). They walked together up the big concrete steps at the front of the beautiful, old town hall. White pillars and ornate doors graced the front. The words of the French national motto, *Liberté, Egalité, Fraternité* (liberty, equality, brotherhood), were once again emblazoned on the stately building. The *Tri-colour* (French flag) proudly announced that France was free.

Suzanne did not have a fancy white wedding dress like the one her mother had worn. She wore the blue coat which had been made for her out of an old blanket. Bing made sure she had a lovely bouquet of white flowers. Her faced was flushed with happiness. Bing believed his bride was the most beautiful bride in the world. Suzanne was his choice.

The mayor of Courbevoie asked everyone present to stand while Suzanne and Bing exchanged the traditional French wedding vows. They were the same promises her parents and grandparents had made to each other. There was a translator for Bing.

Suzanne and Bing promised each other respect, fidelity, help, and assistance. They pledged to ensure the moral and material direction of their family, to provide for the education of their children, and to prepare for their children's future. Both spouses agreed to contribute to the expenses of the marriage in proportion to their respective faculties. They pledged to each other a "community of life."

Suzanne and Bing signed the marriage contract. A record of their marriage, along with their signatures and the signatures of their witnesses, was recorded in the big, black, leather-bound Book of Marriages in the town hall of Courbevoie, France on

October 6, 1945. The mayor declared Bing Yee Ng and Suzanne Chédotal were Monsieur and Madame Ng, husband and wife. Bing and Suzanne were given a *Livre de Famille* (family book). The official book documented their marriage and would one day record the births of their children.

The two couples exited the large front doors of the town hall into the cool, autumn sunshine. Suzanne and Bing paused on the steps to have their wedding picture taken. On the way back to the home of Monsieur and Madame Liebert, they stopped to celebrate the occasion with a dinner of steak and *frites* (French fries) at a café on the bank of the Seine River. Madame and Monsieur Liebert proposed a toast to the newlyweds.

A small, wooden rowboat was tied up at the edge of the river. Even though they did not know who owned it, Suzanne and Bing climbed into the little boat. Monsieur Liebert used Bing's camera to take their picture. A bridge over the river provided a fitting backdrop for the photograph; it seemed to represent the promise of the new path their lives would take together.

Bing and Suzanne on their Wedding Day

Suzanne and Bing spent their wedding night in the attic of the Lieberts' warehouse home on an old mattress on the floor. Suzanne wore a night gown she had borrowed from her friend Therese. The night was perfect.

There wasn't much time before Bing would have to leave again. The young couple took the train back to Nort. They were not greeted with a special dinner, nor a reception, nor a celebration of any kind. There was no toast to honor the newlyweds, nor any words of congratulations. There were no wedding gifts. Suzanne hadn't expected much. The war had left her family poor. The stores continued to have few items available for purchase. Suzanne had only hoped her family would share her joy and bless their marriage. She and Bing were, however, welcome to stay at her parents' home.

Shortly after they returned to Nort, Suzanne became very ill. The doctor was called to come to the house. Suzanne was diagnosed with scarlet fever and quarantined to an upstairs bedroom. No one was allowed to go into her room. Bing did not care about the doctor's orders; he went upstairs to be with Suzanne despite the quarantine. She was very, very sick.

Bing returned to his post in Germany three days after they were married. It was hard for him to leave Suzanne, especially when she was so sick, but he had no choice. He left his bride in the care of her parents. He promised to bring Suzanne to Germany as soon as he could get authorization from the US Army. In the meantime, he would come to see her as often as possible.

At that time, it was against US Army regulations for an American soldier to marry a French national without permission from the Army. Bing was busted for marrying Suzanne. (To be busted means to be demoted in military rank.) He considered it a small price to pay; Suzanne was his wife. (It did not take long for Bing to regain the rank he held before he was married.)

More than 60,000 US servicemen married women overseas during and just after World War II. Two months after Bing and Suzanne were married, the War Brides Act of 1945 was enacted.

The United States promised the soldiers' wives and children would receive free passage to the United States and have expedited immigration status.

These war brides were special. They didn't marry for money or prestige; they married the men they loved and committed to them unconditionally. In fact, the divorce rate of war brides and their husbands is among the lowest of any demographic group. These women left their homes, their families, and their culture. They moved thousands of miles away to be with their husbands. They had little or no hope of ever seeing their families again. Some of these women had spent just days with their new husbands before they were shipped out. For many of them, it was more than a year until they were reunited. When they finally arrived in the United States, war brides were often the objects of curiosity. Sometimes, they were met with disapproval from their new in-laws.

20 NEWLYWEDS

It was the best time of my life. Everyone was happy.
The war was over and the families were back together again.
—Suzanne Ng, recalling the years she lived in Nuremberg

S uzanne drifted in and out of consciousness. She shivered with cold or burned with fever. She was aware of Bing's presence by her side, applying cold cloths to her forehead, coaxing her to take sips of water, holding her hand, and kissing her tenderly. Then, Bing's presence was replaced by her mother. He was gone. She dreamed about Bing and their wedding night. Had it only been a dream?

Suzanne stayed with her parents until she recovered from her bout with scarlet fever. It had nearly taken her life, just when the war was over, and her future seemed so bright. It left her weak and shaken. She was anxious to join Bing in Germany. She understood it might take several months to get the necessary authorization from the US government. She knew Bing would come to see her in France as often as he could, but Nuremberg was 17 hours away by car; weekend visits were not possible.

In the meantime, Suzanne planned to continue working at her job in Nantes. However, when she returned to the *Banque Postal,* her boss told her she could no longer work there because her husband was not French.

She returned to Nort and rented one of the little houses directly across the street from her parents' home. It was tiny and Spartan, with dirt floors and no indoor plumbing. It didn't matter to Suzanne. She wasn't fussy and her living situation was only temporary. Times were still hard in France. Goods were scarce, money was tight, and there was much rebuilding of both infrastructure and lives to be done. Suzanne spent her time helping her mother and studying English.

Albert, Suzanne, Lucette, Raymond, Nicole, Bernard, Marc, 1946

Suzanne's brothers returned to Nort for a visit; Albert was in the French Army and Raymond had joined the Navy. Her parents took advantage of the opportunity to have a picture taken of all seven of their children together. Albert, Suzanne, Lulu and Raymond stood behind the little ones, Nicole, Bernard, and Marc.

Bing's friends in Germany were happy Bing had a new bride. They were anxious to meet her. One of his friends, along with his wife, gave Suzanne and Bing a wedding present—a pound of Maxwell House coffee and a *Good Housekeeping Cookbook*. Those were the only wedding gifts the young couple received. Though Suzanne could neither read nor understand English, she was grateful for their kindness.

Never did a month pass before Bing found a way to come to see Suzanne. He was very generous to Suzanne's family. He always brought them food items and clothing as gifts.

Bing introduced Suzanne's family to peanut butter. Peanut butter was readily available and inexpensive at the American commissary in Germany. It was a staple for American families, but it was new to the French. They were delighted with the creamy texture and rich taste of the novel food item.

He brought blue jeans to Suzanne's siblings. They were the

first young people in their area to have blue jeans. The blue jeans had rivets; rivets were unknown in France at that time. Lulu, Nicole, Bernard, and Marc felt very modern and well-dressed in the newfangled clothes. They were the envy of their friends.

Bing gave Suzanne a second-hand wooden box radio he had purchased from a German woman. Suzanne had not had access to a radio during the war. She was delighted to be able to listen to the BBC (British Broadcasting Corporation). Radio Luxembourg had been her favorite station in the years before the Nazis invaded her country. During the war, it was under the control of Nazi Germany and was used for propaganda purposes. When the war ended, Radio Luxembourg quickly resumed commercial broadcasting. Suzanne enjoyed listening to the news and to the latest music, especially the modern love songs by Perry Como, Frank Sinatra, and Bing Crosby.

Bing bought a small motorcycle in Germany. He secured a week of leave to visit Suzanne. When he was close to Paris, he had an accident; his leg was badly scraped. He wound up in a Paris hospital, attended by the Red Cross. Eventually, he made it to Nort-Sur-Erdre; he spent just two days with Suzanne before heading back to Germany.

Suzanne's family grew to like Bing. Any doubts they had about Suzanne's choice to marry Bing melted away as they got to know him. They were impressed by his energy and initiative. He was observant; often, he recognized problems and figured out how to solve them without being asked. He anticipated their needs and he enjoyed serving Suzanne's parents. Though they could not share conversations, they grew to respect and trust each other. Suzanne was delighted her husband and her parents were building a relationship. Her siblings could not talk to him; they smiled a lot.

Suzanne made two trips by herself to the American Consulate in Paris to get her paperwork processed. No one helped her. Traveling on the train to Paris with Bing had been exciting and comfortable. Suzanne did not like traveling alone to the big city. "When you have something to do, you get it done," she concluded. The end goal was living with Bing in Germany. It took almost six months, but finally the paperwork was complete. Suzanne was recognized by the US Army as Bing's dependent; she had a passport and permission to accompany him in Nuremberg.

It was spring of 1946 when Bing borrowed a vehicle and came for Suzanne. She relished the long drive with Bing. They stopped along the way to buy bread and pâté; they shared a picnic at the side of the road. The scenery changed from the flat lands of France to the hills and mountains of Germany. They passed through thick forests and crossed swiftly moving rivers, the likes of which Suzanne had never before seen.

Suzanne and Bing in Germany

Suzanne brought very little with her when she moved to her new life. She had the radio Bing had given her, her bicycle, the wooden pencil box with the cranes painted on its smooth top, and the orange-colored cloth napkins from the box her father had taken off the train during the occupation. She had very few clothes.

Bing and Suzanne stayed in a room at the American compound for the first few weeks they were together in Germany. Bing promised they would soon have a house to live in. The security of the American compound shielded Suzanne from the devastation in Nuremberg. She and Bing shopped together at the base commissary. Suzanne was amazed at the quantity and variety of food available for the American families to purchase. Everything was inexpensive. The base PX (Post Exchange) was a big room where military ID card holders could purchase cigarettes, chocolate, and coffee. Oh, how Suzanne had missed good coffee! She strolled around the compound or rested while Bing was at work; Suzanne was pregnant with their first child.

Soon, Bing came home with news. They were to be billeted in a house in the Ziegelstein area of Nuremberg, just to the northeast of the city. This section of the city had been spared the heavy Allied bombing during the war.

A uniformed American Army representative had knocked on the front door of every home in the neighborhood and informed each of the property owners, "This house is being requisitioned by the United States Army." The German residents were told to take their clothes and a few personal items, but to leave their houses furnished. The former residents could choose to live with friends or relatives, or they could live in a refugee camp. They were compensated for the rent of their property and they were offered the option of becoming caretakers of their houses. This was an opportunity many of the German property owners seized. Not only would they be able to make sure their property was well cared for, but, also, the American government would pay them for their services. Jobs and money were scarce in postwar Germany; the income was much needed. If they felt resentment, they did not show it. They did not complain to the new occupants of their homes. They understood their position as the defeated nation.

Suzanne was excited as she and Bing drove to their new neighborhood. Deciduous forests framed three sides of the housing area. The trees sported new spring-green foliage, and birds sang as if there had never been a war. At the end of the street was a town center with a school and a few small stores. Bing stopped the jeep in front of their new home, 124 Bierweg Strasse.

Similar two-story houses occupied small lots on both sides of the wide, paved street. The houses were quite new. The steep slate front roofs had two dormers. On the side of each house, six steps went up to a small covered stoop and entry door. Bing unlocked the door of their home; he and Suzanne explored their new living quarters. It was immaculate and completely furnished with everything the newlyweds needed. There was a conspicuously awkward empty place on the wall in the living room. Bing told Suzanne there had been a picture of Adolph Hitler hanging in that place.

An elderly German man named Hier Metz came regularly to fill the furnace with coal. The furnace kept the house warm and comfortable.

The woman who owned the house was hired by the US Army to serve as a maid for Suzanne and Bing. She did not live with them, but she helped with the housecleaning and maintenance, and she did some of the cooking. She had an eight-year-old son; there was no evidence of her husband. Perhaps he had been killed in the war. Suzanne was kind and friendly to her maid. She knew what it was like to be a maid, and she knew what it was like to live in an occupied country. Though the cause and circumstances were different, there were enough similarities to make Suzanne compassionate. Suzanne was careful to treat the house and its furnishings gently. She was grateful for the nice living quarters, but she knew they didn't belong to her. Suzanne was glad she had studied the German language when she worked as a maid in Nantes; it helped her communicate with this German woman. Suzanne often gave her maid food to take home.

Suzanne was happy to have help with the cooking. Bing did most of the cooking for the two of them when he was home. He often prepared steak for their evening meal. During the years France was occupied by the Nazis, there were few opportunities for Suzanne to learn to cook; they had made do with very meager fare. Now that Suzanne presided over her own home, she studied the cookbook she and Bing had received as a wedding gift. Her ability to read and understand English was improving.

She wanted to learn to make American food for Bing.

Those were good times for Suzanne. She always treasured the memories of the years she and Bing spent together in Nuremberg. In fact, it was the happiest time of her life. Despite the difficult conditions surrounding them in Germany, the American military families were happy. The war was over, and the families were together again after being separated for so long.

Suzanne's pregnancy progressed well. The due date came and went. Bing borrowed a government jeep to take her for a bumpy ride, hoping she would go into labor. It didn't work. She was two weeks overdue when labor finally began.

Bing drove Suzanne to the US Army's 116th General Hospital on the east side of Nuremberg. The six-story building, with more than a mile of gleaming white hallways, had been constructed by the German government. It was completed in 1937 and dedicated by Adolf Hitler himself. At the height of the war, it had accommodated more than 1,000 patients. It was controlled by the German Army District Surgeon until April 20, 1945 when the US Army entered Nuremberg.

Though the hospital sustained damage during the Allied bombing raids, much of the building was usable and most of its equipment was in good condition. It had large elevators, state-of-the-art x-ray machines, and modern operating rooms. The last of the German patients was discharged in May. The 116th General Hospital set up operations in the main building. The first American patient was admitted on June 24, 1945. By 1946, the hospital had 500 usable beds. With the war over, most of the patients were Americans who had routine ailments or who had been injured in motor vehicle accidents.

Suzanne was one of the first wives of an American soldier to give birth in that hospital. There was no maternity ward. They simply gave Suzanne a bed in the regular ward with many other patients. The hospital was full. One of the patients was a nurse who had the flu. She gave up her bed so Suzanne could be admitted. That kind nurse left an orange for Suzanne. Suzanne was delighted to have the orange, but, for some reason, Bing was not pleased. That was the first time Bing was ever cross with Suzanne, and it was very bothersome to her. She did not understand the reason for his displeasure.

Fathers did not stay at the hospital with mothers in those days. Bing left, and Suzanne found herself alone in a strange place. Every now and then a nurse checked on her, but she was very lonely, and she had no support. It was not a good experience for Suzanne. Finally, on August 28, 1946, almost 11 months after Suzanne and Bing were married, Francette was born.

Suzanne and Francette stayed in the hospital for four days. When Suzanne returned home with her baby girl, Suzanne's maid fell in love with Francette; the German woman enjoyed helping the young mother take care of the beautiful new baby.

Suzanne's parents and siblings had anxiously anticipated the birth of Suzanne's first baby. They were delighted when they learned of Francette's safe arrival. They could hardly wait for Suzanne and Bing to bring the new baby to meet them. Suzanne often sent letters and pictures; her family eagerly waited for each one.

October 20, 1946 was Suzanne's 22nd birthday. Though birthdays weren't celebrated in her childhood home, she expected Bing would make the day special for her. However, he did not mention her birthday in the morning before he left for work. He didn't say anything when he came home at the end of the day. Suzanne was disappointed, but she did not remind him of her birthday.

Finally, it was time for bed. When Suzanne pulled back the covers, she noticed a package under her pillow. She opened the box and lifted the tissue paper, revealing a beautiful, blue, wool gabardine suit. The perfectly tailored garment had been made by Kirkland Hall, a well-known tailor with shops in London and New York. Bing must have ordered it far in advance.

She could hardly wait to try on the lovely suit. It fit perfectly. The slim pencil skirt was calf-length. The jacket buttoned up the front, had a princess collar, 3/4 length sleeves, and was fitted at Suzanne's slender waist. She had never owned such a beautiful garment. Bing was pleased with himself for surprising Suzanne. She could see in his eyes that she looked beautiful in the new suit.

Suzanne's granddaughter, Molly Ng, wore the treasured suit to Suzanne's funeral in the fall of 2019.

Suzanne enjoyed being a mother. She loved taking walks in the neighborhood with Francette in the wicker pram. Francette was a contented baby and Suzanne could leave her in the care of her maid when she needed to. Bing was delighted with his baby girl; he proudly carried her around, showing her off to his friends. Like most men at that time, he was not very involved with her care.

The American families in the Zieglestein neighborhood were friendly with each other, except for one American woman who lived across the street from Bing and Suzanne. She had a car, and she was stuck-up. The other wives called her Rich Bitch. Suzanne thought that was her name and always referred to her that way; she did not know the English meaning of the words.

Bing and Suzanne made many lasting friendships at that time. Sophie and Ted Goebel lived next door. Ted fought in the Battle of the Bulge and now he, like Bing, had occupation duty. The two couples became very good friends. Bing taught Sophie how to drive because her husband was not patient enough to teach her. Sophie taught Suzanne how to make peanut butter cookies with cross-hatched marks on the top. Suzanne had never made cookies before. In fact, she did not know of anyone in France who made cookies; they were not typical of French cuisine. Suzanne was pleased to learn to make an American treat.

Suzanne was introduced to mail-order catalogs. The Americans in Germany could order from Sears, Montgomery Ward, and Aldens catalogs. The items were delivered right to their front doors. They did not even have to pay for shipping. Suzanne enjoyed browsing through the pages of the catalogs. This was a completely new experience for her.

American women in Suzanne's neighborhood wore pants. (Suzanne had never seen women in France wearing pants.) These pants were made especially for women; they looked modern, comfortable, and attractive. Suzanne found some in the Sears catalog and ordered a pair for herself. She wore them when she went to France to visit her family. She felt very sophisticated, and she wondered what the French people thought when they saw her wearing pants.

Before Suzanne was married, she never wore makeup. There had been little makeup available during the occupation years, but Suzanne hadn't been interested in wearing makeup, anyway. In Germany, she began wearing a little bit of rouge, lipstick, and powder like the other American wives. (She didn't use eye makeup and she didn't wear high-heeled shoes. She always remained a country girl at heart.)

Winter Fun in the Street in front of the Ng's Home

Americans in Germany had a great deal of freedom. There were many fun things for the military families to do. They often gathered in each other's homes. Winters in Germany were colder than the winters Suzanne was accustomed to in France and there was much more snow. The guys brought jeeps home from work and tied sleds behind them—five sleds at a time. They pulled the kids up and down the street. When the weather was warmer, Bing and Suzanne, with Francette, used government jeeps to take rides in the country for picnics. In the summer and fall, they drove to a farm outside the city to buy fresh vegetables. They bought bread, cheese, and cakes at German stores.

Many Americans traded on the black market. The German people were very poor after the war, and, even if they could afford them, most products were not available for the Germans to buy. Some American soldiers purchased cigarettes and coffee at the PX to trade with the German people for beautiful things like china, silverware, and furniture. Suzanne and Bing avoided trading with items they purchased on base because it was against Army regulations. They did occasionally trade coffee for bread at the German bakery. They purchased some silverware and porcelain dishes from a German woman and brought them to Suzanne's mother in France.

As time passed, restrictions about fraternizing with Germans eased. Though some misunderstanding and distrust persisted, the Americans and the Germans were nice to each other. Suzanne observed that the Americans treated the Germans well. Suzanne, the introverted French girl, mingled with the German women more than most of the other American families did. In her mind, she was able to separate the individual people from the German government. She did not blame German civilians for the war. However, she didn't believe they did not know what was going on. They, like she, were victims of a war thrust upon them. Suzanne never talked about the war with her German friends.

This was the time of the Nuremburg war crimes trials. The husband of Suzanne's friend Eloise guarded the Germans who were on trial for war crimes. He was able to get tickets for Suzanne and Eloise to attend the trials one day.

Driving through the Nuremberg ruins was a stark reminder of the havoc the war had raged in Europe. Most of the city had been destroyed. It was gray and dusty. Suzanne saw many people, mostly women and young people, picking through the rubble.

The trials were held near the center of Nuremberg in the Palace of Justice. This complex was chosen because it was relatively undamaged by the war and it included a large prison area. In addition, its location near the site of some of Hitler's major propaganda rallies was symbolic.

Suzanne entered the grand front door of the Palace of Justice. She climbed the marble stairs to the second-floor courtroom. The walls and ceiling of the courtroom were covered with rich, dark, ornate wood paneling. Crystal chandeliers hung from the ceiling. The carpets, as well as the draperies on the windows, were bright blue. Suzanne had never before seen such a place.

Initially, 23 Nazi leaders were tried for crimes against humanity. The courtroom was a busy, somber place. It was important that these trials be conducted carefully. They must be fair, they must bring to light the horrors which had been perpetuated by the evil regime, and they must promote trust between the nations. Many countries took part in the trials. Not only were there judges, lawyers, and defendants, but there were also reporters, translators, and spectators. Everything was done deliberately and thoughtfully.

The defendants offered various explanations for their actions:

- Some of the defendants claimed they were just following orders.

"For a soldier, orders are orders." —Alfred Jodl

- Some claimed they did not know about the horrific things that had happened.

"I am sorry that crimes were committed of which I had no knowledge." —Ernst Kaltenbrunner

"If I have been made guilty of the acts by error or ignorance my guilt is a human tragedy not a crime." —Walthur Funk

- Some were deeply sorry.

"The abyss between the idea of a social community which I imagined as a former seaman and worker, and the terrible happenings in the concentration camps has shaken me deeply." — Fritz Sauckel

- Some expressed their undying loyalty to Hitler.

"Heil, Hitler."

The doctor who was on trial the day Suzanne attended the hearings at the big brick courthouse in the center of Nuremberg had done horrific things; it was rumored he had used human skin to make lampshades. (This charge was never proven, but Suzanne always believed it had happened.) Suzanne didn't understand everything going on in the courthouse that day because her English skills were still limited. She was glad the evil was being exposed for all the world to see and justice was being done.

It is interesting to note that many Nazi soldiers would have been unrecognizable to their family and friends at home in the military roles they played. Men who were loving fathers and Sunday School teachers murdered innocent civilians and children in the name of the Third Reich.

Only the worst of the Nazi war criminals were tried. Most of the German soldiers and many of the German civilian population were implicated in one way or another in the terrible things the Third Reich had done. Regular soldiers were not prosecuted. German people were anxious to move on. Allied Forces did not want to cause resentment that could lead to future animosity.

Suzanne had no desire to go back to the trials. She wanted to put the war behind her and enjoy her new life with Bing and Francette.

Suzanne and Bing made the trip to visit Suzanne's parents in Nort at least twice a year. At first, they went in a borrowed government jeep. Then, Bing bought a government jeep, and he fitted it with an Opal chassis. It was an unusual looking vehicle, but they enjoyed the freedom it afforded them. They usually stopped in Courbevoie to visit the Liebert family on their way to Nort. The Ng family and the Lieberts became good friends.

One time, when Suzanne was visiting in her old hometown, she encountered the wife of the shuttle driver who used to give Suzanne and her siblings rides between Nort and Héric. She asked Suzanne if she might be able to find a needle-threader in Germany; she hoped Suzanne could send her one. Suzanne might have been able to find one, but she remembered the way the shuttle driver had falsely accused her brother of breaking the window crank-handle in the shuttle many years before. Her resentment kept her from searching for the requested item.

In the summer of 1947, Lulu came to Nuremberg to visit Bing, Suzanne, and little Francette. The two sisters enjoyed the time they spent together in Germany. Suzanne and Bing lavished Lulu with an abundance of good food. They went for drives in the car and had picnics in the country. They took advantage of every opportunity to pamper Suzanne's 15-year-old sister.

When they brought Lulu back to Nort, they stopped in Saint-Nazaire so Grandmère-Nazaire could make the acquaintance of Francette. Suzanne was excited to introduce her special grandmother to her precious baby girl. Grandmère-Nazaire loved Francette, just as she loved Suzanne. Grandmère-Nazaire died a short time later. Suzanne forever missed her beloved grandmother.

Suzanne and Bing lived together in Nuremberg for about two years. They enjoyed a time of abundance, freedom, and happiness. Suzanne was content.

21 ARMY WIFE

Home is where the Army sends us.
—Sentiment displayed in the homes of many Army families

S uzanne slid into the passenger seat of their funny-looking POV (privately owned vehicle) and settled Francette on her lap. As the car pulled away, she glanced back wistfully at the German house they had called home for the past two years. Then, she smiled at her husband. She still wanted nothing more than to be with Bing.

In 1948, Bing was transferred to the American military facility located an hour south of Frankfurt. The young family left their friends and the neighborhood they loved so much to move 150 miles west.

Suzanne was learning to understand some of the unique characteristics of military families. They settle into new homes, make friends quickly, and establish routines, only to be uprooted when the military member is transferred. Then, they begin the process all over again in a new community. In contrast, Suzanne's family of origin rarely ventured far from their place of birth. Francette was a toddler when they moved to Auerbach-Bensheim, Germany.

When they first arrived, the Ng family was billeted in a very exclusive area at the base of a mountain on the road winding up to the ruins of Auerbach Castle. The fancy houses lining the street had been home to Nazi generals. To Suzanne, they seemed like mansions. The house was beautifully furnished with large, heavy, ornate furniture. There was a huge dining room table with big chairs around it; the chairs seemed better suited for a conference room than for family dining. Large tapestries hung on the walls. Though the furnishings were elaborate, and the house had everything the family needed, including a maid to help care for the large dwelling, the house felt neither cozy nor comfortable to Suzanne. She was thankful they had been assigned a cook and a maid; she wondered how she could have managed to take care of both a toddler and the big, fancy house at the same time.

All the houses in that area had been taken over by the US Army to accommodate senior officers and their families. There were no other enlisted people billeted in the area. Suzanne did not know how she and Bing wound up in that house; she thought the Army must have made a mistake. She did not connect easily with the military wives who were her new neighbors. She was afraid they might look down on her because their husbands outranked hers.

Enlisted soldiers are the backbone of the Army. They perform specific job functions and have the training, knowledge, skills, and abilities to ensure the success of their unit's missions. Officers manage enlisted personnel; they plan missions, provide orders, and assign tasks. Bing was an enlisted soldier.

Soon after they moved in, Suzanne was invited to an Officers' Wives' Club fundraiser event. Quiet, shy Suzanne assumed the other wives did not know her husband was not an officer. She had no money to contribute, but she went because she was invited. The women played cards. Suzanne had little to say to these American women, whom she perceived to be stuck-up. She felt out of place. She was never invited to another one of their events.

After several months, the Ng family moved to a house that was more comfortable for them. This house also had been requisitioned by the US Army. The Army paid for a cleaning lady to come regularly. The houses the Americans lived in were scattered throughout the area, so Suzanne did not have the opportunity to make as many friends as she had in Nuremberg.

She connected with an Army wife from Liverpool, England who had also married an American GI. The two women had much in common. They had both endured the horrors of World War II in their home countries and become war brides. They now lived with their American husbands in the foreign country which had caused the devastating war. They both anticipated moving to the United States and becoming citizens of a strange, new land across the Atlantic Ocean. They understood the frailty of the peace they enjoyed. They appreciated the lovely homes they lived in, and they relished the abundance of food and clothes they had access to.

Bing brought home a German Shepherd dog named Harold. Harold loved Francette and he would do anything to protect her. He had been trained by the German Army, and he didn't like men. He was prone to biting men if he escaped from the yard, or if he thought a man was threatening Francette. They couldn't keep a dog that was so quick to bite people, so they had to get rid of Harold.

Francette with Harold

Suzanne and Bing decided to explore some of the surrounding countries. They carefully planned an extensive trip and invited Bing's Army buddy, Glen Ermel, to go with them. First, they stopped in Nort to leave Francette with her grandparents. Then, Suzanne, Bing, and Glen toured the south of France, Italy, the French Alps, Germany, Belgium and Luxembourg. It was an exciting trip for the French girl who had never traveled before she was married.

Suzanne was especially pleased to visit Italy. The scenery was beautiful, and the weather was warm, even though it was late fall. It was a nice break from the snow in Germany and the rain in France. Sometimes, when their car stopped at railroad crossings, Italian children recognized American soldiers and asked for chewing gum. Suzanne, Bing, and Glen climbed the Leaning Tower of Pisa. One night, they checked into a small hotel in the Italian Riviera. They awoke in the middle of the night and realized the place was infested with bedbugs. Suzanne was appalled! They left as quickly as possible.

They stopped to eat at a restaurant in the French Alps before heading up a steep mountain road toward Val d'Isere. Soon after leaving the restaurant, a car approached them from behind, honking its horn. Bing stopped the car to see what the problem was. Some people they had met during their stop at the restaurant had learned the road ahead was closed because of heavy snow. They wanted to warn the young American travelers. Suzanne, Bing, and Glen were grateful. They did not have a lot of gas, and they might have been lost in the snow. In fact, two weeks later, the little town of Val d'Isere was destroyed by an avalanche.

When they returned to Nort to retrieve Francette, they decided to spend an evening in Héric with their friends. Suzanne, Bing, and Glen were visiting in the sitting room with Therese and Berik when their daughter, Michelle, came down the stairs. Glen saw Michelle and he was smitten; it was love at first sight. Michelle was only 16 at the time; Glen was six years her senior. Glen visited Michelle often by himself after their first meeting. Eventually the two were married.

Europe was struggling to recover from the devastation of the war. In 1948, The Marshall plan was enacted to help finance the rebuilding efforts on the continent. The United States poured 13 billion dollars into Europe to aid the economic recovery. At first, those funds were intended to help only the countries that had been the victims of the Third Reich. Soon, however, the aide was extended to Germany in the form of loans. The United States gradually granted more liberties to the general population and delegated responsibilities to well-vetted German people. As the nation began to recover, the Germans and the Americans began to trust each other.

Unfortunately, the sector of Germany occupied by Russia experienced more and more oppression. Russia wanted to maintain tight control of Eastern Germany. The capital city, Berlin, was located far inside Soviet-controlled Eastern Germany. The city was divided into four quarters; the United States, Great Britain, France, and Russia each occupied one quarter of the capital city. Russia tried to force the other occupying nations out. They blocked all railway, road, and canal access to the sectors of Berlin under Western control. The United States, France, and Great Britain held their ground. They airlifted food and fuel to West Berlin for almost a year and kept it free from Soviet control.

As the United States, Great Britain, and West Germany worked together to support the free German citizens in West Berlin, something interesting happened. They became friends and allies, standing together against a common enemy, Communism.

Americans in Germany thought the Russians were going to fight for Berlin. It was a scary time; they feared they would once again be thrown into a war. American families were offered the opportunity to go back to the United States, but Suzanne didn't want to leave. Bing and Suzanne decided to stay together and take their chances. They did, however, send Francette to live with Suzanne's parents in France. They wanted to ensure her safety.

Francette was welcome at her grandparents' home. Her young aunts and uncles adored her and relished the opportunity to play with her and care for her. At the time, Francette was two. Mark was only three years older than Francette. Bernard, and Nicole, just a year apart in age, were nine and eight. Lulu, at 16, was older and wiser.

The Chédotal children had great freedom to roam the area around their home. The public launching ramp at the river, about a quarter mile from their home, was one of their favorite destinations. The river was about 50 yards wide at that place. Trees shaded the banks of the slowly moving water. The children fished for catfish or blue gills. Maman cooked whatever they brought home. Sometimes they pulled a slimy eel up from the muddy river bottom; the eels had a muddy taste because of where they had lived.

The children played on the grassy bank or on the concrete launching-ramp. One afternoon they brought two-year-old Francette with them to the river. Mark took a turn pushing her in the baby buggy. Suddenly, Marc lost control of the buggy! It rolled down the boat-launching ramp into the water. The buggy floated like a little boat. Francette sat in the buggy, safe and unconcerned, until she was rescued by her appalled uncle.

Suzanne and Bing continued to bring supplies to Suzanne's family every time they visited. The shortage of goods persisted. Ration coupons were used to help distribute the limited supplies of necessities in France until 1949.

Francette was four when a baby boy joined the Ng family. Once again, Suzanne's pregnancy had lasted longer than expected. George Washington's Birthday was celebrated as a national holiday on February 22 each year in the United States and at American military bases around the world. Suzanne's doctor had the duty on Washington's Birthday that year; he had to be at the hospital for a 24-hour shift. Since there wasn't much going on, the doctor suggested it would be a good day for Suzanne to have a baby. It took one hour for Bing to drive Suzanne to the Army hospital in Frankfurt. Labor was induced. Jimmy was born on February 22, 1950.

Suzanne and Bing named their children exactly what they

wanted them to be called. Jimmy's name is not James; it is simply Jimmy. He was named after Bing's brother. Neither Francette nor Jimmy were given middle names. Their last name often causes confusion for people who first encounter it. Though Ng is a common name in China, many people outside Asia struggle with the fact that the surname has no vowel. The Ngs often explain, "N, G. Two letters. No vowels. Pronounced as if it was spelled I, N, G." (Jimmy maintains that it stands for Nice Guy.)

22 MOTHERS TOGETHER

It's a funny thing coming home. Nothing changes.
Everything looks the same, feels the same,
even smells the same.
You realized what's changed is you.
—F. Scott Fitzgerald

Once again, Suzanne carefully folded her family's clothes and packed their belongings. She was particular about how things were done around the house; she liked everything to be neat and orderly. She hummed as she worked. Each item had a memory attached to it. Moving was not complicated because they did not own many personal possessions. She and Bing had only lived in furnished homes, and they lived simply.

Bing had been promoted to the rank of Master Sergeant; with the promotion came a new assignment. Suzanne, Francette, and little Jimmy accompanied him to the new duty station, 20 miles north in Darmstadt, Germany.

The Ng family was billeted in a German house in a nice neighborhood with sidewalks and a nearby park to play in. The military families' homes were scattered throughout the area. Suzanne longed for a close-knit military community like the one they had enjoyed in Nuremberg. That was harder to achieve when the military families were not next-door neighbors. She wondered what new experiences awaited her in this new home.

The Army assigned a maid to their family and covered the expenses; her name was Frau Kruel. She was efficient, good with the children, and an excellent cook. Suzanne was kind to her, but they did not develop a close personal friendship.

Suzanne communicated with Frau Kruel in German. While Suzanne wasn't fluent in the language of her host country, she knew enough German to get by. Francette rapidly picked up the German language as she experienced life in Germany and interacted with Frau Kruel, who often took care of her. Suzanne and Bing spoke English exclusively to each other and to the children. (Suzanne did not want to exclude Bing from any communications in their home.) Bing never spoke Chinese anymore; Suzanne only spoke French when she was with her French friends and relatives.

Francette was quiet and responsible, much like Suzanne had been when she was a little girl. Jimmy was born with a twinkle in eye; he was much like Suzanne's little brother Raymond had been. He was happy, curious, and extremely active. Suzanne had to watch him very carefully; he was always getting into something.

Bing was strict and impatient with the children. As a sergeant in the Army, he was accustomed to a regimented, rule-bound, hierarchical way of life. He brought some of those expectations home with him. Suzanne tried to keep the children from irritating their father.

Bing's new assignment was managing the NCO Club on the base. The military uses an abundance of acronyms. Not only was Suzanne becoming fluent in English, but she was also learning the unique language of the military. NCO stands for non-commissioned officers. These experienced soldiers obtain their position of authority by promotion through the enlisted ranks. In the Army, corporals and sergeants are considered non-commissioned officers.

Bing's job was part of the Army's effort to encourage good morale for the American soldiers stationed far from home. The NCO Club provided a place to gather, activities, and a restaurant and bar for corporals and sergeants, as well as their families. Bing coordinated dances, parties, Bingo games, movies, and American-style food in a friendly, lively setting. There were dart boards and pool tables.

The Army hired a German woman named Rose Engel to be Bing's secretary. Civilian jobs on the American military bases were highly coveted by the German people. These jobs provided income and access to supplies that were still scarce in Germany. A major perk for people working at the NCO Club was a free meal every day.

Rose was young and single. She had a baby as a result of a brief romance with an American soldier.

In the decade after World War II, 36,000 babies were born to unwed German mothers and American soldier fathers. Most of the men left Europe without ever meeting their children. Occasionally, the children were the result of rapes. Sometimes, the women formed relationships with the soldiers, hoping to get the supplies they so desperately needed. More often, the young German women and the American soldiers simply fell in love. By 1949, more than 20,000 German women had married their American soldiers and emigrated to the United States.

Life was hard for German people after the war, but it was especially hard for unwed mothers and their children. Prior to 1947, American soldiers were not allowed to provide support for the German children they fathered; such assistance was considered "aiding the enemy." Even after the ban was lifted, German women had no recourse in seeking assistance from the fathers of their children. Many of these children became wards of the state, at least for a time.

Suzanne never saw Rose's baby and she did not know where the baby was. She knew the baby was a boy and she knew neither Rose nor her parents had custody of the child. Suzanne felt compassion for this young woman. She and Bing befriended Rose and they did as much as they could to help her. They often invited her to stay with them on weekends. Suzanne and Bing gave her their guest bedroom to use whenever she wanted.

Rose with Jimmy, Suzanne, and Francette

Rose loved Francette and Jimmy. Suzanne thought she must have been thinking about her own son when she held or played with little Jimmy.

Rose and Suzanne sometimes went shopping together to find items Bing could use as prizes for the Bingo games at the NCO Club. Usually, they shopped at the PX. Suzanne looked forward to those shopping excursions with Rose. Neither Rose nor Suzanne had much money of their own to spend, but they enjoyed spending the Army's MWR (morale, welfare, and recreation) money. They shopped carefully to make the budget stretch as far as possible. They tried to discern which items would delight the prize winners. They chose things like suitcases and silverware.

The PX (post exchange) was well-stocked with items shipped over from the United States. American soldiers and their families could purchase cameras, home goods, clothes, shoes, accessories, electronics, toys, candy, cigarettes, alcohol, personal care products, and jewelry. The stores and activities on the base used American dollars.

Bing saved a little money at a time until he had enough to purchase a diamond ring at the PX. He wanted to surprise Suzanne with a replacement for the inexpensive silver ring he had given her soon after she agreed to marry him. Suzanne was delighted with the beautiful symbol of Bing's love. She wore it always.

Rose's parents lived in Trier, an ancient city on the Moselle River. Trier Cathedral marked its center. The charming city was founded by the Roman Empire and still had several well-preserved Roman structures, including the ruins of Roman baths and an amphitheater. An old stone bridge traversed the river. It was a beautiful city; Suzanne loved to go there.

It took two hours to drive from Darmstadt to Trier. Bing and Suzanne made the trip often. It was fun to have a destination, and Rose's parents always made them feel welcome. Sometimes Francette stayed with Rose's parents for several days at a time. They adored her. Five-year-old Francette delighted in going with them to the lightbulb factory they owned. They let her help put the lightbulbs together. Francette placed the filament inside the glass bulb and carefully screwed on the bottom of the lightbulb. She was pleased to be trusted with important jobs, just as her mother had been when she was a little girl.

The Moselle River wound its way slowly through the Moselle Valley to the Rhein River. Vineyards grew on the steep slopes along the river. River boats cruised up and down the Moselle River, passing through several sets of locks on their way.

The Grille was a 44-foot sloop, built in Germany in the mid

1930's. The well-appointed sailboat had one mast, a fore-and-aft mainsail, and a jib. She had been used as a state yacht by Adolf Hitler and other high-ranking Nazi officers. The Grille became known as Hitler's yacht. At the end of the war, she was confiscated by the US Army. Her new mission was boosting the morale of American soldiers and their families. Bing and Suzanne were chosen from among the many American families in Darmstadt to be treated to a river cruise on the lovely vessel. Suzanne enjoyed sailing up and down the Moselle River, passing through the locks, sightseeing, and eating the specially prepared food.

Bing and Suzanne spent as much time together as they could. Sometimes, Suzanne went to the NCO Club with Bing when he needed to attend an evening event. Suzanne was not a drinker, but one evening, when she was at a party at the club, she was offered some champagne. Shy, quiet Suzanne soon became the life of the party. It was the only time in her life Suzanne ever got drunk. Her friends teased her mercilessly after that event. She was never again able to stand the thought of drinking champagne.

Bing was extremely generous. Sometimes he was generous to a fault, offering things or money to people when his own family might have used them. Occasionally, one or another of his Army buddies asked to borrow money ahead of payday, promising to repay the loan as soon as he got his paycheck. Many of those loans were never repaid. Suzanne was not pleased when the loans were for things like cigarettes and alcohol, but she did not complain to Bing.

Bing and Suzanne continued to make the trip to Nort-Sur-Erdre as often as they could. Francette and Jimmy loved to visit their grandparents, aunts, and uncles. The youngest aunt and uncles were not much older than Francette. They made good friends and playmates.

The family usually left Darmstadt early in the morning to make the 14-hour trip by car. They brought Suzanne's family as many supplies as they could fit into the car. Butter, sugar, peanut butter, Jell-O, coffee, and clothes for the growing children were all greatly appreciated items. Once, they surprised Suzanne's mother with a beautiful new coat.

Suzanne carefully packed the gifts on the floor of the back of the car until the items reached the height of the seat. Then, she covered the cargo and used blankets and pillows to make the whole area into a bed. She wanted the children to be comfortable, have room to play, and, hopefully, sleep at least part of the long journey. The children looked at the scenery and sang songs as they traveled. They pretended to be asleep when they passed through customs at the country borders. The guards would not disturb the sleeping children. Consequently, the carefully covered items were not noticed. That made it faster and easier to clear customs. (Suzanne and Bing were concerned the gifts they were bringing to her family might be misconstrued as black-market items.)

Suzanne's family never knew when Suzanne and Bing would arrive; Bing enjoyed devising surprises. He parked the car at the bottom of the hill near the house, out of sight. Then, Suzanne and Bing sent Francette, holding onto little Jimmy's hand, up the hill by themselves to surprise and delight their unsuspecting grandparents. There were always exclamations and lots of kisses all around when the little ones were discovered.

On one of their visits, Suzanne and Bing brought Suzanne's mother an electric wringer washing machine. Bing borrowed a small trailer, loaded the washing machine onto the trailer, and pulled it behind his car all the way to Nort-Sur-Erdre.

Bing and Suzanne's father set the washing machine up in the concrete laundry shed behind the kitchen. The entire family watched as, together, Bing and Maman demonstrated the new-fangled machine. They filled the tub of the washing machine with hot, soapy water. The first load of dirty laundry was added to the tub. (They started with the girls' dresses because they were the least dirty and finished with socks and Papa's work clothes.) An agitator sloshed the clothes in the soapy water until they were clean. Then, they lifted the wet clothes out of the tub by hand and fed each piece between two rotating metal rollers. The rollers squeezed the water out of the fabric. (They had to be careful not to get their fingers caught between the rollers.) Each load of clothes was run through the soapy water and the wringer. When all the clothes were washed, the tub was drained and refilled with clean water. The washed clothes were put back into the tub of rinse water, agitated again, and, then, fed through the wringers one more time. Using the electric wringer washing machine was so much easier than washing and wringing the clothes by hand. Maman was pleased with the work-saving appliance. Papa was delighted to see electricity used in a new way.

Marc and Nicole each took a turn visiting Suzanne and her family in Germany. Always, Suzanne and Bing picked them up and brought them home again. Nicole spent most of the summer she was 12 in Darmstadt. She looked at her big sister with admiration and thought she was a very pretty woman.

Nicole was surprised and impressed when she found Suzanne had a maid to help care for their big, beautiful house; there was no such luxury in the Chédotal household in Nort. She had never seen soft, white toilet paper before; at home they used only newspaper. She thought her sister's lifestyle seemed grand.

The quantity and variety of food available at the commissary and served in her sister's home amazed Nicole. Suzanne made sure Nicole had as much to eat as she wanted. "The profusion of food reigned for our great happiness," Nicole remembered. She felt loved and spoiled. She had a special fondness for the blueberry pies made by Suzanne's maid, Frau Kruel.

Germany experienced a hot spell that summer. Suzanne and Nicole laid together on the cool, hard, tile floor to find relief from the heat. The simple experiences they shared turned into good memories and helped create a strong bond between the sisters, even though there was an age difference of 15 years between them.

Nicole loved her sister and wanted to please her. Suzanne insisted her young siblings obey; she was a little vigorous with both Marc and Nicole when they visited. Nicole surmised Suzanne was worried about Bing's reactions. Perhaps Suzanne did not want Bing to be irritated in any way by their presence. Nicole observed Suzanne was somewhat subject to Bing. Suzanne did not complain.

When they made the trip to bring Nicole home, Bing and Suzanne decided to spend a few days vacationing by themselves in France. Francette and Jimmy stayed in Nort-Sur-Erdre while their parents traveled. The young couple drove along the Coast of Brittany and into Normandy with their new Italian Fiat. (Bing had sold their oddly modified Jeep and upgraded to the new car.) Few people in France had cars at that time. Many of the people they encountered wanted to take a look at Bing's Fiat. Bing was happy to demonstrate its features.

Suzanne wore a new pair of leather sandals on that trip. New shoes were still a scarce commodity in France. During the war, Suzanne had worn wooden-soled shoes that hurt her feet. She was happy to have nice, comfortable, leather sandals. Often, on that trip, people commented on Suzanne's beautiful sandals. They were quite fashionable; Suzanne was amused that she, the simple country girl, was considered stylish.

Bing and Suzanne stopped at the American Cemetery near Omaha Beach in Normandy. More than 9,000 American men and women found their final resting place there. Most of them lost their lives on the beaches of Normandy. Some were killed when the Leopoldville was torpedoed, but that incident was still highly classified. Bing was uncharacteristically quiet as he and Suzanne strolled through the well-kept cemetery. Suzanne was overwhelmed by the sheer number of American men and women who sacrificed their lives to free her country.

(In 1956, five years after Bing and Suzanne visited the American Cemetery in Normandy, the Wall of the Missing was added to honor the men and women whose bodies were never found. The names of 1557 men and women are inscribed on that granite wall, which is set in a beautiful, semicircular garden. Listed among them are the names of the men of the 66th Infantry division who were lost when the Leopoldville sank in the English Channel.)

Next, they crossed the Cotentin Peninsula to Cherbourg. Bing rarely mentioned his war stories, and he never talked about what he experienced coming to France. On that trip, however, as they stood at the edge of a cliff overlooking a beach in Cherbourg, Bing soberly told Suzanne, "There were so many dead bodies floating in the water." She did not press him for details. She assumed he was referring to D-Day and the carnage on the beaches of Normandy. She knew nothing about the sinking of the Leopoldville, and Bing was not at liberty to tell her.

Suzanne and Bing stopped in Nort-Sur-Erdre to retrieve the children before they returned to Germany. While they were gone, Jimmy had fallen out of the highchair in his grandmother's kitchen and broken his collar bone. He was a resilient toddler, however. His injury didn't slow him down much.

In April of 1952, Bing received military orders to move to Fort Detrick, Maryland. The mission of Fort Detrick was to conduct medical defense research against biological weapons. It had an enclosed test sphere which was unofficially referred to as the "8-ball." This unique laboratory was used to test the dispersal of biological agents in aerosol. Bing was assigned to manage the mess hall for the men and women stationed there.

Bing left Germany for his new assignment six months before Suzanne and the children left Europe. They could not join him until Bing was able to get the official documents allowing his European-born family to come to the United States. While they waited, Suzanne rented a two-room house across the street from her parents. It was small and humble. Though she enjoyed living in beautiful houses in Germany, she was comfortable in her temporary quarters. Suzanne was adaptable, and she knew how to be independent. She found pieces of linoleum to cover the dirt floors, and she made the little house into a home for her children.

Suzanne's younger siblings were delighted to have their big sister and her children nearby. They clamored for a turn to spend the night at Suzanne's house. Francette and Jimmy spent much of their time across the street with their grandparents. They loved playing with their aunts and uncles. Sometimes the children explored in the nearby woods where trenches and ruins left by the Germans made a virtual playground.

Suzanne enjoyed the new relationship she was building with her mother; they were adults and mothers together. Suzanne had not felt close to her mother when she was a child. As an adult, she was learning to understand and appreciate her mother. Though it was difficult for the two women to verbalize their feelings, they felt an urgency to strengthen their bond. They knew their days together were numbered. Suzanne wondered about the new land across the Atlantic Ocean. Soon, she would call it home. Her mother worried about her oldest daughter moving so far away. Would she ever see her again?

23 COMING TO AMERICA

Give me your tired, your poor,
Your huddled masses yearning to breathe free,
The wretched refuse of your teeming shore,
Send these, the homeless, tempest-tossed to me,
I lift my lamp beside the golden door!
Statue of Liberty Inscription

Francette and Jimmy pressed their noses against the window of the train as it picked up speed and passed along the back edge of their grandparents' property. They strained to catch a glimpse of Grandpa working in the garden. Suzanne sighed. The long trip ahead was daunting. She was alone with her two children; Francette was six and Jimmy was just two and one half. The paperwork allowing Suzanne and the children to move to the United States was finally in order. Bing sent traveling instructions and money for the journey. Suzanne bade farewell to her family. The Chédotal women did not show their emotions. They did not need to. They were secure in their love for each other, and the future would be what it would be. (*Que sera sera.*)

Picture taken in Héric just before leaving France

Suzanne, Francette, and Jimmy boarded the train at the station in Nort-Sur-Erdre. Suzanne arranged their luggage while the children gazed, wide-eyed, at everything around them. Jimmy felt a need to investigate every square inch of the train. Suzanne had frequently traveled on trains when she was a child, but this was a new experience for her children. They had often seen and heard the noisy trains speeding along the tracks at the back edge of their grandparents' property. Suzanne engaged the children by suggesting they would shortly be passing their grandparents' house.

The whistle blew and the train lurched forward. The train passed the Chédotal property much too quickly, but little Jimmy was sure he had seen Grandpa one last time. The children waved with all their might.

The train took Suzanne, Jimmy, and Francette almost 800 miles to Bremerhaven, Germany. There, they boarded the SS Washington on September 9, 1952. The Army transport ship was 700 feet long; she had been used to move troops during the war. Now she also carried military families between the continents.

Suzanne and the children were assigned to a cabin with eight bunks; they shared the room with five other women. Suzanne thought the food on the ship was very good; she had never before seen so much variety and quantity of prepared food. However, the trip was hard for her. She had two young children, and no one offered to help. It did not occur to her that she could ask for assistance; the shy French girl did not want to be a bother to anyone. Suzanne worried constantly; she was afraid Jimmy would get hurt on the ship. Sometimes she left him in the care of Francette for just a few minutes while she took a quick shower.

One afternoon, the captain of the ship announced they would soon be crossing paths with a famous ship. Suzanne took Francette and Jimmy with her to the ship's railing and watched in awe as the RMS Queen Mary sailed by. The massive ship was more than 1,000 feet long. Her black hull, gleaming white decks and two red smokestacks made a sharp contrast against the blue of the sea and sky. As the Queen Mary passed gracefully on the port side of the transport ship, Suzanne remembered how she had watched the launching of the SS Normandie. She was sad France's rival to the Queen Mary had been destroyed.

The SS Washington traveled at 20.5 knots. After nine days at sea, the ship finally sailed into New York Harbor. Again, Suzanne stood on the deck by the rail with a tight grip on the hands of Francette and Jimmy. The Statue of Liberty came into view, welcoming them to America. The tall, green, copper statue was a gift from France to the United States. It seemed fitting to Suzanne that her native land was part of her welcome to her new country.

Bing was waiting in New York with a brand-new, aqua-colored Studebaker when the ship arrived. The family was happy to be reunited. Bing showed Suzanne his parents' neighborhood, but they did not stop. Bing had already tried to reconnect with them, but he had been rejected.

Unlike most other war brides and their soldier-husbands, Suzanne and Bing spent the early years of their marriage in Germany, home to neither of them. Six years passed before Suzanne came to her new country. Although Suzanne's parents wanted her to marry a French man, they accepted Bing and they came to love him. However, it was a different story for Bing's family. Bing was from a very traditional, old-world Chinese family. They were not happy Bing had married a French woman without their consent. The consequences were severe; Bing was completely disowned by his family. They never met his beautiful bride nor their grandchildren. Bing never talked to his children about his Chinese family or heritage.

Bing, Suzanne, and the children drove on to Maryland. Bing told Suzanne they were going to a friend's house. It was dark when they stopped in front of a house across from 505 Military Street, Frederick, Maryland. When they went inside, no one was there. The little house was completely furnished. There was even a television. Suzanne had never seen a TV before. Bing showed them everything in the house. Then he told Suzanne it was theirs.

Bing had purchased the house, the furnishings, and the new car without telling Suzanne; he wanted to surprise her. There was a big bouquet of multicolored flowers on top of the TV. The house was lovely—all new. The kitchen was completely white. There was a Formica-topped dinette table. Suzanne had never seen such a modern house. It was directly across the street from the base. Bing managed the mess hall on the other side of the fence, within clear view of the house.

Bing bought the TV and the furniture at Sears on credit. He did not have a credit record, so he didn't actually qualify for the loan. The store manager gave him credit, however, because he trusted Chinese people. His experience with Chinese people demonstrated that they were honest and hard-working. Bing purchased the car on credit, too. Bing and Suzanne had to make payments on those loans. Bing's salary did not stretch as far in the United States as it had when they lived in Germany. Many of their needs in Germany, including housing and a maid, had been provided by the Army. Food had been inexpensive. In Maryland, they had no money to spare. They mostly ate beans, hotdogs, tomato soup, and crackers. Suzanne did not like to be in debt. She would have preferred simpler housing and smaller bills.

Bing was drawn to new technology. He had a mechanical device which could be manipulated to change the direction of the rabbit ears on their television; they could receive different stations depending on the position of the antenna. Friends who came to the house were interested in the device; Bing enjoyed demonstrating it.

Television was in its infancy. Their little set had grainy, black and white pictures, but it was amazing. Together the family watched I Love Lucy, Dragnet, What's My Line, The Life of Riley, and The Adventures of Ozzie and Harriett. Watching television shows sharpened Suzanne's ability to speak and understand the English language. The children loved it.

Bing had a propensity for buying and selling cars. It wasn't long before he traded the aqua Studebaker for a light blue Oldsmobile.

Bing often came out the back door of the mess hall when he was at work so he and Suzanne could wave to each other. Eight years had passed since Suzanne and Bing waved to each at the halfway point between Héric and Nort. Those gestures might have seemed small to on-lookers, but they were a tender connection Suzanne and Bing shared.

Suzanne managed their little home and the children herself; there were no maids to assist her. Their neighborhood had many young military families. The fun and camaraderie were much like they had enjoyed in Nuremberg. Suzanne and Bing made friends with their next-door neighbors, a lieutenant named Chick (Cecile) and his wife, Polly. They had two children when the families met, and they soon had another baby. Suzanne and Polly helped each other with their kids. The men fished and hunted squirrels. Suzanne was not accustomed to eating squirrels; she didn't want the squirrels in her kitchen. Another friend in the neighborhood took Francette and Polly's little girl to the Nazarene church for Sunday School.

Jimmy was a happy, gregarious little boy. He continued to be a handful. He was very active, smart, and inquisitive. He was always getting into mischief. Suzanne was sometimes hesitant to go outside of her house; she worried people in the neighborhood would recognize she was Jimmy's mother. They might think poorly of her mothering skills because of Jimmy's hyperactivity and the way he played rough with the other children. Sometimes he threw sand at them.

By the time 1954 dawned, Suzanne spoke English well and she was working on becoming an American citizen. The United States government had passed a law fast-tracking American citizenship for war brides. She was required to study the history of the United States, learn about American government, pass a test, and complete the application process.

Frederick, Maryland was only 50 miles from Washington, DC. Suzanne would have liked to visit the capital, see the monuments, and explore the famous points of interest she read about.

Bing was not interested, so he did not take Suzanne.

In January, Bing was transferred back to Germany. Before he left, Bing sold the house. He and Suzanne stored their furniture and other possessions. The people who purchased the house also wanted to buy the car. Bing gave them the car and they promised to send Bing and Suzanne money every month until the car was paid for, but they never did.

Suzanne, Francette, and Jimmy stayed in the United States for a few weeks after Bing left. Suzanne did not want to leave until her American citizenship was finalized. They stayed with the neighbors who had taken Francette to Sunday School.

Chick drove Suzanne to Washington, D.C. for the swearing-in ceremony. They passed the United States Capital, the White House, and the Washington Monument. Suzanne thought the capital city of her new country was impressive. On February 9, 1954, Suzanne Ng became a naturalized citizen of the United States of America, along with more than 100 other immigrants. The ceremony took place on the steps of the United States Supreme Court Building. John F Kennedy, the junior senator from Massachusetts, officiated. Suzanne noticed his hair was very messy.

Suzanne borrowed money from the Red Cross to buy a suitable dress to travel in. They later paid the money back. Suzanne and Bing always paid their bills and they always kept their word. Honesty and integrity were of paramount importance to them. Suzanne did not want to be indebted to anyone, and she did not want to accept charity.

Chick drove Suzanne, Jimmy, and Francette to Baltimore where they caught the train to New York City. There, they boarded the USNS General Alexander M Patch and set sail for Europe. This military troop ship was 600 feet long. Jimmy was seasick on the trans-Atlantic trip. He threw up on his mother's new traveling dress.

When the ship finally arrived in Germany, Bing was waiting for them. The family was reunited and ready to begin the next chapter of their family adventure.

24 BACK IN GERMANY

Many years are flying by, these happy golden years.
—Laura Ingalls Wilder, *These Happy Golden Years*

S uzanne hushed the children and tidied the two small rooms they were calling home. She snuck into the kitchen they shared with their German landlords to prepare a simple meal of boiled potatoes and vegetables. Bing would cook the steak when he got home from work; Suzanne did not want to spend any more time in the kitchen than she had to. She looked forward to having a kitchen to herself again. Worse than sharing the kitchen, however, was sharing the bathroom. The landlords complained when Suzanne and Bing wanted to take more than one bath a week; they were not happy about the expense of heating the water. Suzanne surmised the walls must be very thin; she could hear conversations taking place in the adjacent rooms of the house. She was sure the other occupants were listening to everything she said. The lack of privacy was bothersome to her.

Almost nine years had passed since Bing had first gone to Germany in 1945, at the end of World War II. Bing and Suzanne were amazed at the changes which had taken place in Germany since then. Much of the country had been in ruins. There was great unemployment, lack of basic supplies, and the economy was a mess. There was no government in place. The Allied Forces occupied Germany and took control of the country. Allied troops and their families were billeted in German houses. German factories were dismantled. German technology and know-how were confiscated. (These were known as intellectual reparations.) Germany was transformed into an exclusively agricultural economy. Every effort was made to rid Germany of lingering Nazi influence.

By 1947, a different approach had taken shape. The United

States and Great Britain did not want to repeat the mistakes made at the end of World War I. They believed a strong, healthy, independent, democratic Germany would make a good friend and ally. Trusted German men were given positions of authority. The Americans supported newspapers and free speech. An effort was made to teach Germans about democracy. At first, the German people did not know how to respond. Gradually, the Germans and the Americans began to trust each other.

Britain and the United States helped Germany rebuild both their infrastructure and their economy. Germany was given its own currency in 1948. Funds were made available to help Germany rebuild. The severely damaged German cities had choices to make; they could rebuild with modern architecture, or they could rebuild to make their cities look as much like they had looked before the war as possible. Frankfurt chose the modern route, while Munich and Nuremberg chose the historical option.

By the time the Ng family returned to Germany in 1954, the Nazi influence was almost completely gone, and the Cold War was the new threat. Preparations were being made to end the military occupation of West Germany. American forces would maintain a presence in Germany (and still do), but West Germany was to become a free, independent democracy. Their economy and their infrastructure were well on the way to recovery. The Germans have a word to describe the transformation of Germany from the ashes of the war—*wirschaftswunder*, which translates to economic miracle.

American troops and their families were no longer billeted in German houses. The Ng family had to find a place to live in a nearby German town until quarters were available for them at the newly established Army housing area called Vogelweh. They found a small apartment in the home of a German family, with whom they shared a kitchen and a single bathroom. They did not know how long they would have to endure the uncomfortable living situation. It might take many months for the housing area to be completed and ready for occupancy.

It did not take long for Suzanne and Bing to conclude that sending Francette and Jimmy to stay with their grandparents was a good idea. Bing and Suzanne drove the children to Nort-Sur-Erdre; Suzanne returned to Germany with Bing. They would come back for the children when housing was available for them on the post.

The arrangement was good for everyone. Grandma, Grandpa, the aunts, and the uncles were delighted with the opportunity to re-establish a relationship with Francette and Jimmy. The children had room to play and they did not have to be constantly admonished to be still and quiet. Suzanne was relieved that she did not have to worry about the children bothering the landlords or irritating Bing in the close quarters.

Grandpa had a special fondness for Jimmy. He was often hard on his own children, and he was sometimes gruff with Jimmy, but Jimmy and his grandfather formed a particularly strong bond. Jimmy followed him around in the garden. He tried to help, often pulling seedlings instead of weeds or stepping on little plants. He got into trouble for picking walnuts from the giant tree behind the house before they were ripe.

Grandma could often be found in the dining room, sitting in her red and gold *fauteuil Voltaire* (high-backed, padded arm chair), working busily with her knitting needles and wool. Her hands were rarely idle. She turned out beautiful sweater after beautiful sweater. While she worked, she enjoyed listening to the radio that sat on the mantle above the fireplace. A tall table beside her chair was a convenient place for her to set her glasses and her knitting needles when she was busy with other tasks.

Francette and Jimmy went to school in the same three-room schoolhouse their mother had attended. They were immersed in the language and the culture of France. They learned to speak French. The children made friends at school. Jimmy was a challenge for his teacher. A picture of his first-grade class is telling; Jimmy is standing next to the teacher and she has her hand on his shoulder. Francette, of course, was a compliant little girl.

Suzanne was happy when they were finally able to move

out of the small, rented apartment and retrieve their children. Though she had not liked the housing arrangement, there was a silver lining. The Ngs developed a lasting friendship with the German family who lived in the house next door. They also met the American family who moved into the rented apartment when the Ngs were finally able to move into government quarters on the post. This new family, Nick and Rose Loveless and their children, became Bing and Suzanne's best friends; they remained friends forever.

Kaiserslautern Military Community, located just outside the city of Kaiserslautern, supports several United States Armed Forces and NATO installations. It became the largest military community outside of the United States. Vogelweh is a housing area in this community. It was built specifically for Army troops and their families; all the needs of the families were met within the gates of the post. The housing areas were carefully planned with sidewalks and playgrounds. There was a school, a chapel, a commissary and PX, a library, and recreational facilities.

The Ng family was billeted on the second floor of one of Vogelweh's brand new apartment buildings. Each four-story building had 16 apartments. The basement was divided into storage rooms by wire walls; each family was assigned one of those storage rooms, so they had a place to keep things like bicycles.

Bing worked as a military policeman. He was soon promoted to First Sergeant and became a supervisor. He was beloved by the people who worked for him.

Suzanne was busy taking care of the children. The Army did not pay for household help at this time, but Suzanne hired a German woman to help with the cleaning. Though most military wives stayed on the post, Suzanne was comfortable in German communities. She often took the bus to the nearby German town to shop.

Bing still did much of the cooking at home, but Suzanne had also become a good cook. She often baked the peanut butter cookies she had learned to make as a newlywed. The dog-eared pages and underlined recipes in her Good Housekeeping Cookbook attested to the fact that she was making good use of her only wedding present.

The family who lived directly above the Ngs was from Puerto Rico. They had quite a few children who became convenient playmates. When the weather was inclement, the kids played together in the basement of the apartment building.

Francette and Jimmy were old enough to play outside by themselves. They went sledding on a nearby hill in the winters. They roamed the woods behind the apartment, and they made friends in the neighborhood. They built forts and played in craters left by World War II bombs. One time, Jimmy found some matches; he took them outside to play, and he accidently set the woods on fire! The post fire trucks came to save the day with their lights flashing and their sirens blaring. Suzanne was oblivious to the fact that Jimmy was the cause of the commotion.

Francette liked to roller skate on the sidewalks in the housing area. One afternoon, she fell while roller skating and broke her leg. Her father did not understand how bad her injury was and he made her walk home. When Francette got to the apartment, Suzanne realized the injury was serious and called an ambulance. (Bing expected his children to be tough, hard-working, independent, and obey his directions without hesitating or questioning. Suzanne tried to compensate for his harshness, without irritating Bing; she did not like conflict.)

Francette was admitted to the Army's 2nd General Hospital. Suzanne was pregnant at the time, but she took the bus to the military hospital every day to visit Francette. This modern medical facility was opened in 1953 to provide primary and specialized care, hospitalization, and medical treatment for American military personnel and their families. (Today it is called Landstuhl Region Medical Center. It is the largest American hospital outside the United States, serving more than 52,000 local American military personnel and their families.

It also provides specialized care for the more than 250,000 additional American military personnel and their families in the European Theater and serves as the primary medical treatment center for injuries sustained by military personnel in the Middle East and Africa.)

Bing and Suzanne welcomed their third child on September 10, 1955. They named him Steve. Nine-year-old Francette was delighted with the new baby. She was a big help to her mother.

The Loveless family came to visit the Ngs every Sunday. Bing always fed them. Suzanne and Rose put their babies in the playpen together. The older children enjoyed having playmates. Nick was a jokester; he was fun to have around. Suzanne and Bing loved Nick and Rose. The two couples considered each other as family. Sometimes, however, just like with blood relatives, there is such a thing as too much togetherness. At times, Suzanne and Bing would have enjoyed having a Sunday alone to do as they liked.

Suzanne was pleased when her brother Albert came to visit them in Germany. Of all her siblings, he was closest in age to Suzanne—only two years younger. She had been worried when she had no news from him during the last two years of the war. They sat together in her home in Germany and reminisced about their experiences. Suzanne learned interesting details about the secrets kept during those difficult occupation years.

Albert was arrested by the Nazis in the summer of 1944 when he turned 18. He was herded onto a train bound for German work camps. During World War II, the Nazis deported thousands of people from conquered countries to work in forced labor camps. The prisoners produced supplies for the strained German war economy or for construction projects. These camps were different from the SS-run concentration camps, but the conditions were still abysmal. There was a complete disregard for the health of prisoners. Food, medicine, and clothing were inadequate. The prisoners were forced to work long hours with little or no time for rest or breaks. As a result, death rates in labor camps were extremely high.

Albert managed to escape from the train before it left France, but, as he jumped from the train car, his hand was slammed in the heavy door. Albert hid his injured hand under his jacket and tried to run away, but he was quickly recaptured. He was taken to a German-controlled hospital for treatment of his injury. The hospital exits were guarded by German soldiers.

Albert was not dissuaded. He tied bed sheets together and made knots in the length of the sheets. In the dark of the night, he snuck out the hospital window and climbed down his improvised rope to the ground below. He managed to get away, undetected by the Germans.

The Allied Forces were already on the European continent by that time. Albert made his way north to General Massu and the Free French. He wanted to join with the forces who were fighting to liberate his homeland. At first, they wouldn't allow him to join the Army. He looked so young; they didn't think he was old enough. When he finally convinced them he was 18, he was accepted into the Allied Forces and assigned to General LeClerc.

Albert was present when one of the concentration camps was liberated. (It was probably Dachau.) Albert and his fellow liberators were encouraged by their commanding officers to take pictures of the concentration camp. The leaders knew it was important to document the horrors that had taken place there. Albert gave some of the pictures he took to Suzanne. (Many years later, Suzanne gave them to Jimmy. I am not including them in this book. They are too hard to look it.)

After the war, Albert married Mary Claire Lorec. She was the granddaughter of a famous sea captain from Saint-Nazaire. Her grandfather had kept a brand-new ocean liner out of the hands of the invading Nazis at the beginning of the war. As the enemy approached, he took a small boat out to the new, almost-finished ship, which was anchored in the harbor. He was able to board the ship and single-handedly take it to a safe port.

When Albert visited Suzanne in Germany, he was no longer in the military. He wanted to go shopping at the PX, but, of course, he did not have the military ID card needed to enter the facility. He borrowed one of Bing's uniforms, put it on, and walked right into the PX. Suzanne was appalled; she was afraid he would get caught. No one, however, asked to see his identification card and he was able to purchase a sweater.

On January 28, 1957, Suzanne gave birth to her fourth child. She named the beautiful baby girl Laurette, in honor of her mother. (Laurence, pronounced with the accent on the second syllable, is a difficult name for Americans who are accustomed to the masculine name Lawrence, pronounced with the accent on the first syllable. Consequently, Suzanne altered the name enough to make it easy for Americans to say, while maintaining a French flair.) With the addition of Laurette, the Ng family had four children, two boys and two girls.

The Ng family stayed in Germany until the end of 1957 when Bing received orders to Fort Lewis. Fort Lewis is a large Army training facility near Tacoma, Washington. Bing's workers were sad to see him leave. They gave him some lovely going away gifts, including a bone-handled carving set.

Bing and Suzanne bought a Volkswagon bus in Germany and had it shipped to New York. Bing left ahead of the rest of the family. He wanted to pick the van up in New York and have it ready to make the cross-country road trip when Suzanne and the children arrived.

Suzanne, Francette, Jimmy, Steve, and baby Laurette boarded an airplane bound for New York City. The Super Connie was the biggest plane of its day; it could make the transatlantic flight without refueling. This was the first time Suzanne or any of the children had ever flown. They were quite excited about this adventure. The plane got as far as the airspace over England when one of the engines caught fire. The plane was forced to return to Germany. Suzanne and the children checked back into the hotel they had left just hours before. Suzanne commented, "It's too bad the maid already changed the sheets. We are just going to use them again."

They finally arrived in New York City. Bing met them with their Volkswagon bus. The family of six embarked on a new adventure. They drove across the country, crowded into the van, with no seat belts, all the way to Washington State.

They stopped along the way to visit Glen and Michelle Ermel on their farm in Fountain, Colorado. (Ten years had passed since Bing had introduced his Army buddy to Michelle when they visited her family in Héric, France.) Bing stopped at a gas station to ask for directions to the farm. The attendant was excited to see them and exclaimed, "Oh! You must be Bing and Suzanne!" Clearly, the Ermel family was pleased the Ng family was coming. The Ermel children had a motorcycle; they showed the Ng kids how to ride all over the farm.

Suzanne's dear friend Therese and her husband Barik had sold the bakery in Héric and moved to Colorado to be close to their daughter Michelle and their grandchildren. Barik became the janitor at a local school and Therese was the housekeeper for the school's principal. Suzanne was happy to see her old friends. The three women conversed contentedly in French.

The Ng family arrived safely in Washington State just before Christmas of 1957. Suzanne settled into life as an American housewife. Her story would continue to develop, chapter by chapter, with new experiences, new friends, new challenges, and even some new children.

EPILOGUE

Her Legacy Remains

*There is a time to write stories
and a time to live your own.*
—Signed, Sealed, Delivered Television Series

I was privileged to be the one who received Suzanne's stories, and the one who was trusted to capture on paper some of the memories she treasured in her heart. I am honored to share these chapters with you. The details of the remaining volumes of her life must be told by Suzanne's children, for they experienced it with her. This, however, is an overview of her life as an American woman.

Bing and Suzanne bought a house in the little town of Roy, Washington, just outside the back gate of Fort Lewis Army Post. The Loveless family soon followed them to Washington State and bought a house near theirs. The two families continued the friendship they had begun more than a continent and an ocean away.

In Roy, Suzanne filled many roles in addition to that of busy housewife and mother to four active children. Among other things, she was a Boy Scout leader, a librarian, and a deputy sheriff. She was an avid seamstress, putting to good use the skills she learned when she was an apprentice to the tailor in Nort-Sur-Erdre. She loved to read. Along with Bing, she and the children picked berries and pinecones to supplement the family income. Bing taught her how to drive a car, which opened new possibilities for her. She got a job as a cashier at the Fort Lewis Post Exchange; Bing and Suzanne set the extra money aside to buy plane tickets for her parents to visit the Ng family in Washington State.

The Ng family moved into the City of Tacoma when Bing retired from the Army. They bought a restaurant, named it Ng's Café, and the entire family pitched in with the work.

Suzanne's fifth child, Bennett, was born on April 11, 1963. Three years later, Francette was married and pregnant with Suzanne's first grandchild when Suzanne discovered she was expecting another baby herself. The two women even shared their maternity clothes. Suzanne was 41 when her youngest son was born. She and Bing named him Jerry. Suzanne, like her mother, welcomed her babies over a period of twenty years.

Bing sold the café and became a chef at Johnny's Restaurant in Tacoma for a few years. Next, he worked as a civilian meat cutter at the Fort Lewis Commissary.

Sons-in-law, daughters-in-law, and grandchildren kept increasing the size of the Ng family. Each of Suzanne's children married and they all contributed to her collection of 21 grandchildren. She had room in her heart for each one of us.

Jimmy grew up to be a tease like his grandfather. Often, I feel the need to apologize for him. I used to say, "I'm so sorry, but it is his mother who raised him."

One day, quite a few years ago, Suzanne overheard me say those words, and she interjected, "Joy, you have had him longer than I did. It's time for you to start taking some of the responsibility for his behavior."

It was important to Suzanne that the entire family gather around the table for meals, just as her family had done in France. She often made peanut butter cookies for her children; in fact, those are the only cookies Jimmy remembers her making.

The well-loved 7th Edition of the Good Housekeeping Cookbook, printed in 1944 and Suzanne's only wedding gift, moved from house to house and country to country with her for 74 years. Its pages have yellowed, and its cover has been reinforced with red and white contact paper. It is mine, now. I cherish the old cookbook because Mom loved it. It gives me great pleasure to prepare the tried-and-true recipes found within its covers.

When Bing finally retired, he and Suzanne lived in a motor

home for eight years. They traveled south to Yuma, Arizona in the winters and north to Tacoma in the summers. One year they spent six months in Cape Cod, Massachusetts with their oldest and youngest sons. They loved their snowbird years, and they made many good memories together.

Bing suffered a stroke in 1988. He and Suzanne sold the motor home and settled into a lovely little house on the property of Francette and her husband Jim. With Francette's support, Suzanne took care of Bing for eight years before she became a widow in 1996. (Complications of diabetes caused his death.) Suzanne and Bing were married for 51 years. It wasn't always "happily ever after," but it was faithful commitment.

Suzanne continued to live in her comfortable home. Francette was always there, her friend and confidant. Jimmy, Steve, Laurette, Ben, Jerry, and their spouses dropped in frequently, often bringing grandchildren and chaos with them.

Marianne, the little German girl from Idar-Oberstein, met and married her American soldier in Germany. Like Suzanne, Marianne left everything she knew to move with her husband to the United States. Marianne and Suzanne were introduced through the friendship of their sons, Mike and Bennett. Marianne became one of Suzanne's dearest friends. Suzanne marveled to Marianne, "I never could have imagined having a German for a friend, but here we are."

While Suzanne, like most of the men and women of the Greatest Generation, was extremely frugal, she took great joy in blessing her children. She was one of the most generous people I have ever known. She delighted in taking her children and grandchildren on cruises. If she knew of a financial need her children had, she found a way to meet the need gently and inconspicuously.

The greatest gift she gave her six children and their spouses was a trip to France in 2001. She introduced us to our French relatives and our French heritage. It was a special time of fun, laughter, and bonding. She was in her element with her children around her, enjoying each other.

Suzanne kept in close contact with her siblings in France, especially her youngest sister Nicole and her brother Marc, who still live in France. Nicole visited Suzanne every few years and the two frequently shared Skype or telephone conversations. Marc and his wife sailed around the world, stopping to spend an entire year with Bing and Suzanne in Tacoma.

Though Suzanne remained independent in her own home until the very end, she eventually needed more help. Her children rallied around her, lending the necessary support. Her eyesight became an issue and she had to give up driving. She continued to indulge her love of reading with Talking Books. During the last five years of her life, she "read" more than 500 books.

Suzanne Chédotal Ng

At her 95th birthday party on October 20, 2019, surrounded by family and friends, she remarked, "This is the best birthday party I have ever had." We played a game called, "Suzanne Ng: Fact or Fiction." Each guest tried to guess the answers to true or false questions about Suzanne's life. Suzanne enjoyed expounding on the answers and sharing her story.

Several days later, she suffered a stroke which took her life. Her friends and children miss her dearly and wonder, "How is it that 95 years seem like not enough time?"

Suzanne left a legacy that is invaluable. She instilled in her children some of the characteristics of the Greatest Generation —humility, a strong work ethic, thrift, faithful commitment, personal responsibility, and silence. Well, maybe not humility. The Ng boys are all avid fishermen, and they love to brag about their catches. And certainly not silence. Suzanne could hardly tolerate the noise when her children were watching the Seahawks football games, and Ng family gatherings are anything but silent. The most important thing she left us, however, is a tight-knit family. The love, commitment, and connection the Ng children have for each other were clearly evident as they supported and cared for their mother. The affection they have for each other continues to be demonstrated in the strong relationships they share. What a blessing it is to be an Ng.

ABOUT THE AUTHOR

If I take the wings of the morning,
and dwell in the uttermost parts of the sea,
EVEN THERE shall thy hand lead me,
and thy right hand shall hold me.
Psalm 139:9, 10

One of four sisters, I grew up on a dairy farm in Woodstock, Connecticut. Our happy childhood revolved around family, farm, and faith.

Jimmy graduated from high school in Tacoma, Washington. Taking the advice of his father, he accepted an appointment to the United States Coast Guard Academy in New London, Connecticut. He was a new Christian when he arrived at the Academy. The chapel program and the Officer's Christian Fellowship became defining parts of his college experience.

Though Jimmy's parents taught him the importance of family, integrity, education, generosity, and hard work, Jimmy did not learn about God at home. He was introduced to the Christian faith when his high school buddy invited him to Sunday School. He liked what he found there: hot chocolate, donuts, and girls. He continued attending that little church where he heard and responded to the Bible's message.

Jimmy and I met on the steps of the Coast Guard Memorial Chapel when he volunteered to be the tour guide for my church youth group's excursion to the Coast Guard Academy. Fifty years later, Jimmy reminisced about the spark in the air that day; he remembered exactly what I was wearing when the "cute, bubbly, blonde girl" caught his eye. Jimmy was wearing his military uniform, just as his father was in uniform when Bing met Suzanne. (I wondered why the other cadets all wore their last names on their uniforms, while Jimmy's name tag sported only two consonants.) Jimmy was handsome, gregarious, and fun-loving. Like his father and his grandfather, he could fix anything, and he enjoyed using those skills to help people.

Our friendship grew into a union that has stood the test of time. We were married in the spring when the rhododendrons were in full bloom. We ducked under an arch of swords as we exited the beautiful, historic chapel where we had first met, four years before.

Like his mother, I left my little country town to follow my military husband all over the world. Jimmy became a highly decorated Coast Guard helicopter pilot; he insists I am the wind beneath his wings. We are a good team.

Together we have three daughters. Suzanne, named after her grandmother, is eighteen years older than our youngest daughter, Sarah. Jenny is in the middle. They have blessed us with seven grandchildren, so far. I love being a mother and a grandmother.

My friendship with my mother-in-law developed slowly until she and Bing came to visit us with their motor home when we were stationed in Cape Cod, Massachusetts. They intended to stay for two weeks, but, six months later, their RV was still parked in our driveway. From then on, we were fast friends.

I cannot adequately express the richness I experienced in the journey of writing this book. I learned so much, and I developed a deep emotional bond with my mother-in-law in the process.

Writing Suzanne's story made me keenly aware of the significance of my own story. I am excited about sharing the adventures and misadventures of a Coast Guard wife in my next book, *Even There*. Life in Alaska, daring rescues at sea, commercial fishing, military transfers and deployments, tragedy, triumph, and the evidence of God's presence are all parts of my story as I share life with Jimmy Ng.

SUZANNE NG: FACT OR FICTION

(Game played at Suzanne's 95th Birthday Party)

1. Suzanne, born in 1924, was the oldest of seven children.
(Yes. Albert, Raymond, Lucette, Nicole, Bernard, and Mark followed over a span of the next 20 years.)

2. Suzanne played on a basketball team when she was a teenager.
(Yes, indeed. Basketball was a new sport at the time.)

3. Before she was married, her main means of transportation was a motor bike.
(False. Suzanne received a bicycle as a gift when she graduated from junior high school. It served her well for many years.)

4. The convent where Suzanne was living in Nantes, France was bombed during World War II. (True .)

5. Suzanne met her husband at a dance that both French girls and American soldiers were invited to attend.
(False. They met in Suzanne's uncle's butcher shop.)

6. On her wedding day, Suzanne wore a beautiful, white lace gown that had been made by her mother.
(False. The war was just over, they were very poor, and there were no such supplies to be found in stores. Suzanne wore a blue coat that had been made from an old blanket. However, she was, indeed, a beautiful, radiant bride.)

7. Suzanne spent most of her honeymoon in bed battling scarlet fever.
(True. In fact, she almost died.)

8. Suzanne was sworn in as an American citizen on the steps of the US Supreme Court building on February 9, 1954 by then Senator John F Kennedy.
(True. She remembered how messy his hair was that day.)

9. Suzanne made her first trip to the United States aboard the iconic ocean liner RMS Queen Mary.
(False. She traveled on a military troop ship, but, during the crossing, the Queen Mary passed them going in the opposite direction.)

10. Suzanne was present on October 29, 1932 for the launching of the SS Normandie. At that time, it was one of the greatest, most luxurious ocean-liners ever built.
(True)

11. Suzanne attended the Nuremberg Trials.
(True)

12. More than 60,000 US servicemen married women overseas during and just after World War II. Suzanne married her handsome American soldier in Courbevoie, France just a few months after World War II ended. They were married for more than 50 years.
(True)

13. Suzanne's oldest grandson is older than her youngest son.
(True. In fact, Suzanne and her daughter Francette were pregnant at the same time.)

14. Suzanne's parents hid a Jewish couple in their basement during World War II.
(True)

15. In 2001, Suzanne gave her six children the gift of a lifetime when she took them and their spouses to France where she introduced them to their relatives and their heritage.
(True)

16. Suzanne was an avid reader.
(True. Even when her eyesight failed, she continued to enjoy books with the Talking Book program for the visually impaired.)

17. Suzanne loved to watch Seahawks football games with family and friends.
(This is most definitely false.)

18. Suzanne was an avid computer gamer.
(True. She loved to play Solitaire on her computer. By making the cards on the screen very large, she was able to make out what they were and play the game.)

19. Suzanne and Bing lived together in more than ten different homes.
(True)

20. (This is the bonus question, provided by Jimmy.)
Jimmy was Suzanne's favorite son.
(False. We all tease that Jerry, the youngest, was her favorite.)

NOTES

Preface
1. Orlean, Susan. The Library Book. (Simon and Schuster, 2018)
2. Davis, Claude. (26 October 2017). "Six Essential Differences Between the Greatest Generation and the Ones that Followed." www.askaprepper.com/6-essential-differences-greatest-generations-ones-followed/
Chapter 1: Hushed Rumors
1. Reagan, Ronald. (31 May 1982). Arlington National Cemetery, Arlington, VA, Memorial Day Speech
Chapter 2: Unexpected Encounter
1. Dickens, Charles. Great Expectations (1860), Chapter 9, page 6.
Chapter 3: Suzanne's Heritage
1. Eisenhower, Dwight. Speech at Carnegie Institute in Pittsburgh, Pennsylvania, October 10, 1950
2. Alphonse's mother, and, later, his father were buried in Toutes-Aides Cemetery in Saint-Nazaire. The graves are "in perpetuity."
Chapter 4: Formative Years
1. Verigo, Elena. "Early Years and Character Formation." M.A. Education & Coaching, Liverpool Hope University (2020), Answer to question on Quora web site. www.quora.com/What-is-meant-by-formative-years
2. Rene was eight when she came to work for Aunt Juliette. She never married. She lived with and worked for Aunt Juliette for her entire life. When Juliette's daughter Dede was gown and widowed with two mentally handicapped children, Rene loved those children and helped care for them, as well.
3. Costello, Meg. "Church Bells and Death Knells." Untold Tales of Falmouth from the Archives of Museums on the Green. museumsonthegreen.org
Chapter 5: The New House
1. The original address of the Chedotal home was 18 Rue des Brosses, Nort-Sur-Erdre, France. The street address was later changed to 60 Rue Francois Dupas.
Chapter 7: The Pride of France
1. Silvin, Richard Rene. Normandie: The Tragic Story of the Most Majestic Ocean Liner. Silvin Books LLC; 1st Edition (January 1, 2016)
2. Hilton, James. "The Sinking of the SS Normandie at NYC's Pier 88." The New York Hisotry Blog, September 23, 2014
Chapter 8: Growth and Change
1. Many years later, a descendant of Suzanne's friend Madeline Pauvert bought the Chédotal family home in Nort-Sur-Erdre.

2. Sometime after Suzanne was married, her mother received an inheritance from her parents. She used the money to buy Berilise, a stone and stucco house near the beach in Pornichet. As the Chédotal children became adults, each one who lived in France had a room at Berilise for their family to use. Jimmy and I stayed at Berilise in 1975 when we visited France. It did not have a water view, but it was a short walk on a path to the beach. The Chédotal extended family enjoyed congregating at Berilise for many years.

3. Suzanne regretted not being able to attend high school. She never told her children she did not go to high school. That fact was the one thing she asked me not to mention at her funeral, though she did not mind sharing it in this book. She wondered aloud to me what it would have been like to be able to go to high school and college. She was convinced she could have done well. There is no doubt in my mind, Suzanne Chédotal would have excelled.

Chapter 9: The Arrival of the German Army

1. Werthman, Kitty. Speech, April 2011, "She Survived Hilter and Wants to Warn America." On the Front Lines of the Culture Wars. www.beliefnet.com

2. Roger Menoret married Suzanne's sister Lucette after World War II. Together they moved to Nantes where he followed in his father's footsteps, eventually owning his own butcher shop. Roger shared his memories with me when I visited him at his apartment in Nantes in 2019.

Chapter 10: Occupation

1. Lauritsen, Aaron. *100 Days Drive: The Great North American Road Trip.* (Create Space Independent Publishing Platform, January 24, 2016)

2. Suzanne learned about her father's hidden radio from her brother when she was 94 years old. Suzanne was delighted to finally know the truth. She marveled, "I knew my father had a radio. So, that's where it was."

Chapter 11: On Her Own

1. Even at the age of 94, Suzanne harbored bitterness because her employers did not believe her when she told them she had not touched the picture that had broken the vase. She did not like to have her integrity questioned, and she did not easily forget offenses.

Chapter 12: Love Blossoms

1. World War II Exhibit, Nantes History Museum, Castle of the Dukes of Brittany, Nantes, France

2. Frank, Anne. *The Diary of Anne Frank.* Anne Frank wrote about the hatred of Jews in her diary on April 11, 1944.

3. Shirran, Arthur. "The Helpful Engineer, U-Boat Base in Saint-Nazaire: Too big to knock." August 15, 2011, www.thehelpfulengineer.com/index.php/2011/08/u-boat-base-in-saint-nazaire-too-big-to-big-to-knock/

4. Submarine base at Saint-Nazaire, Submarine Espadon, and Saint-Nazaire Heritage Museum, Avenue de la Forme Ecluse, 44600 Saint-Nazaire, France

5. Grand Blockhaus, War museum in Batz-sur-Mer, France

Chapter 13: Bing's Story

1. Kleiner, Sam. *The Flying Tigers; the Untold Story of the American Pilots Who*

Waged a Secret War Against Japan (New York: Viking, 2018)

2.   Andrade, Allan. *Leopoldville: A Tragedy Too Long Secret* (United States of America: Xlibriss, 2009)

3.   Goodwin, Doris Kearns. *No Ordinary Time: Franklin and Eleanor Roosevelt: The Home Front in World War II* (New York: Simon and Schuster, 1944), 288

4.   Panther Veteran Organization – Official Website of the 66th Infantry Division, www.66thinfantrydivision.com

5.   Caen Memorial Museum. Esplanade General Eisenhower CS 55026 – 14050 Caen, France

6.   Cherbourg Liberation Museum, Fort du Roule, 50100 Cherbourg-Octeville, Cherbourg-en-Cotentin, France

7.   A Navy Press Release in 2019 announced its newest guided-missile destroyer, the USS Quentin Walsh, would be named after Captain Quentin Walsh, USCG. Richard Buckingham related his memories of his father's stories about Captain Walsh to Jimmy in an e-mail message dated June 10, 2019.

Chapter 14: Promises

1.   Zhou, Christina and Xiao, Ban. Marry first, the fall in love: "The evolution of love in marriage in China since Mao Zedong's era." ABC News Australia, Article 9641958, April 21, 2018, www.abc.net.au/article/9641958

2.   "Saint-Nazaire Celebrates its D-Day," Smartappart, May 25, 2019, www.smart-appart.fr/en/news/post/336sainy-nazaire-celebrates-its-d-day

3.   Bing gave the German binoculars to his son Jimmy.

Chapter 15: Marianne

1.   Idar-Oberstein is about 46 miles from Koblenz. It is within the area of Germany the 66th Infantry Division initially secured.

2.   Mariane recounted her story to me as we sat together in her comfortable home in Tacoma, Washington in January of 2020.

Chapter 16: Perspective

1.   Coons, Philip M. *Letters Home: From a World War II Black Panther.* (iUniverse, Incorporated, Bloomington, Indiana, March 28, 2012)

2.   Svan, Jennifer H. and Kloekner, Marcus. German POW asks: "Why did America give their young men for us?" Interview for Stars and Stripes, April 23, 2019. www.stripes.com/news/special-reports/featured/d-day/german-pow-asks-why-did-america-give-their-young-men-for-us-1.583219

Chapter 17: Shifting Gears

1.   "George Catlett Marshall," marshallfoundation.org

2.   Bob and Delores Hope Foundation, www.bobhope.org

Chapter 18: Americans in Germany

1.   "Your Job in Germany," War Department Orientation Video Official O.F.-8

Chapter 19: War Bride

1.   "Red Cross History – Supporting Our Nation's Military," American Red Cross official web site, July 24, 2019, www.redcross.org/about-us/news-and-events/news/2019/red-cross-history-supporting-our-nations-military.html

2.   Wilt, Brenda J. "War Brides," America in WWII magazine, August 2005 issue, www.americainwwii.com/articles/war-brides/

Chapter 20: Newlyweds

1. 116th General Hospital, Nuernberg, USAREUR History Office official web site, www.usarmygermany.com/Sont.htm?https&&&www.usarmygermany.com/Units/Medical/USAREUR_USAH-Nuernberg.htm

2. La Cambe German War Cemetery, Information Center, Les Noires Terres, 14230 La Cambe, France. The cemetery commemorates the memory of the losses of Operation Overlord, where more than 100,000 people died. Human fates and reconciliation are special themes.

3. Memorium Nuremberg Trials, Nuremberg Palace of Justice, Barenschanzstrabe 72 90429 Nuremberg, Germany

Chapter 22: Mothers Together

1. Fitzgerald, F. Scott. The Curious Case of Benjamin Button (short story) published in Collier's Magazine, May 27, 1922

2. Wiltenburg, Von Mary and Widmann, Marc. "WWII GI Babies: Children of the Enemy." Der Spiegel (Germany weekly news magazine published in Hamburg, Germany. February 1, 2007. www.google.com/amp/s/www.spiegel.de/international/spiegel/wwii-g-i-babies-children-of-the-enemy-a-456835-amp.html

3. Rose Engal eventually married and regained custody of her son.

4. Memories from Suzanne's sister, Nicole Kerlau, shared via e-mail, summer 2020.

Chapter 24: Back in Germany

1. Wilder, Laura Ingalls. *These Happy Golden Years*. Harper Collins; illustrated Edition (May 11, 2004)

2. SS stands for Schutzstaffel (Protective Echelon). It was a paramilitary organization under Hitler and became one of the most powerful and feared organizations in all Nazi Germany.

3. Jimmy now owns the precious carving knife his father received as a parting gift from his workers in Germany.

Epilogue

1. Williamson, Martha. "Signed, Sealed, Delivered" television series, Hallmark Channel, Episode #1001, "Time to Start Living" (April 20, 2014)

Made in the USA
Monee, IL
08 October 2021

SECRET OF THE
STORM

LAND OF
DRAGONS

Beth McMullen

ALADDIN

New York   London   Toronto   Sydney   New Delhi

ALADDIN

An imprint of Simon & Schuster Children's Publishing Division
1230 Avenue of the Americas, New York, New York 10020
First Aladdin hardcover edition March 2023
Text copyright © 2023 by Beth McMullen
Jacket illustration copyright © 2023 by Vivienne To
All rights reserved, including the right of reproduction in whole or in part in any form.
ALADDIN and related logo are registered trademarks of Simon & Schuster, Inc.
For information about special discounts for bulk purchases, please contact
Simon & Schuster Special Sales at 1-866-506-1949 or business@simonandschuster.com.
The Simon & Schuster Speakers Bureau can bring authors to your live event. For more information or to book an event contact the Simon & Schuster Speakers Bureau at 1-866-248-3049 or visit our website at www.simonspeakers.com.
Jacket designed by Laura Lyn DiSiena
Interior designed by Ginny Kemmerer
The text of this book was set in Chaparral Pro.
Manufactured in the United States of America 0123 FFG
10 9 8 7 6 5 4 3 2 1
CIP data for this book is available from the Library of Congress.
ISBN 9781534482883 (hc)
ISBN 9781534482906 (ebook)

FOR MAX AND KATIE.
GO CHANGE THE WORLD.

CONTENTS

Chapter 1

MERCY GROVE. AGAIN.

PLANS ARE ALWAYS PERFECT right at the beginning, before any action has been taken, before they encounter reality. For example, this morning, on the first day of Thanksgiving break, I was convinced I was fully capable of opening a rip, a kind of doorway to the dragon dimension. All I had to do was rub my hands together and produce the necessary golden mist, just like Albert did in this *very* spot, a mere seven days ago.

Albert, in case you are wondering, is my kitten, who is actually a dragon, who came to our dimension to hide out from the vengeful dragon King Vayne, who wanted to kill him because he might be the marked dragon prophesized to end Vayne's reign. Simple, right?

The reason I need to generate the glitter, open the rip, and jump through is to *rescue* Albert. I mean, Albert gave me the means to make the glitter, and I know I can do it because I have done it before. But right now, when I *really* need the glitter to happen, nothing. Total fail. The only thing that happens is my palms get hot and sweaty from all the rubbing. No golden mist. No rip. No Albert.

"This is not working," I say. My mother, Miss Asher, and Joe watch me. This is partly their fault, as they helped with the rescue plan. I drop my arms to my sides.

"You said you practiced," Joe says, unable to hide his exasperation. Joe is my best friend. My best friend used to be Mia, but it turned out she wasn't any sort of friend at all, and Joe is a way better friend. This does not mean we don't annoy each other sometimes.

"I *did* practice," I shoot back.

"Maybe the missing element is the weather," he suggests, eyebrows furrowed in concentration. "Whenever Albert turned into a dragon, there was horrible weather. And when he opened the rip, it was like the storm of the century."

"It wasn't *that* bad," I counter.

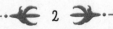

"It was pretty bad," Joe replies.

Okay. Fine. It was bad. But maybe I should add a few more details before this gets even more confusing. I found Albert the black kitten in a dumpster here in Lewiston (the most nowhere of all nowheresvilles, if you ask me) during an extreme weather event—think lightning, thunder, hail, wind, freezing rain, and mini tornadoes, all at the same time.

And Albert was the best kitten! Cute, soft, funny, and curious, but he was also . . . strange. Odd things started to happen, and before too long, I discovered Albert was a dragon. After that, things took a turn for the seriously weird. Like, grade-A, eyes-crossed bizarre.

But the most important thing to know is that Joe and I figured out how to open a rip to the dragon dimension and help Albert get back to his dragon family. Which is what he wanted. Or we think it is what he wanted. Hard to be sure because Albert couldn't speak our language and we couldn't speak his, but we'll get to that.

Another thing we've learned is that nothing is simple when it comes to cats who are really dragons. Almost as soon as we sent Albert back through the rip, we discovered that bit about Albert hiding here. Once the dragon world prophecy claimed that the ruling class, the Silvers, would be overthrown by a dragon marked with a golden blaze, Albert was doomed. There is no missing the golden blaze on his chest. When Vayne declared all marked dragons were to be terminated, whoever loved Albert pushed him through a rip, disguised as a kitten, to hide him from certain death.

And we sent him *back*. Not good. Really not good.

Of course, once we figured that out, we had no choice but launch a rescue. But the plan requires that we go to the dragon world, and to do that, we need to open a rip, and to open a rip, we need the golden mist. Do you see the problem here? The mist illuminates the rip, almost like invisible ink revealed by the primer.

Now, before Albert left, I absorbed some of the mist from his golden blaze into my hands. It's there just beneath my skin, making my hands shimmer in a certain light. With a little experimentation, I figured out how to rub my hands together in a certain way and generate the mist myself, just like Albert does. Unfortunately, now, when I really need the mist, it is not happening. Our plan is not working.

Miss Asher, the town librarian and also the smartest person on the planet, chews her lip. "There has to be something we aren't doing right," she mutters.

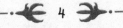

"Maybe it's because you're not a dragon," Joe says.

"If I need to be a dragon," I reply flatly, "then we are doomed. Because I'm not, you know, a dragon."

We are in the Arcata wilderness, a million acres of green that come right to the edge of the Pacific coast, just north of Lewiston. More specifically, we are in Mercy Grove, a circle of old-growth redwood trees stretching high into the sky. This is the place where Albert went through the rip. There is something about Mercy Grove, a sense of magic, of otherness. If there is a doorway to the dragon world, it makes perfect sense that it is here. The last rays of daylight seep through the canopy above, which is better than the usual November (or any other month) weather in Lewiston: rain and more rain and then rain again, just to be sure you got the message. I intend to go to college somewhere sunny, but I'm only twelve, so I'm practicing patience.

Joe, thin brown legs poking out of his baggy basketball shorts, begins to pace. It's what he does when he's trying to unravel a puzzle or solve a mystery or answer a complicated question. Because we are best friends, I understand these things about him and know better than to ever say such things are weird. I watch him. Usually when he paces, he eventually comes up with something, even if it's an oddball theory about an alien invasion or whatever.

"It's okay, honey," my mother says quietly, slipping an arm around my shoulder. "We'll figure it out. We'll get Albert." Now, this may seem all very normal, if you discount the fact that we are deep in the woods trying to figure out how to get to a dimension where dragons live. But until recently, my mom was a ghost. I don't mean that literally, of course. It's just that she would float around, wordless and expressionless and seemingly not connected to anything solid in the world. The description for what was happening to her is "situational depression." The situation was my dad died in an accident and she struggled to get back on her feet. It wasn't until the incident with the FBI agents that she kind of snapped out of it.

Yes. The FBI. We'll get to that, too.

In the meantime, I'm standing here unsuccessfully trying to figure out how to make the gold mist rise from my palms.

"Maybe we need rain?" Joe asks thoughtfully.

"The first time I did it," I say, "I was in the house and it wasn't raining."

"Okay. Fine. No rain." He continues pacing.

Since Albert went through the rip, whenever I think of him in danger, afraid, alone, on the run, hurt or worse, my heart pulls toward him. While I know the organ in my chest isn't *actually* moving, the sensation is real. My pulse quickens. My breathing gets shallow and my cheeks flush. It's not a pleasant experience, so I have come up with a mantra to get myself back under control. I close my eyes and repeat over and over:

I'm coming to save you, Albert. Just hang on. I'm coming to save you, Albert. Just hang on. I'm coming to save you, Albert. Just hang on.

Eyes closed, I say the mantra now while Mom pats my back, Joe paces, and Miss Asher mutters. Slowly, the squeeze in my chest loosens. All of a sudden, the silence is interrupted by Joe yelping.

"You're doing it, Cassie! Look! It's working!" Joe leaps in front of me. Miss Asher fist-pumps the air. My mother eyes me warily. A cloud of golden mist, like glitter, floats up from my hands and drifts in the air before me. It is beautiful, like the sparkle of sunlight on ocean waves.

But there is something I have not told Joe, my mother, or Miss Asher. It's not because I don't want to tell them; it's just I'm not sure how to explain it. The mist makes me feel strange, like there is an unfamiliar electric current charging through my body, like I am a beacon gathering up the energy circulating around me and concentrating it into the tangible mist. It makes me think that if I focused never indicated that I would explode, or worse, if I did. Joe was horrified by my confession.

"You were just going to leave me there in the woods *alone*?" he bellowed.

"I didn't *do* it, did I?" I snapped back.

"No," he said, eyes narrowed. "But you *thought* about it, and that is almost as bad."

I decided not to argue because, with Joe, that can sometimes feel like what I imagine an infinity loop of nothingness would.

But Joe also took issue with the idea that Albert would have warned me in advance if going through the rip was going to scatter my molecules across the galaxy. He pointed out that Albert and I could not generally communicate, and when we did, it was by the occasional odd message showing up in my head as if he were texting it directly into my brain. And even with those, I can't be 100 percent sure I wasn't making them up.

However, my argument remains. Albert would never do anything to hurt me. It's the one thing I know beyond a shadow of a doubt. It has to be safe, or safe *enough*, for a human to pass through the rip.

And honestly, even if it's not safe, I'm going anyway.

The golden mist rises from my outstretched palms. It's

like I have an electric ball of sticky spiderweb that I can stretch and bend, like I have the ingredients for storms. My mother clutches my shoulder. There was a lot of negotiation leading up to this moment about who would actually go through the rip, if we somehow managed to open it. The conversations got downright heated.

Me: I'm going.

Mom: No way. Not an option.

Miss Asher: We will figure it out.

Joe: If Cassie goes, I go.

Mom: Your parents won't allow it.

Joe: My parents don't *know*.

Mom: Besides the point.

Joe: Is it?

Me: I'm going.

Miss Asher: It should be me.

Mom: I'm the oldest with the most life experience. I'll go.

Me: Ugh. Really?

Mom: No need to be snotty, Cassie.

Miss Asher: I know the most about the dragons. It should be me.

Me: I have to go. I'm the only one who can open the door.

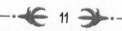

Mom: Theoretically.

Me: (rolling eyes)

Miss Asher: Cassie does have a point.

Joe: Hey, I have an idea. What if we *all* go?

When it came down to it, that was the only option. No one wanted to stay behind, even if we might be disintegrated going through. And so the decision was made. Me, Joe, Miss Asher, and Mom would go through the rip. As such, we are outfitted for an expedition into the unknown, bulging backpacks full of water and snacks, a first aid kit, flashlights, extra batteries, and gloves. We wear hiking boots with thick socks and wool hats and sturdy pants. Except Joe, who will not give up his shorts for any reason, even interdimensional travel. His argument is that this dragon world we are attempting to enter might be tropical, in which case we will be sweaty and gross. Miss Asher tried to lecture him on the importance of layers, but she should have saved her breath. Joe can be stubborn about certain things. Fact: he will gloat hard if the dragon world is, indeed, tropical.

But right now, with the mist leaping and swirling around us, as things get real, I can sense reluctance in my teammates. I'm about to suggest I go alone. After all, I'm the one who promised Albert I would never let any harm come to him. He was my responsibility and I let him down.

"Look, Cassie," Joe whispers, pointing to the mist. Just like when Albert opened the rip, the mist leaping from my palms begins to form an oval, the edges sparkling and bright. I can't believe I'm doing this! The sense that I am harvesting the energy all around me and controlling it comes in sharp relief. I feel it in my veins. Eyes closed, I breathe in the damp rich smell of the surrounding forest while envisioning the one on the other side of the rip that I glimpsed briefly when Albert left. It is brighter and bigger and glossier than our forest. But we have no idea if there are wicked creatures waiting to eat us immediately. Or if there is, you know, *oxygen*. Miss Asher, of course, modeled it out and determined that we should be able to breathe and function as normal although she could not say either way about the wicked creatures.

Stop it, Cassie! It's Albert! He'd do it for you.

He would. The golden sparkling oval hovers before me. Now what? Okay. The rip is a door. I need to open it. I imagine plunging my hands into the golden oval and prying it open. A surge of energy racing through me indicates it might be working. I tug again with my imaginary hands.

"Cassie!" Joe yells. I open my eyes to see the rip expand. Joe and I have seen one before, but Mom and Miss Asher have not, and they stare, jaws slack, as the oval widens and reveals the other side. There is nothing quite like the first moment you look directly into an alternative reality. And if you think about it for too long, like *really* think about it, it kind of hurts your head.

Miss Asher regains her wits and peers through the rip. "It's so . . . glittery over there," she whispers. I don't think she really believed until this very moment. I mean, she *saw* Albert in his dragon form, but still, this takes it to another level.

Mom edges closer to the rip, hands out in a defensive posture, as if it might suddenly turn on her. "Do we just step through?" she asks tentatively.

"We think so," Joe replies. When Albert left, he walked through the rip and it sealed closed behind him, like a great mouth swallowed him up. It's important that the rip close behind us. The last thing we want is a parade of humans following us through. Especially Agents Fox and Dana, who work for the FBI's Project Analog, where they investigate strange phenomena that have no obvious explanation. To be clear, Agent Fox and Agent Dana are not our friends.

The rip trembles before us.

"It's destabilizing," Joe says. "Just like the last time."

"We'd better go," I reply. This is it. It's time to rescue my Albert. I take a deep breath, and it hitches in my throat. But I don't share that I'm scared, for Albert, for me, for Mom and Joe and Miss Asher. We all feel responsibility in some way for Albert, but really, I am at the center of this. It is hard to put those you love at risk, even if the reasons are good ones.

"Okay," Mom says. It's her steely voice, the one she uses when she is psyching herself up. It gives me confidence. The version of Mom that uses that voice is tough, as in you don't want to mess with her. "Let's do this."

We link arms. The rip sputters and hisses. But just as we are about to step over the threshold, there is a loud crack, and something crashes through the rip at great speed, colliding with us full-on. We tumble backward, scattered about the forest floor. I land sideways against the base of a tree, my hip throbbing from the impact. And I can't *see*. There is so much darkness. Where are the others? Are they okay? I try to call their names, but my voice won't work. My face is hot and wet. Am I crying?

No. It's not that. Something is *licking* me.

Chapter 3

THE RETURN OF ALBERT

I TURN MY HEAD violently, side to side, trying to get away from whatever is licking me. It's scary. And gross. "Stop!" I yell finally. "I can't see!"

The licking ceases. Hot puffs of air hit my face as I sit up and wipe away the slime. And when I open my eyes, there he *is*, in full dragon glory, wings tucked in tight, mossy-green eyes bright and expectant, flames leaking out between jagged, sharp teeth.

Albert. My kitten. My dragon.

"You're back! You're alive!" I scream, flinging my arms around his neck. His spiked tail thumps on the ground, shaking the forest. I bury my face in his leathery black skin. "I missed you so much," I breathe. My tears spill, hit his warmth, and fizzle to nothing.

Joe runs up and elbows into my hug. "Albert! We had no idea what happened to you! Why didn't you *tell* us about the prophecy?" My emotions are soaring, but even so, I recognize this is not a fair question, and not just because he can't tell us anything, let alone something complicated. Miss Asher even suggested that Albert would not have remembered much from his brief time in the dragon world before he was sent here to hide. The chances that he knew about the prophecy were slim to none.

We hug Albert for a long time. I can feel his big heart beating slow and steady as his muscles ripple under my touch. "I will never let you go again," I whisper. In response, Albert exhales, a hot blast that makes my skin tingle.

"Um, excuse me?" This is from Mom, standing over my shoulder. Her stunned expression says it all.

Seriously. Her eyes are wide, her lips parted, her eyebrows near her hairline, her hands clenched into fists, her shoulders up by her ears.

"It's just Albert," I remind her.

"I know," she says slowly. "But the last time I saw him he was, you know, a tiny *kitten*. This is a bit . . . jarring, that's all."

I get that. I remember the first time Albert turned into a dragon in front of me, during a sleepover at Mia's. I was shocked right down to my scuffed-up sneakers, but on another level, it was wonderful. Just knowing that such things can happen in the universe, that the possibilities are endless, that the fantastical might be real, felt so wild. Don't get me wrong. I was terrified, too, because . . . *dragons*. All things considered, I'd say Mom is handling it quite well.

Miss Asher stands beside me, hand outstretched, hovering right above Albert. She wants to touch him but is kind of frozen.

"It's okay," I say. "He won't hurt you." Slowly, she lowers her hand, and as she connects with Albert, she exhales a breath I know she has been holding for years.

"Amazing," she whispers.

As my pulse slows and I get ahold of my feelings, I have a thought. "Wait a minute, Albert," I say. "Did *you* open the rip or did I?"

He steps back from me, his long tail practically knocking Joe over. Lowering his eyelids and fluttering his lashes, he shrugs. He really does! Oh, he definitely opened the rip. And he made the weather! Was the powerful feeling of harnessing electricity all in my head? How disappointing. It's not that I want to be a superhero, but . . . come on . . . it would be pretty great.

"I'm so glad you are here," I say, hugging Albert hard.

Miss Asher clears her throat. "But . . . um . . . *why* are you here?"

Does it matter? Maybe he just missed me too much. Or he could not live without me. Or he really missed his cat treats. Or . . .

"That's a good question," Joe responds, peering into Albert's eyes.

When we sent him back, it was because he wanted to go home but also because he was in grave danger here. People fear what they don't understand, and Albert was *really* outside the realm of understanding. So he must have a good reason for returning beyond just missing me. The forest stills. A little flare of mist bursts from my hands. As I take Albert's face in my hands, so we are nose to snout, I ask, "Did they hurt you?"

He shakes free of my grip. No. "Did you learn about the prophecy? Is that why you came back? Because it's not safe?" Albert huffs, the dragon equivalent of an exasperated sigh. I'm not getting it.

Finally, Albert's mighty wings unfurl, wide enough to bump the trees that form the circle we stand in. With a clawed paw, Albert reaches into the space where the wing connects to his back, kind of like a wing armpit, and pulls out a piece of what looks like parchment paper but upon closer inspection is some sort of large tree leaf. He holds it out to me, cocks his head to the left, just like a golden retriever might, and waits.

With trembling fingers, I take the leaf from him. Joe shines his flashlight on it while Mom and Miss Asher move in close to see. Albert's eyes stay focused on me.

"What is it?" Joe asks.

On the leaf is a tracing of an image, rendered in a dusty, waxy red, almost like clay dust. It looks like a rising sun behind a dragon shadow, the dragon's tail displayed predominately in the foreground. What it means is not immediately obvious. The last time Albert showed us a symbol, it was carved into my closet door with his sharp nails and was much less fine than this one. It turned out to be a map to the location of the rips, but that was not obvious on the surface. Joe had to render it in 3D and stretch it out on his computer to see what it was. Is this the same sort of thing? Is there something hidden in the symbol that our regular eyes cannot see? It would be nice if it were just a little bit straightforward, but that might be wishful thinking. When it comes to dragons, I'm learning, nothing is straightforward.

Albert? What is this? Can you tell me?

But no dragon text messages show up in my head. Albert just continues to give me a look. Anyone who knows cats knows they never belong to anyone but themselves. There is no ownership. Cats are independent thinkers. They do not lose sleep wondering how to please us. They do what feels right and good to them. Sometimes that might include us, and other times, not so much. No one really has the upper hand in the cat-human relationship.

Dragons, on the other hand, take those cat traits and bring them to the next level. From the expression on Albert's face, he clearly thinks humans are daft and a little hopeless. Some disgruntled birds squawk in the branches above.

Behind me, my mother's breath grows shallow. "A dragon is passing us notes," Mom says, sounding winded. I glance back at her. "What's next? Unicorns falling from the sky?"

"Ugh. Unicorns," Joe says. "So not a fan."

"You look funny," I say to my mother. "Like a weird-color green. You should sit down."

"Good idea," she replies. Her legs buckle, and she plops to her butt right there on the damp earth.

"Better?" Miss Asher asks.

"Much," Mom responds. She kneads her temples with her closed fists. This is hard for first-timers, so I totally understand. Joe swipes the cloth from my hand and examines it up close.

"Well?" I ask.

"Clueless," he replies. "Miss Asher?"

She shakes her head. "It's going to take some research," she responds, her eyes bright. Research is her favorite thing. It's one of Joe's favorite things too. If there is an explanation in our world as to what the tracing means, they will find it. A girl has got to have good teammates. Otherwise, everything is a major pain in the butt.

I'm about to ask Albert again about the tracing, just to be sure he isn't holding out on me, but when I turn back, he's a small bundle of black fur, cute pointy ears, and twitchy whiskers, dead asleep at my feet.

Chapter 4

AGENT FOX AND AGENT DANA WATCH THE WEATHER

ABOUT A TWO-HOUR DRIVE due east of Lewiston is a town called Redmond. Redmond is exceptional in exactly no way except that anyone who wants to go anywhere from Lewiston must drive through Redmond to get there. As rainy, gray, and lush as Lewiston is, Redmond is the opposite: hot, dry, and relentlessly bright. The moisture that comes in off the ocean bumps up against the mountain range between the two towns and travels no farther. Rain rarely falls on Redmond.

In a nondescript office park, off the Elmer Drive freeway exit, is a door with the name "Acme Supplies" etched into its glass. There is no other information on the always-locked entrance. Inside, a hallway disappears into the shadows, and in those shadows sit Agent Dana and Agent Fox of Project Analog, a subdepartment of the FBI, which investigates phenomena that are otherworldly. Unexplainable. *Different.* Once people know certain things exist, everything changes, so Project Analog tries to keep that to a minimum.

Certainly, other FBI departments get more respect. No one pokes fun at the agents who work bank robberies or cybercrimes. But Project Analog is like an adrenaline rush. There is nothing quite like it.

There are two desks in the office, each facing a bare wall so Dana and Fox sit with their backs to one another. Fox has wrinkles, a sleek gray bob, and gray-green eyes. Dana is a redhead with eyebrows so pale, they are practically invisible. The office has a temporary feel, as if the two occupants are just here for a heartbeat. Which is true. Fox and Dana never stay anywhere for very long. They go to where the action is and stay there until they can explain it away. Or they can't.

And while they aren't seated face-to-face, this does not mean they don't talk. And for the last week, that talk has been mostly about dragons.

"Have you checked today's weather data?" asks Fox.

Specifically, Fox is interested in the storms that accompany a dragon moving in or out of its dimension. And because no wild weather has been recorded in the last week, she is sure the dragon they encountered with the kids on the Lewiston library roof is still *here*. Somewhere. Of course, finding this dragon is her job; it is what she is paid to do.

Fox returns her attention to Agent Dana, who confirms the weather data offers nothing of interest. Dana is new to Project Analog, handpicked by the director herself for the role. At first Dana was hesitant. She joined the FBI to catch bad guys, not chase down space aliens or, you know, *dragons*, but after just one mission, she was hooked. Besides, she is young and seems to find living out of a suitcase pretty fun.

"There's nothing new," Agent Dana reports. "The patterns are steady, no surges or weather anomalies."

Fox sighs. This is good and bad. No weird weather means the dragon is still around. But it doesn't help them find it. And as the days go by with no progress, the bosses get antsy. There is *always* a backlog of weirdo world events waiting for attention. They want this dragon thing wrapped up quickly.

"Do you think you can talk the bosses into a few more days?" Dana asks. Fox understands Dana has found a coffee shop here in Redmond that she really likes, but that won't be enough to convince the bosses they need more time. Sitting around this sad, dusty office without coming up with a single new idea on how to catch a dragon is not considered a good use of their time.

"I can try," says Fox. "It would be better if we had something to give them." She returns her attention to studying social media and local news information for any hint of a dragon sighting. People don't usually come right out and say they saw a dragon because, well, they don't want to come across as bananas. This is something Fox understands from experience. But they *will* often describe a bizarrely giant eagle or a huge hawk and post blurry photos. If you know what to look for, and Fox definitely does, it's not hard to zero in on potential sightings. This helps create a map of sorts. And the map leads them to the dragon.

And *then* what? The point of the FBI is to investigate crimes and make sure justice is served. But that is not what Project Analog is about. Their directive is twofold. First, it is to explain the unexplainable to the extent that is possible. Sometimes action is necessary and sometimes it isn't. Sometimes the aliens are just curious and then they leave. Second, it is to control the narrative. If people run around claiming that they are seeing dragons, things can get wildly out of hand.

"Maybe we should question the kids again," Dana suggests. "They must know more than they are letting on."

"And that is exactly why we can't talk to them," Fox replies. "Two teenagers with phones, and the whole world will be hysterical by lunchtime. Not good. No. We need them to be too scared to say anything. It's the only way to keep it quiet."

Fox leans back at her desk, stretching her arms above her head and leaning side to side. She has been sitting for too long. Her feet are falling asleep.

"How about Slack?" Dana asks. She's referring to Sheldon Slack, the youngest professor of atmospheric science in the history of Lewiston University and also a firm believer in the existence of dragons. Back in high school, Slack stumbled on some information suggesting that dragons were among us. It also suggested that dragon blood could cure any human ailment. Cyrus, Slack's twin brother, was gravely ill at the time, and Slack, determined to save him, became obsessed with finding the dragons. Cyrus died, but Slack never let go of his obsession. It only grew stronger in the dark, something Fox understands.

But while the kids are easy to control, Slack is not. Right now, he is under lock and key in an FBI safe house, although, in this case, it is to keep everyone else safe from him. "We should talk to him again. He knows a lot."

"Agreed," Fox says. They have talked to Slack many times over the last week, but really, it's been more like talking *at* him. He has not said a word since they brought him out of Mercy Grove that night. He just sits in his room, wearing a slightly dopey smile and hums a little tune to himself, completely out of character and likely the result of a close encounter with a dragon. But Fox and Dana don't have a lot of alternatives. "It's not like anything is happening here anyway."

"How about a stop for coffee on the way?" Dana suggests.

"Brilliant idea," Fox replies.

As the two agents leave the lonely little office, the weather-monitoring station that has been idle all week suddenly explodes with activity. But they are already gone.

Chapter 5

A CHANGE OF PLAN

WE WERE PREPARED for an adventure to another world. Our adrenaline was high, our backpacks were full, and our pep talks were done. We were committed! But here we are, trudging back up the long trail to the car, amid a cloud of many questions. But Albert, asleep in my hoodie pocket, more than makes up for the abrupt change of plans.

As we move along the muddy path, Miss Asher asks, "How long does Albert usually sleep when he is in, you know, cat form?"

"Normally, he is *always* in cat form," I respond.

"Ninety-nine percent of the time he is all cat," Joe adds.

"We think because he's obsessed with salmon and chicken cat treats."

Miss Asher grins. "Who wouldn't be?"

"But if we are threatened in some way," I continue, "he will turn dragon, like, in a flash."

"It can be a little bit surprising," Joe adds, which might be the understatement of the week.

"I believe that," Mom says. All things considered, Mom is being really calm about this dragon stuff.

"I have to say I'm a little disappointed we didn't get to jump dimensions," Miss Asher adds. "It's not the sort of opportunity that comes around every day."

"Our mission *now* is to figure out the meaning of that symbol and why Albert brought it to us here in our dimension," Mom says.

Really, all I want is to go home and live my life with Albert, my sweet, occasionally naughty kitten. And while I call him mine, anyone who knows cats knows they never belong to anyone but themselves. There is no ownership. Cats are independent thinkers. They do not lose sleep wondering how to please us. They do what feels right and good to them. Sometimes that might include us, and other times, not so much. When we are feeling sad, they will crawl in our laps and purr, because comfort, they understand. It's a two-way street, this cat-human relationship. No one really has the upper hand.

I just want to fall asleep with Albert's warm little body pressed to my chest, feeling his heart beat strong and steady. But nothing can make Albert and me normal. I squeeze him gently as he rides along in my pocket. Mom is right. He is here for a reason, and that reason is linked to the symbol on the tracing. My job is to protect him, which means I need to figure out what the symbol is and what we have to do next.

It takes a while to drive from the trailhead back to Lewiston, down a series of punishingly curvy roads. The last time Joe and I came to Mercy Grove, we arrived via dragon, and that, surprisingly, made me much less carsick. In the back seat, we do our best not to barf.

Joe's parents and four siblings are on a college tour road trip for the two oldest brothers. Joe's grandma, who was called in to babysit, thinks Joe was on a night hike with a school group for science class, after which he was spending the night at our house. Which is kind of true, if you keep the dragons out of it. Before he climbs out of the car, we agree to regroup the next day and figure out the symbol's meaning.

"But in the meantime, it is probably best not to

mention that Albert is here," Miss Asher says. "As in don't tell anyone."

Her warning hangs in the air. The FBI wants Albert. Sheldon Slack wants Albert. The Lewiston Police want Albert, although they are sure he's just a lost mountain lion with wings or something. The point is, Albert is very popular and not in a good way. We will say nothing.

Back at home, Mom kisses me good night and tucks the blankets in around me and Albert, who stretches out contentedly on my pillow with both paws resting on my face. I sleep hard, dreaming of tornadoes made entirely of golden mist. They are pretty but also kind of terrifying. I'm almost grateful when Albert starts his furry wake-up call, tapping my cheek progressively harder, with more and more claw, until my eyes fly open.

"I'm up!" I bellow. Immediately, he jumps off and pads to the door, glancing back over his shoulder to make sure I follow. How can he be so hungry for breakfast when he ate a five-pound bag of cat food last night? Then again, that was *hours* ago in cat time.

I am not moving fast enough. "Mew," he complains. It's the tiniest sound, completely at odds with the roar he can produce in dragon form. And it is delightfully cute.

"Mew yourself." I stumble over a pile of laundry, hike

up my pajama pants, and dash after him. He circles back and headbutts the back of my legs. The message is clear. Go faster!

"What is the rush?" I ask, untangling him from my feet. "You are not going to starve between here and the kitchen, are you?"

Albert throws a disgusted look my way, which can only mean I am missing something. He is not very tolerant of human stupidity, I guess.

"What is this about?" I ask, because I'm starting to think it is not just his empty stomach. We pass right by the kitchen and head to the front door, where Albert stands on his hind legs and starts scratching to get out.

Maybe he has developed an aversion to his litter box in the short time he was gone. "Do you need to go to the bathroom?" This time his expression is pure pity. For *me*. For being so clueless. I throw open the door. He bolts, racing toward the sidewalk as fast as his little legs will carry him. My pants are falling off, and my bare feet are freezing, but I run after him anyway.

Where are we going? Why are we going there? What is the urgency? Why didn't I stop and get my shoes? And another layer? Great. It starts to rain. Undeterred, Albert charges on. Soon it becomes clear we are going to Joe's house. I could have just called him! Albert plops down in front of Joe's front door, not even winded while I'm panting and hopping from foot to foot to stave off frostbite.

Joe finds the scene before him hysterical. I can tell from the smirk. "Nice pj's, Cassie," he says.

So they have Baby Yoda on them. So what? He's really cute!

"What's going on?"

I glance down at Albert. "I have no idea," I say. "Why don't you ask him? He's the one who ran over here."

Joe gets down on his knees and bends forward, eye to eye with Albert. "Can I help you?" he asks. Just as he did with me, Albert circles behind Joe and gives him a tiny shove. He meows loudly. And we're off. Joe at least has the sense to throw on his sneakers. And grab an umbrella.

Ten minutes later, when I really think my feet have reached the point of being beyond saving, we pull up short in front of the library.

"I think he wants us to go inside," Joe whispers, looking down at Albert, who is tiny, wet, and bedraggled but still somehow full of energy.

"You think?" I snipe. Even if we can't speak to each other, I have got to teach this cat charades or something. This could have been way less complicated. Not that *any-*

thing in Albert's world is uncomplicated. The library doesn't open for another two hours, but Miss Asher's car is already in the parking lot. I wonder if she came straight here last night to work on figuring out the symbol from the tracing. It would not surprise me.

We knock on the door. It takes a minute, but finally Miss Asher appears. She is still wearing her expedition-to-another-dimension clothes, so that answers that question.

"What happened to you two? Cassie, where are your shoes?" Before we can answer, Albert runs between Miss Asher's legs into the library, leaving a tiny wet trail of evidence behind him.

"I think we are on a mission," I explain.

"We just don't know what it is," Joe adds.

Typical. Albert runs to the maps room, a small alcove at the back, and plops down in the middle of the floor. We have arrived at our destination. If only we knew why we were here.

"He wants us to find something on a map," Miss Asher says with authority.

Joe rolls his eyes. "Well, *yes*." Thankfully, she doesn't notice.

"Did you find out anything about the symbol?" I ask.

Miss Asher's shoulders sag just a bit. "Not yet," she says.

"But I'm eliminating possibilities." This is what she says whenever she finds a question that is difficult to answer. It is certainly better than saying her efforts have been a complete failure so far.

"Albert," I ask. "Why did you bring us here?" He stares back at me. So cute but not helpful.

"I have an idea," Joe says suddenly. "It's a little kooky, but it might work."

I am totally willing to entertain "kooky" if it helps us figure out what we are meant to be looking for.

Joe clears his throat. "Albert, can you understand us? Blink once for yes or twice for no."

Albert stares. He doesn't blink. "Wait a minute," I say. "How would he know to blink twice if he can't understand the question?"

"I don't know, Cassie," Joe says with a scowl. "I'm just winging it here."

While we argue, Albert leaps forward and grabs Joe's shoelaces. This is one of his favorite games. Did he bring us all the way here just to play the shoelace game? We could have played the shoelace game at home! But really, Albert is trying to get our attention. He regards us, wide-eyed, ears perked.

"Ask again, Joe," Miss Asher commands.

"Can you understand us? Blink once for yes. Twice for no."

And Albert gives us one exaggerated, unmistakable, firm blink.

Yes.

Chapter 6

MAP SESSION

HE BLINKED ONCE! He understands! Joe and I leap around and cheer like total idiots while Miss Asher stares at Albert as if she has just seen a cat-dragon from another dimension in her library. (Sorry. Couldn't help it.)

"Joe!" I cry. "You are a genius!"

"I am!" Joe agrees.

"Kids!" Miss Asher's sharp tone brings us back to the library maps room. "Let's see if we can figure out what Albert wants us to know."

I try to settle, but I'm still shivering from the thrill of it all. I have so. Many. Questions!

"Albert, were you in danger in the dragon world? Is that why you came back?"

One blink. "That's a yes!" Joe yells. It's a good thing the library isn't open yet. We are being very loud.

My hands shake. I ball them into fists. I want to know what they did to him, and I want revenge. These are not helpful emotions, so I bury them. "Are you okay?"

Blink. Yes. I exhale the breath I did not know I was holding.

"Do you know about the prophecy?"

Yes. My heart pounds against my ribs.

"Are you here to do something? Like, some kind of mission?"

Blink. He stares at me intently, like he is trying to beam a message right into my head, but even as I try to quiet my thoughts, nothing shows up.

"Ask him why we are here," Joe urges. Which he could do himself, because he is standing right next to me. But okay.

"Albert," I say. "Why are we here? Oh, wait a minute. That is not a yes-or-no question. Let me try that again." Albert sits, his tail thumping impatiently. "Are we supposed to find something here in the maps collection?"

Yes.

"Is it a map?"

"Duh, Cassie," Joe says.

Albert blinks once.

"So we are looking for a place on a map, right?"

Blink.

"Is it near Lewiston?"

Blink. Blink.

"That's a no!" Joe hollers, right in my ear. "The first no!"

In a fit of inspiration, I scoop Albert up and bring him over to the wall-sized map of the United States. I point to Nevada. "Is it here?" Nope. I move on to Washington. "Here?" No. I slide my finger down to Oregon. "This one? Oregon?"

Blink.

"Oregon!" Joe yells. "He wants us to go to Oregon!"

Miss Asher runs to a shelf and pulls off an upright file box of maps. Spilling them onto the table, she quickly finds a road map of the entire state of Oregon. My dad used to joke that we kids were going to grow up so reliant on GPS that the parts of our brains necessary to read proper paper maps would never develop. As Miss Asher unfurls a huge road map of Oregon, I think he might be right. What are *all* these lines? I plop Albert onto the table right in the middle of the map. He pads around it, nose down as if trying to sniff out a location. We watch, breathless. Albert pauses to wash his face. I resist the urge to tell him to stop being so *cat*. Nothing is linear when it comes to cats. Everything has detours. Including this process.

"How long will this go on for?" Joe asks through gritted teeth.

I shrug. "Hard to say."

"If he was a dog, we could give him a command and he'd do it," Joe says.

"He's not a dog," I reply.

"Tell me about it," Joe says with an exasperated sigh.

After some face-cleaning, Albert prances around on the map like it is just the most fun thing he has ever done, swatting at the folds in the paper and even taking time to chase his tail. I want to scream, but it wouldn't help. Finally, after what feels like an eternity, Albert plops down and goes to sleep.

Carefully, I slide him over. The town he chose to snooze on is Midhurst. Miss Asher, who has a part in her brain that can read maps, says it looks like a small mountain town surrounded by dormant volcanos. Can this be where he wants us to go, or did he just get tired and randomly lie down on it?

"You guys." Joe's face glows blue in the light of his phone screen. "Look at this." He holds it out.

The Midhurst Dragon Festival

What the heck? I grab the phone for a closer look. It's the town of Midhurst's website advertising the annual dragon festival, which takes place every year during Thanksgiving week. Turkey, mashed potatoes, and . . . dragons? Okay, I guess. The website promises food trucks, a parade, entertainment, boat races, vendors, crafts, kids' activities, and more. Pictures from previous festivals make it look like one big colorful, wild party.

Miss Asher, peering over my shoulder, says, "It *can't* be a coincidence. No way. For some reason, Albert wants us to go to this festival. Maybe it has to do with the symbol."

"I one hundred percent agree," Joe says.

I give Albert a little nudge with my hand. "Wake up." He opens one eye and forms his cute little facial features into a seriously grumpy expression. The problem is that sometimes when Albert gets mad or annoyed or scared—*poof!*—he turns into a dragon. So I try to be careful of his emotional state. "Sorry, buddy. Just tell us if Midhurst is where we are supposed to go. To this dragon festival thing? Then you can go back to sleep, and I'll give you a handful of salmon treats later."

He winks at me. Once. And promptly goes back to napping. Boy, he really let go of that sense of urgency he had dragging us over here.

"That was one eye," I say. "Does it count?"

"Let's say yes," Joe replies.

"The festival starts tomorrow," I say. As my feet warm, they begin to tingle uncomfortably. I jump up and down to get them back to normal faster. Miss Asher looks at me like I have sprouted another head. "My feet hurt."

"You shouldn't run around without shoes in the rain," Miss Asher says.

"You sound like my mother," I reply.

"Your mother is right," she says. "And speaking of your mother, we better loop her in. It looks like we are going on a road trip to the Midhurst Dragon Festival."

Good thing it is Thanksgiving break. If we had to miss school, how would we explain it? *Sorry, we have to rush off to Midhurst, Oregon, because my pet dragon has a mission of some sort that none of us quite understand but are committed to following through on anyway?* The truth is, we are used to plans that are vague, where we are missing major pieces of information, where we are pretty much clueless.

But this is the way it is when dealing with dragons.

Chapter 7

THE RETURN OF SHELDON SLACK

WE LEAVE MISS ASHER at the library and head home to tell Mom of the latest developments and also let her know that she will be driving us to a dragon festival in Midhurst, Oregon. I bet she will be surprised. I think she had plans to paint the living room this week.

After his map nap, Albert is back to being full of energy and urgency, even though I have explained to him we are going to Midhurst ASAP. First, we have to get Mom on board, not too challenging, and make up a story to tell Joe's grandmother, possibly more challenging. I try to ask Albert questions, stuff like whether he is happy or scared or excited or if it really is him sending messages to my head, but he does not want to play along. He's clearly sick of blinking at me. Which I get. It's like Mom asking me a ton of questions about my day when I really just want to get a snack and decompress. Joe agrees that I am being very annoying.

As soon as we come through the door, Albert leaps from my grasp and charges to the kitchen, anxious that, in all the activity, I do not forget the promise of extra treats. He claws my ankle and mews. "Relax!" I command. "They're coming!" I scoop out a small handful of fishy-smelling pellets and place them on the floor. Albert's eyes turn glowing red as he pounces on his prize. His tail flicks back and forth rapidly, and little puffs of steam rise from his flared nostrils. The treats are instantly demolished.

Joe and I watch him. "I was going to make a joke about how if Albert were bigger, he'd eat us," Joe says. "But maybe that is not so funny."

"Nope. Not funny."

Done with the pile, Albert turns his glowing eyes to me, asking for more. I immediately scoop out an additional handful. Don't want him going all dragon here in the kitchen and burning down the house. Mom would be super mad.

Speaking of, there is a note on the table. Mom went to help do Thanksgiving prep at the food bank. Out of the kindness of her heart, and this being school vacation, she let me sleep in. If only she knew I was running around shoeless in the rain after my cat! She'd be super mad about that, too.

Joe and I can spend the two hours before she returns home further investigating this dragon festival and trying to figure out why Albert wants us to go there. Or we can pack our stuff. Or figure out how to best convince Joe's grandma to let him go. Or we can heat up frozen waffles and watch TV. We choose waffles. As Mom so generously pointed out, we are on school break. Settled into the couch with our plates balanced precariously on our knees, we argue about what shows are good and what shows are terrible and manage not to pick anything to watch. Albert, eyes back to mossy green, jumps into my lap. His breath smells like fishy pellets. It's not a gross smell but also not so good. I bury my face in his fur.

"Your breath stinks, but you're still the cutest thing ever," I whisper to him. "Cuddle face. Cutie pants. Sweetie paws. Honey buns. His Royal Adorableness."

Joe eyes me over his plate. "You are making me physically ill," he says, gagging for dramatic effect.

"I can't help it," I reply. "Albert is just delicious."

"Gross, Cassie. He's not a plate of waffles."

"Of course he's not. Jeez, Joe." Albert peers into my eyes, questioning. "Don't worry, Albert. You are not a plate of waffles. And as soon as Mom gets home, we will get this trip to Midhurst sorted out. I promise."

I commandeer the remote from Joe and pick a show with lots of singing and dancing. Joe is not pleased. He insists the show is 95 percent garbage. He threatens mutiny, but his heart isn't in it, so I'm not too worried. Albert, dead asleep, rolls off my lap into the space between the couch cushion and my arm and practically disappears. I'm just about to explain to Joe why this show is completely excellent, when the doorbell rings. Maybe it is Miss Asher coming to see where we are with planning. Or . . . I don't know, but the bell chimes again, this time with more urgency. Okay! Coming!

I peer through the side window to see who it is. A man stands there, bedraggled and wet but grinning wildly. A man I am not particularly happy to see. A man in an orange jacket.

Sheldon Slack.

What is he doing *here*?

Slack's trademark puffy orange down jacket is still

streaked with dirt from when Albert knocked him out with sleeping gas in Mercy Grove and he ended up in a heap on the muddy ground. The reason he was in Mercy Grove in the first place was to kidnap Albert, and he went so far as to bring a Taser to help get the job done. He even threatened *me* to motivate Albert to do as he wanted. It didn't work. To which I say this: Don't make a dragon mad. You won't like what happens next.

But something interesting occurred when Slack regained consciousness in the forest. He was oddly *happy*, marveling at finding himself surrounded by so much natural beauty even though it was nighttime and he could barely see anything. It was like the sleeping gas had rewired his brain. He didn't even remember why he was there to begin with. And from the look of the man standing at the door, his brain has not returned to its pre-Albert-sleeping-gas state. His grin is loopy. His eyes dart every which way.

My second thought, after "What is Sheldon Slack doing at my door?" is that Albert *cannot* see Slack. I don't know if dragons hold grudges, and I don't really want to find out. Fortunately, he is wedged between the couch cushions, hopefully dreaming of mountains of fishy treats. Slack sees me through the window and gestures wildly. I have to open the door.

As soon as I do, Sheldon Slack throws his arms wide as if to sweep me into an embrace. "Cassie! My dear, dear friend! I'm so relieved I found you."

Dear friend? Huh? The last time we met, he thought seriously about Tasing me and stealing my dragon. I cross my arms against my chest. In the doorway, Slack hops from foot to foot as if he has ants in his pants. His hair fringe, a little long to begin with, sticks straight out like porcupine quills. He twirls a bit of it around his index finger anxiously.

We stare at each other until I realize I should probably say something. "What are you doing here?" A soft rain begins, and the dirt on Slack's jacket turns muddy.

"Might I come in?" he asks. There are purple bags under his eyes, like bruises, and his fingernails are gnawed down to nothing. While Slack may have seemed threatening a mere week ago, I realize he is mostly pitiful now, like a wet puppy. I step aside and gesture for him to enter. Joe appears in the hallway, eyes wide. He gives Slack the once-over, taking in the muddy jacket and the wild hair.

"Sheldon Slack?" he says. "For real? *Why* is he here?"

I shrug. "We are getting to that."

Slack wrings his hands. "I would have come sooner, but it took me a bit of time to figure out how to get away from my new friends Agent Dana and Agent Fox." He reports this without irony, as if they really *are* his friends, when, let's be clear, they are *not*.

"Wait a minute," Joe interrupts. "You escaped the *FBI*?"

Slack takes a step back and bumps into the wall. "It seems I did," he says, as if this is the first time he's considered his actions. "I went through a window. I don't think they thought I could fit, but I can make myself quite compact when necessary. And I really had grown weary of their hospitality."

I glance at Joe. Is Slack serious? He makes it sound like the FBI was a hotel where he didn't like the service. Having met Agents Fox and Dana, I can say they will not be pleased when they realize their guest has slipped through a window and disappeared. They will be even more unhappy when they realize where he is. I slam the door shut against potentially prying eyes. That orange jacket is like a beacon.

I head to the kitchen with Slack trailing me and Joe bringing up the rear. I give Slack a glass of water, which he gulps down, making me think he wasn't kidding about the hospitality thing. I refill his glass and pause for him to finish before asking again, "Why are you here?"

Slack sighs. It might be with relief. The guy was thirsty. He puts the glass gently in the sink and wipes his hands on his jacket, smearing the mud around, but he does not notice. "I don't feel myself," he says quietly. "Actually, that's not true. I don't remember what I used to feel like, but part of me thinks it was not like this." He glances from me to Joe as if waiting for us to weigh in on this thought. We say nothing. The silence grows awkward. Slack clears his throat.

"In any case," he continues, "my memory is spotty, but I do remember you two in the woods. And I remember . . . a dragon. Yes. I believe I do." His eyebrows furrow as he wrings his hands together. "Do you remember . . . a dragon?"

This is our moment to tell Slack that his faulty memory is playing tricks on him and that dragons do not exist. It's no guarantee that his real memories won't come roaring back at some point, but that is a worry for *later*. We glance at each other, and I can tell from Joe's expression he is thinking the same thing. But Slack is not done talking, and what he says next changes *everything*.

Chapter 8

EDWARD TENBROOK'S DIARY

THE TEMPO OF SLACK'S hand-wringing increases and his eyes grow frantic. "Because here is the thing," he says. "The dragon, if he *is* real, is in grave danger. Now I probably sound like I got hit on the head or something. And maybe I did."

"No," Joe mutters, "it wasn't that." I elbow him in the ribs and serve up my best glare. *Shut. Up.*

"But anyway, the dragon I *think* I saw, black and golden, he is in danger, and I feel quite certain that the diary has information that is important to help him."

"The diary?" I blurt. "*What* diary?"

Slack sighs. "It's a long story, but suffice it to say there was a diary written long ago that I stole because it had dragon information in it. Wait a minute! That's a new memory! I didn't know that before!" He seems pleased as punch with himself.

And I am 100 percent confident that the diary Slack *stole* was written by Edward Tenbrook in the 1800s, when he and his family followed the whiff of gold to Lewiston, then a speck on the map suddenly overrun by forty-niners. We intended to steal the diary, but it was missing. And now we know it is because Slack stole it back when he was a teenager.

"You swiped it from the Lewiston University archives, didn't you?" Joe says with a grimace.

Slack hangs his head. "Yes. I remember that part now too. My friend and I were tasked with bringing it to the university archives so it could be restored. It was in terrible shape, the second half literally falling to pieces. The journal itself was unusual, too, a product of an artisan bookmaker. Red leather with a gold-embossed redwood tree on the cover. I'm sure it was quite beautiful in its prime. My research said only a handful of such notebooks were ever produced. Intact, it would be quite valuable."

This history lesson is all well and good, but let's get to the point. "But instead of bringing it to the archives, you took it?" I interrupt.

"Oh, no," Slack says, waving me off. "We brought it to the archives and turned it over as we were asked to do. But then I could not *stop* thinking about it. It filled my head, leaving no space for anything else. And I knew I must have it. I had to try to decipher those disintegrating pages, even at risk of ruining the book. Which I did."

"Wait a minute!" Joe barks. "You murdered the diary? Like, *destroyed* it?"

"Indeed." Slack nods thoughtfully. "The whole thing just fell to pieces."

Joe throws up his arms in disgust. "I can't believe you! You are a book murderer!"

Slack hangs his head in shame. "I don't know what I was thinking."

But I do. He was desperate and desperation makes people do things that they normally wouldn't do. There is a reason everyone wants the diary. It has the only firsthand account of a dragon.

Remember, it was the year 1854, and dirt-poor twelve-year-old Edward, the youngest of eight kids, was hungry, cold, and miserable *all* the time. Plus, his siblings were so mean to him! Walking among the giant redwoods that came right to the edge of town back then was his only happiness. But one day, out in the forest, Edward met Alvina, a dragon.

Alvina had run away from her tyrannical father, Vayne, who happened to be king of the dragons and pretty awful. The Silver dragons, like Alvina and Vayne, were the ruling class and had a lot of everything while other dragons struggled to survive. The Silvers centuries-old grip on power seemed unbreakable.

But there was a prophecy offered up by a revered elder, who claimed one day a dragon would come and bring an end to the rule of the Silvers. This dragon would bear a special mark, a golden blaze on his chest. Determined to hold on to power, Vayne ordered all marked dragons to be executed.

This horrified Alvina, and she tried to intervene and save the marked dragons from their terrible fate. But Vayne was enraged and thought Alvina weak for caring. Frightened, Alvina ran away through a rip between dimensions, landing among the Lewiston redwoods. She had learned of the rip from her grandmother, who was forbidden from sharing it but did so anyway. Information is power, and Vayne did not want his dragon subjects to have that—no way.

In the diary, Edward goes on to explain how Alvina caused crazy weather whenever she passed through the rip, and how being here for too long made her weak. And then when Edward got himself run over by a horse and

Chapter 9

SLACK THE HERO?

SLACK, OVERWHELMED with this outpouring, collapses into a kitchen chair, breathing hard. I give him another glass of water and an apple from the fruit bowl on the counter. He looks like he could use it. But as soon as I hand over the apple, Joe yanks me out of the kitchen and into the hallway.

"*Destiny?*" Joe blurts. "I had no idea that Albert's sleeping gas would knock him for such a loop. It has changed his personality completely."

"I can't argue with that," I reply. "But destiny or not, he has a copy of the diary."

"Believe me," he says, gaze narrowed. "I heard that

part loud and clear. And do you know what?"

"What?" I ask.

"We are taking it," he replies.

"Like, from Slack?" I ask. We had to break into the library last week when we were running away with Albert, and that felt like crime enough for one lifetime.

"Not like that," Joe responds, as if reading my thoughts. "He's going to give it to us. It's his destiny to save dragons; he said so himself. Giving us the diary will help him fulfill that destiny."

My adrenaline spikes at the mere thought of holding the actual-but-not-really diary in my hands. "Let's tell Slack," I say.

"You do that part," Joe says, nudging me back into the kitchen. Joe is good at some things, and I am good at others, which is why we make a great team.

In the kitchen, Slack munches thoughtfully on his apple. He looks serene, the creases in his forehead, so prominent before the sleeping gas, now gone.

"We want to help you with your destiny," I say, breaking the silence. Slack jumps a little at my voice. He places the apple core gingerly on a napkin, making sure to keep the table nice and clean.

"You do?" he asks.

I nod vigorously. "Yes. Absolutely. And to do that, we need the diary."

"Of course," he says quickly. "But as the FBI is sort of . . . after me . . . might I suggest you go alone? They will surely be watching my house and my office and probably even the sandwich shop I frequent."

My heart sinks. The FBI is watching us too. Not every minute, of course, but if we show up at Slack's house, it's not like they won't recognize us. "And is that where the diary is, your house?"

Slack laughs. It sounds like fingers dragged along the high notes of a piano. "Oh goodness, no. I'm not an idiot. All of my research is hidden away, including the diary. But I trust you, so I will tell you where to find it."

This makes me feel guilty, although I'm not sure why. It's not like we are taking the diary. Slack is offering it up. He wants us to have it. He wants us to help him fulfill his destiny! Or, you know, something like that. I take a step toward him.

"So, where is it?" I ask.

"The Starlight," he replies. "I hid a bunch of books in a building full of books. Smart, right?"

The Starlight is the shiny metal-and-glass central

library for Lewiston University. From a distance, the Starlight looks like the city of Oz, shimmering on the horizon. But that is not important right now.

"Wait a minute," I say. "You just stuck your research journals and the diary in with all the other books at random?" Miss Asher will have a heart attack when she hears this.

"Of course not!" Slack fires back. "I have a system!"

Joe's expression drips with disdain. Despite Slack's change in personality, I don't think Joe will ever forgive what he did in Mercy Grove. Or intended to do. "What kind of system?" he asks.

Slack drums his fingers on the tabletop. "Numerical," he says finally. "And alphabetical. And categorical. And by time frame. And, of course, hierarchical."

"Of *course*," Joe says, rolling his eyes.

Slack's fingers stop, and he frowns. "Although, I may have the order wrong. Perhaps category is first followed by numerical? Oh dear. It seemed so simple when I thought of it."

I get the creeping sensation we will never find a single trace of the diary buried in the Starlight, especially if the man himself can't remember the system he created to hide it.

Joe sighs. "Hopeless," he mutters. "We seem to specialize in hopeless."

My urge to tell him to stay optimistic is doused by the fact that he is right—we *do* specialize in hopeless. Hopeless and complicated and sometimes even dangerous. Great. Now what?

Suddenly, Slack jumps to his feet. The apple core rolls off the table. "Hurricanes!" he yells.

And I have no idea if that means one is coming or *what*.

Chapter 10

FOX AND DANA SEARCH FOR SLACK

THE FBI SAFE HOUSE is on the edge of town, a small cottage that looks like the setting of a fairy tale on the outside while the inside is basically a jail. It is the kind of place only a person made of water could escape. And yet, when Agent Fox and Agent Dana arrive, steaming cups of fresh coffee in hand, Slack is *gone*. This is bad.

Dana checks the locked windows and doors. "How did he do it?" she wonders. "It's impossible."

"Maybe he is double-jointed," Fox suggests. She'd once met a man who had so many double joints, he could flatten himself out like a piece of paper and slip under any door, without even screaming.

"I'm so disappointed in him," Dana says, shaking her head. "We were being so nice!" Dana is right, but he wasn't allowed to leave, and apparently, he wanted to.

"Of course it would be Sheldon Slack to bring down my career," Fox mutters. After all, they go way back to when Slack was just a teenager and happened to find that diary, which he continues to insist disappeared after he and his friend Ellen Asher turned it over to the university archives. "The bosses are not going to be happy."

"Are we in trouble?" Dana asks.

Definitely. Getting more time to work the case now seems unlikely. "We might be," Fox replies, not wanting to alarm Dana.

"If Slack's not here," asks Dana, "where is he? Would he make a run for it?"

"Slack?" Fox replies with a snort. "No way. He's at home or at his office. He lacks the imagination to run. Besides, he's not even sure who he is right now. But that will likely wear off in time."

Or she thinks it will. Fox takes a sip of coffee. She was really looking forward to it, but now it just tastes bitter.

This case is getting complicated. The guy who was going to help them sort out this dragon mess has vanished into thin air. "Let's go check his house," she says to her partner.

"Affirmative," replies Dana. They stalk out the door like two people on a mission.

Which they are.

Chapter 11

ALBERT HOLDS A GRUDGE

"HURRICANES!" SLACK YELLS again when we stare at him with total confusion. "You know, hurricanes, those big storms with lots of wind and rain?"

"We know what hurricanes are," Joe says defensively. "What we don't know is why you are yelling about them."

"Oh. Of course." Slack twirls his hair fringe, looking sheepish. "It's the basis for my system, the system I used to hide the diary and the other research materials."

We are still confused. This seems to be our default state lately, and I sure wish it weren't. Being confused all the time is not that fun.

"You better explain," I say.

"Fine," he says, settling back into his chair as if this might take a while. "Hurricanes are given proper names, the kind you might name a person. Andrea. Barry. Karen. Jerry. Pablo. You get the idea?"

"We get the idea," Joe says flatly.

"Well, last year, for example, there was Hurricane Nana. Not very substantial but still caused quite a lot of property damage for those folks down in Florida. Blew off some roofs, trashed some boats, mangled some lovely palm trees."

"Hurricane. Florida," I say impatiently. "Go on."

"*Okay.* I had a Nana Slack, may she rest in peace, whose real name was Margaret, which happens to be the same first name as my favorite author, Margaret Atwood."

Miss Asher's favorite author is Margaret Atwood too. I wonder if they read her books together back when they were friends. I glance at Joe, suddenly aware that I don't know what types of books he likes to read, which is a huge oversight in a friendship. Huge! I make a mental note to ask him later.

"Are you even listening?" Slack asks, peering into my face.

"Yes! Yes. Sorry."

"Now, do you two know that novels in the library are organized by the author's last name?"

And this is enough for Joe to lose it. "We go to school!" he yells. "We know things! *Where* is the diary?"

Slack holds up his hands defensively. "I just want to make sure you are well informed, that's all."

I lay a hand on Joe's shoulder. "We know how libraries work," I say. "What does Margaret Atwood have to do with hurricanes?"

"Hurricanes?" he asks, surprised. "Nothing at all. It's just a way in. The diary is on top of the shelving unit where the Margaret Atwood books are."

"*That's* your system?" Joe blurts. "It's totally random!"

"Not to me," Slack says with a sniff. "I'm quite sure I know where everything is."

"Let me get this straight," I interrupt. "The diary is on top of a shelf in the fiction section of the Starlight, above the Margaret Atwood books."

"Correct," Slack says. He has the nerve to look smug. I mean, Joe is right, the only constant to his system is that he doesn't have one. But we can find the fiction shelves, and if he is telling the truth, we can get the diary.

I'm about to say as much when I hear growling from

the hallway. Uh-oh. Albert finished his nap and probably figured he'd check to see if his food bowls miraculously refilled during his absence or at least insist on some more salmon treats. Instead, sitting in the kitchen is the man who tried to hurt us in Mercy Grove, the man who Albert knocked out with sleeping gas.

Slack leans around me and peers at my tiny puffball of a kitten. "Why, isn't he just adorable?" he exclaims, full of joy. It's hard not to be happy when you are in the presence of a kitten, but this is no ordinary kitten. Slack, of course, has no idea that this same delightful creature is the very dragon he sought to kidnap in the woods. However, if Albert goes bananas, the cat will be out of the bag, so to speak, not to mention a whole host of other bad things will happen. We could have a serious situation here any second now.

"Albert," I say, keeping my tone neutral. "It's fine. Everything is okay. This is Sheldon Slack. He's going to help us find out some things about . . . some stuff."

Albert, stay calm! Slack has information we need. Do not go all dragon on me right now. Are you listening?

I watch Albert's eyes. If they turn red like fire, we are in trouble. But he remains crouched in the doorway, rumbling with displeasure and staring at Slack.

No dragon, Albert.

Uh-oh. His eyes begin to burn red. Outside, the light breeze turns ferocious.

"This is going to be bad!" Joe yells above the sudden pounding sound of the rain.

Slack grips the table. "What's happening?" he cries.

You'll see. Just give it a second, I think.

The kitchen fills with hazy smoke. Slack leaps from his chair and flattens himself against the refrigerator. "Help!" he yelps.

I swear Albert emerges from the cloud of smoke for maximum dramatic effect. First, his leathery snout, jagged teeth, like an alligator, followed by glowing red eyes that seem to spark, and then the magnificent rest of him, wings pulsing, iridescent skin rippling. Slack turns a funny shade of green. He clutches his chair for dear life. I think he whimpers.

"The cat is a *dragon*?" he whispers. "He's back? He's here? Is this true? Is it real?"

Oh, it is plenty real. Albert takes up most of the kitchen. The edge of the kitchen table is singed and the upholstery on a chair, melted. There is a black streak across the refrigerator and the linoleum floor buckles. Albert growls.

"Albert, be good," I command, sounding much more

confident than I am. He's not a dog. He will not necessarily listen to what I say.

"He probably won't hurt you," Joe offers. He smiles benignly, thoroughly enjoying Slack's terror.

"Probably?" Slack wheezes.

"Eighty percent," Joe confirms.

"I might be having a heart attack," Slack says.

"It's the shock," I confirm. "Just try to breathe normally."

"Nope, not working," Slack replies. Albert growls and thumps his ample tail, which stretches clear into the living room. I hear a crash that has to be the stained glass table lamp that my mother loves. Oops. Slack shrinks back. A plume of fire scorches the ceiling.

"Maybe you can apologize to him," Joe suggests. "You know, for trying to Tase him in the woods."

"I did *what*? Me? Are you sure?"

"Pretty sure."

Slack takes a tentative step toward Albert, hands out, quivering. "I'm so sorry, dragon friend. I don't know what came over me, but I'm different now. I swear I am. My destiny is to help you."

"His name is Albert," I say.

"Albert, please forgive me."

As apologies go, it sounds sincere to me. Albert eye-balls him, thumps his tail (and there goes the glass bowl of fake chrysanthemums), and finally settles down on his haunches, a clear sign that he is not planning on eating Slack. At least not right now.

"He's good," I say to Slack, who exhales loudly and leans back against the sink, a sheen of sweat on his forehead. I'm sweating too. The kitchen is ten degrees hotter than a minute ago.

"Well, now that we're all friends," Joe says snidely, "I think Cassie and I should go to the Starlight ASAP."

"Um . . . are you going to leave Albert here with me?" Slack asks quietly.

But before I can answer, I watch as Albert's eyes fade from red back to green. A moment later, he is asleep at my feet, a tiny ball of kitten fuzz. Acting out as a dragon is apparently exhausting.

Slack's jaw hangs open. "Amazing. Just amazing. *A dragon-cat.* What a marvelously perfect disguise." I scoop Albert off the ground and stuff him in my pocket. We leave Slack in the kitchen with the fruit bowl and another glass of water to contemplate what he just saw and what it means.

"Ready?" Joe asks, grabbing his backpack. I can feel

the nervousness coming off him in waves. The idea of the diary, even if it is a copy, is next-level exciting. It could explain *so* much, starting with this new interpretation of the prophecy.

"Ready," I reply.

"Should we call your mom?" Joe asks. "Or Miss Asher?"

We should. If Mom comes home and finds Slack sitting at the table eating grapes, she will have questions. But will that be before or after she sees the damage to the house? Who knows? Still, I don't want to waste time explaining right now. I feel a sense of urgency that does not allow for even a five-minute conversation with my mother or Miss Asher.

"We'll do it later," I say, waving off the suggestion. "Let's *go*."

Chapter 12

THE STARLIGHT

THE STARLIGHT IS BARELY two years old. The grand opening was quite an affair, with VIPs coming from as far away as Sacramento. Most of Lewiston is old and covered in moss (and I mean literally!), so this building, all sharp angles of glass and steel, is visually shocking. And pretty great. Somehow, its mere presence pushes back on the perpetual grayness of Lewiston, radiating light even when the sun hasn't shown itself in days.

Can you tell I love it? Because I totally do.

Inside, the building smells of the lavender planted in the surrounding gardens. A burbling fountain of stars and moons occupies the main atrium. The marble floors glow with warmth. Joe and I agree it is much too fancy for a place like Lewiston.

We stand on the wide plaza outside the Starlight, which is edged by giant planters bigger than we are, overflowing with blooms. One of the nice things (the only nice thing?) about living in a climate like ours is that flowers blossom all year round. A night freeze is pretty unusual, so the flowers just keep chugging along. Students stride with purpose through the plaza, in and out of the library, heads bent, thoughts large.

The last time we needed to get inside the Starlight, we got lucky. The student sitting at the desk right beside the entrance turnstile where actual students, as opposed to imposters like us, swipe their student ID cards turned out to be a Dungeons & Dragons fan. Joe dazzled and distracted him with D&D conversation until he let us into the archives. It was genius. But it seems our luck has run out.

A student with blue hair sits at the entrance, chewing on a pencil and muttering to herself as she works out something mathematical on a piece of paper. The chances of her being a D&D fan are about zero.

"Maybe she's a fan of just the dragon part?" Joe asks, his tone laced with sarcasm.

"What? You thought this would be easy?" I respond.

"Nothing is *ever* easy," he replies with a sigh.

"Easy is boring," I snap.

"Is it?" he shoots back.

"We can't stand here all day," I say.

"Can't we?" he asks.

"Now you are just being annoying."

"Am I?" I glare at him. His lips form a tight thin line. "Sorry. What's the plan?"

"I think we just ask to come in," I say. "Try to look like a desperate book reader."

"What does a desperate book reader look like?" he asks.

"I don't know," I say. "I'm making this up as I go." With that, I stride confidently toward the library entrance, my heart pounding against my ribs. On the other side of the wall is the diary. And I *want* that diary.

Both of my hands rest on Albert, sleeping soundly in my pocket. It's like I'm some sort of strange mother kangaroo, but I like him there. He gives me confidence I don't know if I'd have without him. Joe scurries after me.

"I have a bad feeling about this," he whispers.

"It will be fine," I reassure him, lending him some confidence because that is what friends do.

"If you say so," Joe says. Another thing a friend will do is go along with your stupid plans even if the chance of success is low. The wide glass doors slide silently open, and warm, scented air wafts out. My heartbeat ratchets up a notch.

The blue-haired student glances at us as we approach and just as quickly looks away. We simply do not register on her radar as . . . well . . . anything.

"Excuse me?" I ask. "Hi. Sorry to bother you."

Beside me, Joe stands statue-still. He doesn't even blink. I wish he'd stop that.

"Hi?" I repeat. Blue Hair again looks up. This time her eyes focus on us, and her eyebrows, not blue, rise just a touch.

"Kindergarten is that way," she says, pointing vaguely out the door.

"Oh, we are way past kindergarten," I say.

"That was a joke," she replies flatly.

"I know," I say, blushing. "So we really want to come in and look in the fiction section for a book by Margaret Atwood. Do you know who she is?"

Okay. From the look on her face, I can tell this was not the right question to ask. Her gaze narrows. "Are you Lewiston University students?" she asks, her tone frosty.

"No."

"Do you have some sort of special exemption allowing you to access this library?"

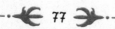

"Um . . . no?"

"Well, then I suggest you hurry back to kindergarten before you get in trouble for missing class."

Ouch. She returns to her equations. Joe and I slink away, regrouping out of Blue Hair's line of sight, tucked behind a giant planter, overflowing with pink, orange, yellow, and white camellias.

"That went really well," Joe comments.

"Not our best work," I reply.

"What do we do now?"

"Do you suppose there is another way in?"

"We could ask Albert to create some chaos and then sneak in," Joe suggests.

"Are you kidding me? He already wrecked the kitchen. That's enough for today."

Joe sighs, deflated. I feel it too. But what if we gave up every time we felt that way? We probably wouldn't even know each other. We'd just be boring middle school students with no dragon.

"Let me think," I say.

"Hurry up," Joe says, glancing skyward. Heavier rain begins to fall.

Rain.

This makes me pause. And think, specifically, about the strange feeling I get conjuring the golden mist, like if I concentrated, I could gather up the energy circulating around me and fold it into the mist and possibly, just maybe, turn the mist into something like a mini tornado. A small one. A *distracting* one.

What happens if *that* happens?

Chapter 13

IN MY HANDS

THE PROBLEM WITH my golden mist power idea is that I have not mentioned it to Joe, and if I suddenly start whipping up tornadoes, he's going to have questions. Plus, there is the small problem that I don't exactly know how to do it. Just because I feel like I can doesn't mean I actually can. But if there is anybody who can help me figure it out, it is Joe.

"Okay, there is something I have to tell you," I begin, "but I don't want you to freak out. Can you promise me you won't freak out?"

"I don't like it when you start conversations like this. It makes me want to freak out."

This is not going the way I want it to go. But Joe believed me right away when I told him Albert was a dragon, so I should not doubt him now.

"You know the golden mist?" I begin, my voice a little shaky. "The stuff from my hands?"

Joe narrows his gaze. "Yes?"

"Well, I think there might be more I can do with it." I pause, swallowing a few times, gathering up my courage. "More than open the rip, I mean. I think it gives me . . . abilities."

Joe takes a step back, as if pushed, and bumps hard into the concrete planter. "What did you just say?"

"You heard me."

"I did, but I want to be sure."

"I think the golden mist gives me, like, powers or something."

"*What* powers?"

I stare at my open hands, the glitter always present just below the surface. "Like I can make storms," I say.

"Storms?"

"Rain, wind, lightning," I say. "You know, storms."

"You've *made* lightning?" Joe asks in disbelief, shock, or horror. I really can't tell which.

"No!" I bark.

"But you think you *could*?"

"Yeah."

"Oh boy."

"Yeah."

"Why didn't you tell me?" he howls. I jump, caught off guard by his outburst. "How could you keep a monumental thing like storm powers from me? Your best friend? We found a dragon together!"

"I'm sorry," I say meekly.

He scowls. "Describe."

I try to pick the right words. This is not easy. "It's like I can channel energy from my surroundings and put it into the mist and then command the mist to do things."

"Like you could tell the mist to do your math homework?" Joe asks.

"Not homework," I reply.

"Okay. I'm mentally regrouping." Joe paces and runs his hands through his hair. "So does this energy come from inside you or outside?"

I stumble in my reply. I'm not sure of the answer. I don't really know how this works, or *if* it does. Joe waves me off.

"Never mind," he says. "We can talk about that later. Right now, do you think you could get us into the library?"

"Fifty-fifty?"

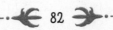

Joe frowns. "Not great odds, but so far we are batting a zero. Is that a thing? Can you even bat a zero?"

I shrug. I know nothing about baseball *or* golden-mist superpowers, as it turns out.

"Do you want to practice?" Joe asks. "Maybe make it rain harder?"

We are both soaked. I glance at the sky. "Not possible for it to rain harder," I reply.

"You're right."

"But I might be able to make a tornado. A small one to blow all the papers around and give us an opening."

Joe grins. "I love that you just said you were going to make a tornado."

"*Might* make a tornado," I clarify. In my pocket, I plunge my fingers deep into Albert's downy fur.

"Well, we never seem to know what we are doing, so that is comforting in a way," Joe comments. "Here we go." Shoulder to shoulder, we march back in through the wide glass doors to the desk, behind which Blue Hair sits, still gnawing away on her pencil. I try to keep my breathing normal, although the panic is rising steadily in my chest. What are the chances she calls campus security and gets us dragged away for being weird? My guess is pretty high. Trying to be inconspicuous, we stand to the side, allowing other students to enter the turnstiles into the library. I turn my back, tucking in behind Joe to be out of view. I stare at my outstretched palms.

Focus, Cassie. A small tornado. Really more of a whirlwind. Just to blow her papers around.

Nothing happens. Joe peers over my shoulder. "Well?" he asks.

"It's not exactly easy," I shoot back. "I need a mantra."

"A what?"

"Specific words that I repeat to help me calm down and focus."

"Oh yeah," Joe says. "My mom has one of those she uses when she wants to kill me and my brothers for destroying the furniture or whatever. Does it need to rhyme? How about . . . let me think . . . *wind, wind, blow, blow; make a storm, make it snow?*"

"That's ridiculous."

"*Rain, rain, don't go away; come around, and please just stay?*" Joe suggests.

"Being as it rains here all the time, I don't know how we would know the mantra was working," I reply.

"True. Thinking." He pauses. "*How about this? Rain, snow, sleet, hail; clouds, twister, wind; come on, weather, do it right; blow me up a storm tonight.*"

"Oh. I kind of like that one. Say it again?"

"*Rain, snow, sleet, hail; clouds, twister, wind; come on, weather, do it right; blow me up a storm tonight*," Joe repeats.

I place my hands in prayer position, close my eyes, and repeat the words slowly, under my breath so I don't appear like a complete weirdo to anyone in close proximity. I like their rhythm, even if the words themselves are kind of silly. Not that I came up with anything myself, so I should be appreciative and not complain about it.

My third round through the words, the air around me crackles. I pull my palms apart. Mist begins to rise, slowly at first but suddenly thicker and denser. It feels almost heavy in my hands. I close my eyes and imagine the mist forming a small twister, swirling and whirling from me to the desk to the math papers, scattering them all around the floor.

"Cassie!" Joe nudges me. "You're doing it!"

I open my eyes to see the rotating spiral of gold moving toward the desk. The map of its path is laid out in my head. Like I am playing a road-race video game, I direct the mini tornado to the desk. It is small, only about five inches high, and decently camouflaged by the bright light of the Starlight. As I drive it closer, I have the fleeting thought that I do not know how to make it go away. Like, where is the off switch? Will it just stop being a mini tornado when I stop thinking about it?

So many questions!

"Cassie," Joe hisses. *Oh. Wow.* While I was pondering how to turn it off, my tornado has doubled in size. It reaches the desk, sucking up everything in its wake. The papers, the jar of pencils, a stamp pad, a notebook, Blue Hair's phone.

We wanted chaos but maybe not at this level. Students are yelling and pointing and taking videos. Blue Hair, trying to retrieve her phone, sticks her arm into the mist, only to be lifted two feet off the floor. She begins to scream.

"Tornado! Stop! Cease! End! Quit!" I whisper-yell. Suddenly, the golden mist loses its funnel-cloud shape and dissipates, evaporating like fog in the sunshine. But the pandemonium does not dissipate. If anything, the chaos grows. I get it. A very strange thing has happened right before the eyes of these people. They cannot quite believe what they have seen. And Blue Hair still wails like a lion with a thorn in her paw, despite appearing unharmed.

I can't believe I did this. I'm staring at the disarray when Joe shoves me through the turnstiles. "Go! The diary!"

He's right. The whole reason for this chaos was to get past Blue Hair to the diary. I race after him as he plows through the unattended and utterly ignored turnstile.

We are *in*.

Chapter 14

NO BIG DEAL

TRYING NOT TO draw attention to ourselves—not that anyone is paying attention—we race up the central stairs to the third-floor fiction section. As we climb, we pass a sprawling mural of an ocean scene, rendered in bright blues and greens. I wish I could come here all the time. It's not as homey and comfortable as Miss Asher's library, but I like how grand it is. It matches the treasures inside.

It doesn't take long to find the *A* section and the Atwood books in particular. The stacks are eight feet tall. While we take a moment to consider how we can get to something hidden from view on the very top, Albert breaks free of his pocket, landing on the floor and giving a big stretch.

I point a finger at him. "No shenanigans," I say. He turns his back on me with a sniff, licking a paw and running it over his face. "I'm serious. Trouble follows you. And I think we have made enough of that here for one day. See if we can find a stool or a chair to stand on."

We search the surrounding area, but the only chairs are much too big to move, and there are no ladders anywhere. I bet they never dust the tops of the shelves.

"You can get on my shoulders," Joe suggests. This is a ridiculous idea. I'd crush him.

"You can get on *my* shoulders," I counter. But before we can negotiate the finer details of what this will actually entail, a blur whizzes past my face. A black fuzzy blur.

"Albert!" I squeak. "I said no shenanigans!"

Too late. With remarkable ease, he has launched himself eight feet from the floor straight to the top of the bookshelves, to a perch above our heads. I swear he is smirking. Was I not clear on the definition of "no shenanigans"?

Albert disappears. All we can make out is the very tip of his tail, switching and straining as if he is doing something difficult. And he is. With his little paws, he's pushing the hidden notebook to the edge of the shelf.

"I can't believe Slack was telling the truth," I say.

"It's really here," Joe responds, mirroring my surprise.

A snowstorm of dust flutters down on us. Albert's eyes glow red with the effort. I say a silent prayer that he doesn't erupt into his dragon form while on top of the shelving unit. Talk about shenanigans. He'd bust clear through the ceiling and certainly terrify whoever is above us in the ancient languages section or whatever. Not to mention the rest of the library.

But he seems to have it under control. The book tumbles over the edge and literally falls on my head. Joe catches it as it bounces.

"You won't be playing varsity basketball anytime soon," he comments, clutching the diary. It is a faded green composition notebook, held together with several rubber bands and thick with dust. Tucked inside are additional pages scribbled with notes, sticking out past the covers. Joe holds it like it is an egg. "Do we open it now, or do we get out of here?"

Although I want to absorb every single word between the covers immediately, we created a whole lot of chaos downstairs, and leaving ASAP is probably the smart thing to do. We are not supposed to be in here in the first place. "The second," I say. "Albert! Come down immediately!"

Cats are not obedient. If you call them, they are just as likely to head off in the other direction. If you want them to sit on your lap, they will refuse. If you *don't* want them to sit on your lap, they won't get off it for all the treats in the world. Headstrong. Strong-willed. And on occasion, just downright rude. But Albert obliges by leaping off the edge right to my chest, where he clings to my hoodie with his sharp nails.

I peel him off and stuff him back in my pocket. We have the diary. Time to get out of here.

Joe zips the diary inside his jacket because the rain is getting more enthusiastic and there is no way this ordinary old notebook survives getting wet. My fingers itch to open it, to reveal its secrets. The rain comes harder. We run faster. When Joe tries to leap over a puddle, the notebook dislodges and drops out of his jacket right into it, where it lies like a thirsty sponge, soaking up the water.

You would think we had seen a dragon for how we both start shrieking. I have the drenched diary in my hands in negative seconds, blowing on it and waving it in the air and doing all the things I think might save it, none of them particularly effective.

"This is not good," I say through gritted teeth.

Joe, frantic, wrings his hands. "We need a blow dryer, *stat!*"

"Shortcut!" I yell. If we cut down the alley between

Main Street and Broad Street, we will come to a park, and if we sprint straight across the park, we will save about five minutes. The park will be a bog from all the fresh rain, but it doesn't matter. This is urgent.

"But then we go right by Slack's house!" Joe yells back.

It's a risk but one we have to take in order to save the book. "I don't think we have a choice," I reply. We take off running. I hold the diary like a fragile piece of blown glass as we navigate the small lakes that fill the sunken patches in the park, trying our best not to fall in and just make things worse.

Chapter 15

WHAT ARE THE CHANCES?

AGENT FOX AND AGENT DANA SIT outside Slack's house, located on a tree-lined street in the historic section of Lewiston. In this case, "historic" means small and a little run-down. Most building materials suffer in the constant fog and rain. Fox can't blame them. This town smells of wet dog and mold. Utterly unappealing. What self-respecting dragon would choose to come here when he could go . . . virtually *anyplace* else? This would be a good question when she finally finds the dragon and gets a chance to ask him questions. Of course, if she does find the dragon, there is no way her bosses at the FBI would let her have time to ask silly questions like that one. No. They will take the dragon away, and Fox will likely never see or hear of him again. There is no glory or recognition for the hard work, the risk, the danger involved. There is nothing but the expectation that she will move quietly on to the next case, whatever that may be.

In the past, there have been strange things that Fox was more than happy to hand off to the bosses, things that smelled bad or were slimy or rude or just basically unpleasant, but the dragon is different. Fox wants to *talk* to the dragon.

A small voice in the back of her mind tells her to stop being ridiculous. Her job is to find the dragon. What happens next is not her department. Normally, this small voice, which sounds a bit like Fox's grandmother, is enough to clear her thoughts of such nonsense. But not today. Today she wants to tell the voice to be quiet.

There is no chatter in the car. Usually Fox and Dana have an easy banter. It's one of the things that makes them good partners. But the only sound now is the rain pounding on the roof, reflecting their general sour mood. Slack escaping is a major error, and unless they find him soon, they will be forced to explain what happened, and they would really rather not have to do that. Not today. Not ever.

Slack's house is partially hidden behind shrubs that are meant to be trimmed and tidy but have gone berserk, growing wildly in all directions. The foot-high grass is run through with feathery weeds. The cracks in the walkway to the front door sprout steely yellow flowers.

Even with nature trying so hard to hide the house, the agents can see the inside is dark. If Slack is here, he is likely hiding in a closet or under his bed. With a sigh, Fox shoulders open the car door. "Let's go have a look," she says with zero enthusiasm.

"I get the sense he's not home," Dana replies sharply. The agents climb out of the car and pick their way through the jungle to the front door. They ring, they knock, they call out Slack's name. Nothing. When the coast is clear, they pick the lock and invite themselves in for a peek.

All houses have distinct smells, and this one is musty and unloved. Dana crinkles up her nose and sneezes. "Ugh. Dust."

"Not the best housekeeper," Fox comments.

"Are we surprised?" asks Dana.

"Not at all," replies Fox. "He's not here, but let's look around anyway."

Dana nods in agreement, and they part, Fox up the stairs and Dana around to the kitchen, where she discovers the refrigerator is bare except for a container of strawberry yogurt well past its expiration date and some dehydrated celery stalks. A coffee mug is stuck to the counter as if by glue. There is no sign the sink has been turned on in recent days.

Upstairs, Fox finds an office, small and tidy. On the desk is a pile of the brightly colored flyers that Slack was handing out, asking for information about dragon sightings. Fox takes the stack to shred later. Can't leave stuff like that just lying around.

Back downstairs, the agents agree there is nothing of interest here, including Slack. More disappointment. But just as they are about to leave, Dana says, "Hey, look at that." She points across the street. And there, running down the sidewalk, dressed in oversized soggy hoodies, are two kids. One of them cradles something precious to her chest. Fox's first thought is local kids should know better and wear rain jackets. Cotton hoodies are terrible in any kind of weather! But the second kid wears shorts, which is even more inappropriate. Who does that in Lewiston in November, or any other month, for that matter?

Oh, who *indeed*. "Joe Robinson," they say at the same time.

"What are the chances of him running by right now?" Dana asks.

If there is one thing Fox has learned in all her years, it is that coincidences don't exist. Yes, Lewiston is a small town where running into people you know probably happens all the time. But Fox and Dana aren't from Lewiston, and these aren't *any* kids. "Basically zero," Fox says.

"Are you thinking what I'm thinking?" Dana asks.

"Follow those kids," Fox responds with a sly grin. And Dana smiles back.

Chapter 16

MOM MEETS SLACK. UNEXPECTEDLY.

OH, THE PUDDLES ARE DEEP! At one point the water is up to my ankles. About a block from my house, I see my mother standing outside our front door, arms crossed defensively against her chest, feet planted hip width apart. Happy people don't stand this way. How could she possibly know we dropped the notebook in a puddle when she doesn't even know about the notebook in the first place?

Joe stops abruptly. "She found Slack," he says.

Slack! I left him at my kitchen table, with just the fruit bowl for entertainment! What is *wrong* with me? Granted, he gave us a lot to think about, but I should have called my mother. Or left a note. Oh well. Too late now. The cat is out of the bag. (Sorry, Albert. What kind of person would put a cat in a bag? How awful. A pocket is just fine, thank you very much.) We can't even make a run for it. She sees us and waves her hand that we should hurry up.

"Do you think Slack explained?" Joe asks. "I mean, told your mom why he is here?"

"He might have tried," I reply. "If she let him get a word in edgewise. I hope she didn't hurt him."

My mother does not change her stance as we approach. "What on earth is Sheldon Slack doing in the kitchen eating grapes?" she barks. "And what happened to my kitchen? *And* my chrysanthemums?"

"About that . . . ," I say.

"And *where* were you two?"

"Yeah . . . that's part of it," Joe says.

"And what is that?" She points to the soggy mess in my hands.

"Also part of it," I reply.

Mom relaxes her arms and flings open the door. "Explain. Inside. Immediately."

We trail her to the kitchen, where Slack is just where we left him. There is an apple core, orange and banana peels, and grape stems in a tidy pile on the table. He seems perfectly content, grinning at us as we enter.

"Did you find it?" he asks. His eyes latch on to the book. "*What* did you do to it?"

"It was an accident!" I clutch it to my chest so he can't grab it. If he does, it will surely disintegrate. "Is there another copy?"

Slack looks at me like I sprouted an extra head. "I didn't think I'd need two copies!" he shrieks.

"Everyone, quiet!" demands Mom. She puts her nose practically to mine. "Start the explaining part."

"He just showed up here!" blurts Joe, gesturing to Slack, who only has eyes for the soggy diary.

"He may have escaped from the FBI," I add.

"And he said the diary had important information that could help Albert," Joe continues.

"He just couldn't remember what it was," I say.

"So we went to the Starlight," Joe says.

"To get the copy of the diary that Slack made after he stole the original and ruined it."

"Do you two tell all your stories this way now?" Mom asks. "In tandem?" I throw a look at Joe, who shrugs. Yes. Yes, we do. "Go on."

Albert picks this moment to emerge from my pocket,

yawning and stretching. All over again, he's not happy to see Slack.

Be good, Albert!

"How about some treats?" I say, hoping to distract him. Albert plops his tiny butt on the ground and waits. As soon as I put the diary down to fetch the treats, Slack grabs it up, and without exercising any caution, he flings it open and starts flipping madly through the pages. Joe yells that he's going to ruin it. Albert jumps in the air. I shout at Joe to stop yelling. Slack barks that the diary belongs to *him*, and Mom bellows that we should all just be quiet.

It gets moderately out of hand until the moment Slack pulls free a page taped to the inside cover of the book. It is a photocopy of an entry from Edward Tenbrook's *actual* diary. Edward Tenbrook, friend of Alvina, daughter of Vayne. "I wanted to preserve a sample of Edward's handwriting," Slack explains. "It can tell you so much about a person."

This pretty much shuts us up. Mom moves in behind Slack and so does Joe, focus glued to the page. I slide in next to them. Edward's handwriting is loopy and uneven, broad and exuberant. Just from his letters, I imagine Edward was bold and fearless, even when life overwhelmed him. Slack's handwriting, on the other hand, is tight and controlled and small and precise. He continues to turn pages until he is close to the end. The ink is faded, and the paper's edges are swollen with water.

"Where is the important information?" Joe asks.

"I'm getting there," Slack responds.

"You are taking a long time," Joe snaps.

"Patience," Slack says, adding a *tsk-tsk* that does not go over well with Joe.

Finally, after what seems like an eternity, Slack jabs a page with his finger.

"Here," he says triumphantly. "This is what I was thinking about!"

"Read it already," Joe urges.

"Might I have a glass of water before I begin?" Slack requests. "My mouth is a bit dry."

Boy, Slack really knows how to draw things out. I jump up, fill a glass halfway, and slam it down in front of him. Water sloshes all over, but the notebook is already waterlogged, so I'm not too worried.

"Read!" I command.

Chapter 17

THE PROPHECY, REVISITED

SLACK SLURPS SOME WATER and clears his throat. "Let me preface this by mentioning that Edward Tenbrook was not the most straightforward of writers. He certainly could have been clearer. But he does mention that communication was a challenge because he and Alvina did not speak each other's language."

"Hurry up!" Joe and I shout at the same time. Slack jumps a little in his chair, offering us a wounded look, and returns to the page.

"'I continue to meet Alvina on the mossy hill in the forest,'" Slack reads. I think he is doing a weird interpretation of what he thinks Edward would sound like. It isn't working, but if I interrupt him, who knows how long it will take to get the guy back on track? I stay quiet. He continues to read. "'It does not matter how many times we meet. I am always surprised to see her. A dragon! A real dragon! My friend, the real dragon. When she first made me understand she had run away from her tyrannical father, Vayne, King of the Dragons, I did not know what to do with her story. I still don't. Her family belongs to the dragon-ruling class, the Silvers. The Silvers hold all the power and wealth. Silvers have everything while the others have nothing. Their grip on power is unbreakable, as it has been for eternity.'"

"Are these the critical details?" Joe interrupts.

"Be patient," Slack replies, obviously irritated. "I'm getting there." He continues on with reading. "'Today, I finally worked up the nerve to ask Alvina why she had come here. Although I had to act out my question, she quickly understood and grew agitated, breathing out a plume of fire and accidentally singeing my eyebrows. But I remained steadfast and did not flinch. And soon she helped me understand the event that drove her to my mossy hill.

"'*It is a prophecy.*

"'This is how it goes, I think. Although I might be wrong on the finer details. 'On an ordinary, nothing kind of day, the royal oracle arrived unexpectedly at the royal dragon lair.'"

"Is that like the dragon castle?" Joe interrupts again. "Where the fancy dragons live?"

"Is it possible for you to think something and not say it aloud?" Slack asks.

"Well, *is* it?" I demand.

"Yes," Slack responds. "But from what I understand, a lair is more like a series of platforms built into the trees and cliffs. There are underground tunnels, too, sort of like catacombs, for storing loot and food and things. Dragons would have no use for a proper castle with walls. It would make no sense. May I continue now?"

We nod. He finds his place on the page. "'The arrival of the oracle was cause for great concern, as the oracle was not known for spontaneity. But her message was urgent, and she wasted no time in bringing it to the king himself. The oracle foresaw the end of the Silvers' reign of power. Her vision showed the ruling class overthrown and driven to ruin by a dragon marked with a golden blaze who would bring to bear the power of *two*.' A golden blaze! The power of two!'" Slack raises his eyes, triumphant. "It is exactly as I thought! Critically important information!"

Huh? "I don't get it," I say flatly. Slack waves off my confusion.

"Pay attention," he admonishes. "'This dragon will travel great distances and overcome many challenges. And there will be a mighty storm. This storm will protect the warrior dragon from malevolent forces.

"'Chaos will follow the downfall. In the vacuum, a new power will rise, a benevolent leader who gives everyone a voice, even to those downtrodden who have given up. This leader will have love in their heart rather than greed or selfishness or anger. They will be brilliant, a bright light to all, a promise of a better future.'"

Slack narrows his gaze. "Do you *still* not get it?"

"No!" we shout in unison.

"I always assumed that the power of *two* was a quirky translation, that it just meant a supercharged dragon. Already this marked dragon had to be extra powerful to overthrow Vayne, so of course it made sense that he would have the strength of two dragons. Are you with me so far?"

"Sort of," Mom says, forehead creased.

"But what my subconscious was trying to sort out all along is that this is *not* about individual dragon power but more about . . . *help*." Slack's eyes flash. "I suddenly remembered the power of friendship and how it can make you feel so much stronger and better than when you are alone, like you can do things you couldn't do before."

Mom pats him on the shoulder. "We still don't get what you are saying, but it's nice that you have some clarity on friendship."

"What I *mean* is that Albert is not meant to do this alone. He is *meant* to have a partner. A dragon friend. Someone to help him with his mission. If he attempts to fulfill the prophecy alone, he will fail. The words are the same. I just needed to change my point of view to see a different meaning! Isn't that wonderful?"

I remember flying with Albert over the treetops on the way to Mercy Grove the first time, right before we sent him back through the rip. I had never seen the trees from that vantage before, and they looked completely different. But the trees themselves had not changed; only my point of view had. Is this what Slack means? After getting zapped with Albert's sleeping gas, his brain started to see things in a different way. I like this idea, that as situations change, so does our understanding of them.

I think this is what Mom means when she says something is in a "gray area." But more importantly, I don't want Albert to do this alone. Of all the ideas, and there are many, that one terrifies me the most.

"Do you think that the prophecy means we are going to Midhurst to find this other dragon?" I ask. "A dragon that is meant to help Albert on his mission?"

"Midhurst?" Mom asks.

Oh. Right. We explain the how Albert dragged us to the library this morning and we think he wants us to visit Midhurst, Oregon. "He confirmed it with eye blinks," I say.

"The eye blinks were my idea," Joe adds.

"A *really* good idea," I confirm.

"Eye blinks? Oregon?" My mother glances at Slack. "Do you have any idea what they are talking about, or am I the only one without a clue?"

"No idea," says Slack, popping a grape into his mouth.

"Joe figured out that Albert can answer yes-or-no questions with eye blinks, and he basically said we need to go to Midhurst, Oregon," I repeat, slowly, so she gets it.

"To the dragon festival," Joe adds.

"The *what*?" she asks.

"Dragon festival," Joe repeats.

"It might be where it all comes together," I say.

"It makes sense," he says. "A journey, challenges, storms. All that stuff. It fits. Albert uses the clue to help him find what he needs in Midhurst. And *maybe* that is another dragon."

Joe offers me a high five and I slap his hand. *Yes!*

Or not? Mom sighs, a wrinkle of concern forming

between her eyes. "We are pretty much broke, Cassie. The house is in shambles. Sheldon Slack is eating all the fruit. And you two want a spontaneous trip to a dragon festival in Midhurst because it might be related to . . . something?"

I recognize the need to do something here, and fast. "I don't need the phone you promised," I blurt. "And we can skip Christmas."

"And I'll sell my baseball hat collection," Joe adds.

Mom sighs and rubs her eyes. When she opens them, Albert is sitting at her feet. He taps her shoelaces to get her attention, and when he does, he simply stares up at her, eyes wide and unblinking. Imploring, somehow. She cannot look away. The seconds tick by. No one moves. Even Slack pauses midbite of an apple.

When the connection is broken, Mom says, "Fine. We'll go to Midhurst. I will figure it out."

And Albert adds an appreciative little "mew."

Chapter 18

MIDHURST

JOE'S GRANDMOTHER is more than happy to give Mom permission to take him with us to the Midhurst Dragon Festival. His family is out touring colleges, and his grandmother explains she has cooking to do in preparation for the Thanksgiving holiday, so she is pleased someone else will take responsibility for Joe having fun. Besides, if she had said no, Joe would have stuffed himself in the trunk of the car. No way he was missing out on this next chapter of our dragon tale. Unthinkable!

It's Miss Asher's car, but Mom drives because Miss Asher is still working on figuring out if the symbol from the tracing means anything useful. She is literally squished into her seat beside the many books she just *had* to bring along. She does not look comfortable, but she does not look like she cares that much, either.

It's a three-hour drive to Midhurst from Lewiston. The route travels inland over the mountain range and then due north. I worry that Albert won't be able to hold his pee for that long, and cats are not like dogs. You can't just pull into a rest stop and take them for a walk, can you? As a precaution, I toss a roll of paper towels in the trunk. Miss Asher's car is new and shiny, and I just don't think she will appreciate Albert peeing on it, even if he is a very special cat.

As soon as we are driving, Joe pops in his headphones and vanishes into a digital world that I have no ticket to enter. Mom has promised me a phone of my own but has not had time nor money to get it yet, so instead, I look out the window and narrate for Albert, who is curled up on my lap, what I see. But in my head, of course. Don't want to be totally annoying.

There are a lot of trees. I mean, not super interesting because there are a lot of trees in Lewiston, but it's just trees, trees, trees as far as the eye can see. Remember when you flew me and Joe up to Mercy Grove? That was wild, seeing all the trees from above like that. They were the same but not. I like how something that is absolute can still be so many things at once, you know? Like, it is what it is, but depending on how you look at it, it can seem completely different.

Albert's eyes pop open. I can't tell if he's mad that I interrupted his nap or that I'm rambling, not so much describing the scene rushing by the car window as editorializing on it. Can he even hear my thoughts? Do I sound like an idiot? Is he rolling his eyes but I just can't see it? *Oh boy.* I lean over and tap Joe on the shoulder. His head jerks toward me as if he forgot I was there.

"What are you doing?" I ask.

He pulls out an earbud headphone. "What? Huh?"

"What are you listening to?"

He removes the other headphone. "Just listening to a podcast about Venus. The planet. Did you know the temperature is hot enough to melt lead? And it's covered with volcanoes?"

This is Joe we're talking about, so I'm not surprised. Had he said he was playing Candy Crush, now, that would have surprised me.

"Venus is indeed fascinating," says Slack.

Oh, did I forget to mention that wedged between me and Joe in the back seat is Sheldon Slack? Well, there you go. Slack, too, was keen to see what happened next in the evolving dragon story. He begged and pleaded and said that if we left him behind he would surely be snatched up by the FBI and disappeared forever. While in normal circumstances, this tale of woe might sound exaggerated and dramatic, in this case, he was almost certainly right. Plus, Slack is a treasure trove of dragon lore, having been marinating in it for years. He is the one who suggested that dragons hiding as cats made perfect sense because they are so similar. He then went on to list all the many ways that dragons and cats overlapped, physically and personality-wise, to the point where it started to sound true to me.

The fact that Slack has no luggage helped his cause, too, and now he sits squished between me and Joe because that was part of the deal. He could come, but he had to ride in the middle.

And he must have been willing to do anything because he didn't even argue that he is at least six inches taller than Miss Asher and therefore should have the front seat. Not that she would have given it to him, but still, he could have tried. It's not exactly roomy in the back, shoulder to shoulder as we are, and Slack keeps shooting furtive glances at Albert on my lap, as if he's afraid Albert might transform and explode the car.

Albert, don't turn dragon, okay?

I'm sure he is aware, but it doesn't hurt to remind him.

I suspect that sometimes when he is startled or afraid, it just happens. I rub my dragon-cat between the ears and he purrs, pushing his head into my palm. There is something soothing about his purring, like it syncs up with my heart and paces it at a nice, calm rhythm.

I love you, Albert.

He doesn't answer, just rumbles away in my lap, content as can be. My mind drifts to the diary entry Slack read us. Is he right about another dragon? Is it something else? Will it be a dragon-cat? I wish I had a phone. We could watch cat videos on YouTube. Albert loves cat videos, especially the ones of cats riding around on vacuuming robots. He can watch them over and over again, ears curved forward, whiskers twitching, completely mesmerized. He is very easy to amuse.

"Excuse me, Ellen?" Slack asks politely, interrupting my jumble of thoughts. "Might we stop for a bathroom break?" They are so formal with each other, it is hard to believe they were ever best friends. Miss Asher glances at Slack in the rearview mirror and offers up her crisp, no-nonsense, all-business smile. It's the one she reserves for people at the library who are really getting on her nerves, like when they use books for coasters and stuff.

"Sure," she replies evenly. "The next opportunity."

Right there in the back seat, I make a silent vow never to let my friendship with Joe reach this place, a tense, icy, awkward dance where both parties cannot wait for the music to end.

Chapter 19

THE GREAT ANNUAL DRAGON FESTIVAL

MIDHURST IS SIX THOUSAND FEET above sea level, nestled in the long shadow of the dormant volcano Midhurst Mountain and several other ancient volcanic peaks. A ribbon of shimmering blue river cuts through the heart of town. I can imagine in the hot summer months the cold and glossy water dotted with people in rafts doing a lazy float. We have to drive a big loop around downtown because the dragon festival is in full swing. Even with the windows up, the sound of people gathering and having fun is unmistakable.

We pull up in front of a shabby yellow house. Mom says

we were lucky to get anything last minute as the entire world seems to have converged on Midhurst for this festival and lodging was in short supply.

"Who knew people were so into dragons?" Mom muses. I step out of the car onto a carpet of brittle pine needles, fallen from the tall trees that fill my nose with their scent. The air here is dry and thin. In Lewiston, every inhale is damp with the ocean. This is the complete opposite.

And there is sun! A glorious yellow orb hangs in the sky, bathing us in light. We are usually some degree of soggy, so I wonder if we might start to steam as we heat up. That would be something to see. Pulling off my jacket, I close my eyes and invite the warmth to soak into my skin. It feels so good. Albert pops out of my pocket, his nose twitching with all the new smells. He leaps to the ground and scatters a heap of leaves every which way.

There is a winding path to the front door of the house. But running up it leaves me winded.

"It's the altitude," says Mom, entering a code to unlock the door. "You don't get as much oxygen up here, so your body must learn to be more efficient. We are spoiled with it in Lewiston."

I never really considered plentiful oxygen as a gift, but maybe I should be more grateful for Lewiston. Or not.

Albert seems fine, scampering along at my feet, batting at the leaves and twigs and stopping once to chase his own tail. While I know somewhere in his cat body is a dragon, he still seems so *cat*. He bounds up the stairs and plants himself in the open doorway. His eyes narrow and his ears push forward in annoyance. We are not moving fast enough for him. Whatever we are meant to be doing, he'd like us to get going.

On the dining room table, the owners of the cottage have kindly left us a stack of dragon festival information because clearly no one comes to Midhurst for any other reason. We spread out the flyers and brochures. Albert has been exactly no help in narrowing down *specifically* what we are here to do, even if his sense of urgency is palpable. That part is clearly up to us. Mom, being Mom, doles out sandwiches to help us focus.

I lay out the symbol that Albert brought through the rip. Albert sits right next to it, looking expectant. Slack, who has never seen it before, bends in for a closer look. "This is what he brought through the rip? What is it?"

Well, if we knew that, we wouldn't be sitting here, would we?

"We don't know," Miss Asher says. "Does it mean anything to you?" Slack is so close to the tracing now, he could blow his nose in it. Finally, he leans back and takes a deep inhale.

"Nope. No idea." The energy in the room goes flat. Why did we let him come along again?

"Maybe we just go to the festival and see if we can find any evidence of anything that looks like this dragon tail?" Mom suggests.

Miss Asher grimaces. "It's a dragon festival. There are going to be hundreds of tails."

"I think we will know it when we see it," Slack suggests. Miss Asher shoots him an unkind look, like his mere existence is aggravating her. I'm glad he doesn't notice.

"I agree," Mom says. "If we see it, we will know." She glances at Albert. "How does that sound, kitty cat?" He blinks once. Great. Our plan is to wander around clueless. At least it is a plan with which I have some experience.

Mom instructs us to eat our sandwiches and put on our shoes. "We have work to do," she says.

The shabby rental is very shabby, but it is also within walking distance of the downtown core, where the festival action is. Even with people running around in dragon costumes, downtown Midhurst is way cuter than downtown Lewiston. But it might be because I'm dazzled by all the sunshine.

"I wish I owned sunglasses," Joe says, squinting under his baseball cap.

"I just never considered it," I reply.

"Let's go to college someplace sunny and warm," he suggests.

"That is my plan," I say. I hold a hand up to shield my eyes, and we push on down the sidewalk, blinded by the light, in search of dragon tails.

Chapter 20

FOX AND DANA
GO TO MIDHURST

AS EXPECTED, the bosses were not happy to hear Slack went missing even when Fox explained they had found him again. They were given twenty-four hours to resolve the dragon case; otherwise their orders were to return to headquarters. Not willing to risk losing track of Slack, Fox and Dana bypass a stop to pick up even a toothbrush and arrive in Midhurst with nothing more than the clothes on their backs. No big deal. Fox once wore the same pair of pants for twenty-one days while chasing a yeti in the Himalayas, where the FBI had no business being in the first place.

Are they surprised to find Midhurst overrun with people in dragon costumes? Nope. In fact, it fits perfectly. Of *course* there is a giant dragon festival going on!

"I want to say something smart about this festival," Dana says, "but I don't know what that would be. Do you think they really drove up here for this? Like, just to have fun because school is out and they are really into dragons?"

Fox reminds her that this festival has nothing to do with real dragons. And even if it did, they are here to watch Slack and the kids and see what happens next. Much of the work they do in Project Analog involves waiting. It can be quite dull at times, truth be told. Sitting in their car outside the shabby little rental house, Fox picks at her cuticles. Dana twirls her hair.

When the silence gets too much, Dana asks, "Any guesses on why they are here?"

Only a new agent would ask such a thing. Fox's old partner told her very early on that guessing in their line of work will only lead to disappointment and confusion. "Nothing is as it seems," he told her. "When you guess, you are coming from a deep well of cluelessness. This is because there is so much we don't understand and probably never will. Which means your guess is always going to be wrong."

Fox has never forgotten those words, but they have time to kill, as surveillance is super dull. Might as well indulge in random theories.

"They plan to throw themselves into a volcano," Fox suggests. After all, they are sitting right beneath one, the majestic Midhurst Mountain, with several others looming on the horizon.

"Like a sacrifice?" Dana asks with complete seriousness.

"No," Fox says flatly. "Why do *you* think they are here?"

"I think it is all to do with Slack," she replies. "I think he knows something he didn't tell us."

"He didn't tell us *anything*," Fox reminds her. "Remember, he could barely recall his own name?"

"What if that was an act? Or his memories came back? Or . . . I don't know . . . something."

Fox wonders for a flash if Dana's desire for concrete answers, for explanations that make sense, will eventually drive her from Project Analog to bank robberies or cybercrime or something more concrete. It's possible. But before Fox can formulate a response, the whole crew, including Slack, tumbles out of the shabby rental and onto the sidewalk.

"Oh, *thank* the powers that be," Dana blurts. "If I don't get out of this car and stretch my legs, they are going to *fall* off."

And just like that, they are back on the dragon trail.

Chapter 21

A NEEDLE IN A HAYSTACK OF DRAGONS

I STOP EVERY half block to turn my face toward the sun, like a flower in the early morning. Albert rides along in my pocket with his head out, eyes closed, whiskers still, soaking up the rays into his dark fuzzy coat. All the stopping gets on Joe's nerves.

"We are never going to find what we are looking for if you keep sunbathing," he snaps.

"Not sunbathing," I reply. "Sun-*absorbing*. I'm storing up for later. Like a sponge."

"That's not possible," he says.

"How do you know?"

"Science?"

"Fine, but it feels good."

"Cassie, come *on*!"

"Okay! Okay!"

Scanning every festival-goer, every vendor, every shopwindow, for something that we can't exactly define is giving me whiplash. Is that it? No. Is this it? Nope. Over there? Not a chance. We do see some pretty great costumes, embroidered with thousands of sequins and bedazzled with crystals and tulle. Main Street is shut down and dragons dance along the pavement to a vibrating bass line. The music is loud enough I can feel it through the soles of my shoes. We walk up and down all the streets. We even take a turn past the boat docks where a crowd gathers. Nothing. Nada. We expand our circle to the area just outside the main festival action, but other than some cute shops and people sitting in outdoor cafés enjoying themselves, there is nothing noteworthy.

We stop at a kiosk selling dragon brew, AKA hot chocolate with whipped cream. Mom buys for Slack because the FBI confiscated his wallet. It's delicious, but that's about it. I begin to despair. We are never going to find what it is Albert sent us here to find. I slump against a storefront, sloshing a little hot chocolate on my shirt. Joe leans up beside me.

"Do you think Albert meant to sit on Midhurst on the map? Maybe it was just the moment he got tired, and the festival is just a coincidence."

"What are the chances?" I reply.

"I know. Zero percent, pretty much. But still. Don't you feel like we are missing something?"

I can't argue with him. That feeling is strong. Whatever we are supposed to see or find *has* to be here. But where?

Mom, Miss Asher, and Slack huddle up, heads together, no doubt brainstorming what to do next. Slack stands under a green-and-yellow flag advertising the name of a store. It catches the breeze and tangles around his head. He swats it away. This happens repeatedly. Just move already!

As if reading my mind, Miss Asher takes him by the arm and pulls him out from under the flag. And when she does, the flag, still clinging to Slack, unfurls.

"Cassie," Joe whispers, eyes pinned on the flag. "Are you seeing what I'm seeing?"

Oh yes, I am. It's a flag advertising a rare and unique books shop, right around the corner, down a narrow alley.

And the store is called Dragon Tales.

Albert leans out of my pocket, suddenly alert, whiskers twitching, tail swishing, eyes focused.

"Mom! You guys!" I shout above the thumping music. "Look." I point down the alley toward the bright green-and-yellow awning bearing the name of the store.

"Okay. Wow," Miss Asher says, breathless. We creep down the alley as if we might somehow be caught in the act of doing something naughty, approaching the store tentatively.

The window display is full of books, all of which look old and dusty. There are none of the fun new and colorful ones like Miss Asher has in her library.

Slack presses his nose up to the glass. "Oh my," he breathes. "Will you look at that?" He points to a book on display with a red leather cover and a gold-embossed image of a redwood tree. "It's the same journal that the original diary was written it. The redwood journal maker!"

"What are the chances?" Mom says, pressing in next to Slack to stare at the book.

"About two percent," Joe responds, gazing inside.

"It really should not be sitting here in the window in direct sunlight," Slack says, brows furrowed. "It is quite valuable and should be in a climate-controlled environment."

"Just like the diary?" Joe asks, unable to stop himself.

"You will never let me live that down, will you?" asks Slack.

"Never," Joe replies.

I peer into the gloomy store, trying to focus my eyes on the dark interior, when suddenly there is a face pressed up to the glass on the other side, nose to nose with me.

"Aaah!" I yelp and jump back, crashing right into Joe. It's a man. He's super old and so wrinkled, he looks like that shriveled-up apple left behind in the fruit bowl.

And in his arms, he holds a silver cat.

Chapter 22

DRAGON TALES

THE CAT FIXES her glowing amber eyes on us. Comfortably cradled in the old man's arms, her tail twitches just enough so we know she is watching. Albert gives a pathetic little "mew" and tucks his head back in my pocket. It's part of the misinformed "if I can't see it, it isn't there" magical thinking of cats.

"It's okay, Albert," I whisper. "She's not going to hurt you." Honestly, I have no idea if this is true, but it feels like the right thing to say.

"We should go in," Miss Asher says quietly. "Right?"

"Yes," Mom responds. "Of course. It's a bookstore. What's the worst that could happen?"

Oh, Mom. That is the sort of thing you say when you don't have dragons in your life. You have a lot to learn.

Miss Asher takes a deep breath and pulls open the door. A small bell chimes overhead. The shop smells musty and dry, like old books. The man remains in the window, backlit by the sun, face obscured by shadow. The cat tracks us as we squish into the store. Slack has gone terribly pale, appearing to lean on the doorjamb to keep from collapsing to the ground. Joe grips my arm. As my eyes adjust to the low light, I take in a crowded room, with bookshelves groaning under too much weight. There's an overstuffed faded green velvet couch in one corner, sagging in the middle and covered in cat fur. A few other hard wooden chairs are scattered among the shelves. An old-fashioned cash register sits on a glass counter, thick with dust. It's as if no one has come into this store in years.

"Welcome to Dragon Tales," the old man says after a long quiet moment. Up close, his face is like a grooved walnut shell. His eyes, which might have been blue or green at some point, are watery and clouded. His flannel shirt is frayed at the neck, and his blue jeans thin and soft at the knees. On his feet are fuzzy bunny slippers, strange but also somehow fitting. He eyes us, his lips pressed into a thin tight line.

The silver cat jumps free of his arms. She's big and fluffy and round, and she comes right to me, plopping down at my feet and scanning me with those eyes.

"That's Ali," the old man says, gesturing toward the cat. "She's my protector and dearest friend."

Protector? That is a strange choice of words for a twelve-pound animal. Is he trying to tell us that Ali is really a dragon? Is she the one Albert is meant to team up with to save the dragon world? More importantly, how does one go about asking for clarification?

Fortunately, I have Joe, who never met a question he didn't want to ask. "Like, she guards the shop?" he asks. We collectively hold our breath. Dust, illuminated by sunbeams, floats in the air.

"In a way," he replies. "But she also looks after me." He watches Ali watch me. "She either likes you or you smell like fish." He speaks with a cadence that feels as old-fashioned as the cash register. "She's keen on tuna."

I really hope I don't smell like tuna. That would be humiliating. And my guess is Ali smells Albert and not me.

"Now, is there something I can help you with on this fine Midhurst day?" the old man asks. "Are you in the market for a used book? Something old, perhaps?"

Okay, we probably should have taken a moment to figure out our story before we barged in here, right? I mean, how exactly do we explain ourselves and what we are doing here? Major oversight. This is Joe's fault. I rely on him to think things through while it is my job to just plow forward. I glance at him. He looks like a deer in the headlights, frozen. *Great.* What we need is a diversion so we can get our bearings, look around, and maybe figure out *why* we are here.

And who should come to our rescue? Why, Slack, of course. Wow. The world really is upside down. He steps forward and smiles. It's not even the usual creepy smile that reminds me of a vampire. This is an almost-regular smile. Or maybe I'm just getting used to him. That is equally disturbing.

"I see you have a redwood journal in the window," Slack says. "I had one once. My research suggested it was quite rare. And unusual. Might I see it?"

The old man studies Slack, as if trying to take his measure. Slack, for his part, does not seem to notice. He keeps on smiling while the rest of us just stand back like giant dorks, doing nothing. "I like a person who knows his books," the old man says finally. He leans deep into the bay window and pulls out the journal Slack was referencing, blowing a cloud of dust from its cover. Slack gingerly takes it from his hands. Other than the dust, it appears to be in pretty good shape. Slack flips it open, revealing the intricate illustration of a towering redwood on the first page.

"Extraordinary," Slack whispers, holding it up to Miss Asher. She is right by his side. It is the closest I've seen them get to each other since this whole dragon thing started.

"Amazing," Miss Asher concurs.

"Is it okay if we look around?" I blurt.

"We love books," Joe adds.

"Especially old ones," Mom says. That's not true. I like new books, but I don't think that is important right now.

"Of course," the man says, gesturing for us to go deeper into the store. Ali comes along, entangled with my feet to the point where I almost step on her. Albert stays completely hidden, which is surprising because he never misses an opportunity to be disruptive. Is he afraid of Ali? She is rather impressive, with large tufted ears and a long tail that reminds me of a snow leopard I saw once on a television show. I wrap my hands around Albert in my pocket. I want to ask him to please tell me if this cat is actually a dragon and the reason we are here, but when I try to remove him from my pocket, he clings with all his claws. Great. He will need a moment to get it together.

"Eyes up," Mom whispers. We each take a different aisle and move slowly down them. There are a lot of books. They are all old. None of them look particularly interesting. I mean, nothing I want to actually read. I run my fingers along their spines, creating a little cloud of dust in my wake. Nothing jumps out at me. Nothing seems out of the ordinary. I pull on Albert, and he clings harder.

You're a dragon! Come on! Be brave!

Ali does not take her eyes from me for a moment. Actually, she is staring directly at my hoodie pocket. She knows Albert is in there. We are fooling no one, at least not the felines.

Okay. Fine. I will do it myself. In the softest voice I can manage, I whisper to Ali, "Are you a dragon?" Ali raises her eyes to meet mine, and in them, I see . . . nothing. They are unusual amethyst cat eyes, but there is no recognition that she understands what I'm asking. Maybe I *do* smell like tuna. That is so not okay!

"So you're *not* a dragon?" I ask. Maybe she is just as the old man said, a cat to keep him company. Ali returns her attention to the pocket. She really wants Albert to show himself, but he still clings like lint. I remember the stray we encountered when we were hiding out in the park that time and how scared Albert was of her, even though at the time he was in dragon form. It's possible my dragon is afraid of cats. This is kind of funny, not that I want to make Albert feel bad. All feelings are real, even if they don't make sense.

I'm thinking about dragons being afraid of cats when Ali starts to meow. And she's got lungs.

"Meow! Mrrrr-ow! Owwww! Rruh!"

"Whatever I did," I yelp, "I'm sorry!"

"Grrr! Mrrr-owww! Grrrr!" Ali's tail fluffs up. Her ears flatten. I have not been a cat companion for very long, but I know this is a displeased look. Ali is mad at me.

Or maybe not me. Albert suddenly peaks his head out, just barely.

"Meep?" Albert's voice is small and timid.

"Mrrreeee!" Whatever he just said, Ali is not satisfied. "Hssssss!" She bares a little bit of fang to make her point.

"Mew." I would give anything to understand what they are saying! Albert jumps down from my pocket and sits down in front of Ali.

"Rrak!"

"Waaoooh!" It's a guttural sound from Albert, something I have never heard before. But honestly, I have never heard most of these sounds. Albert just isn't that chatty unless there is food on the line. Joe, drawn by the sound, appears silently behind me, as do the others, including the old man. "Waaaaooooooh!"

"Meow. Mreep." At least Ali isn't hissing and growling at him anymore. Albert lies down and covers his head with his paws, in full submission. Or maybe he doesn't like what she is telling him.

The cat conversation goes on for a few more rounds. And the old man, right at my shoulder, leans in and whispers, "Why don't you tell me why you are really here?"

Chapter 23

FOX AND DANA
ARE ON THE CASE

FOX AND DANA ABANDON the car and set out on foot, keeping a discreet distance behind their marks in the growing crowd of dragon festival people. Losing Slack for a second time is not an option.

"Do you think they have a plan?" Dana asks. "Or are they just going to wander around all day?"

Fox shrugs. Right now, it looks like wandering around might be it.

"I have a question," Dana continues. "If we just grab Slack and force him to tell us where the dragon is, what happens?"

"Everyone notices, Slack included," Fox replies. "And then we have to pull out badges and explain ourselves, and things quickly get complicated."

"So not an option?"

"No!"

"Okay!" Dana replies, throwing up her hands defensively. "I just want to know what he knows. What they know. It's kind of driving me crazy."

"Ninety-five percent of this job is patience," Fox lectures.

"I *know* that," Dana snaps. "You tell me that *all* the time."

"That is because it is true."

In all the back-and-forth, Fox and Dana lose track of Slack and friends. This brings on a wave of panic until they spot them at the mouth of an alley. A flag flies above Cassie's head, a flag with a giant dragon tail on it. It's advertising the name of a bookstore. Dana shakes her head. "Dragon Tales?" she replies. "For real? This town is obsessed."

The group turns down the alley. Fox and Dana lag at the corner, and Fox takes a moment to regret not having a costume. They look weird in their dark suits and shiny shoes. Nobody around here wears a suit, like, *ever*.

Fox nudges Dana. "Look, they are going into the store."

"Is this why they came here?" Dana asks in a rush. "Can we count this as progress?"

"Maybe?"

"Now what?"

"We watch. And wait."

"No chance we can just bust in there and demand to know what is going on?" Dana asks hopefully.

"None," Fox replies. Dana sighs and leans up against the wall of a building.

And they wait.

Chapter 24

A CONFESSION

IN A SPLIT SECOND, I run through a range of possible answers, including I'm a huge fan of dusty old books to I am traveling with a librarian who insists we visit every single bookstore, none of which are very good. I'm about to say that we were just in the neighborhood, when Ali stretches out a paw and bops Albert on the head. Unprovoked!

What happens next is complete pandemonium. Albert rears up, hissing and spitting, puffed up like a bad hair day. His eyes go instantly red. Oh no!

"Albert!" I yell. But it is too late. They are off. Albert races toward the front of the store, defying gravity by charging up the sides of the bookshelves, just like a snow-boarder on the half-pipe, to avoid Ali, in quick pursuit, and her long claws. Ali howls. Albert banks in a tight curve around the end of the bookshelf and leaps to the relative safety of the cash register counter. But Ali is no slouch. She is hot on his tail, and I mean, she is literally about to get it in her teeth. Sensing her proximity, Albert hurls himself into the air, bounces off the saggy old sofa, and flies to the top of a shelving unit.

Mom, Miss Asher, and Slack stand, mouths gaping, watching the show. As if she is climbing a tree, Ali scales the bookshelf. Albert gingerly makes his way across the top shelf of books, just ahead of Ali. When he reaches the far side, he turns to face his pursuer. His eyes are blazing red, and he growls, low and rumbling.

"Albert!" I yell before I can stop myself. "No dragon! Not okay!"

"Did you say *dragon*?" The old man's runny eyes fix on my face. From his perch, Albert glares down. Ali is a foot away, ears flat, hissing wildly, whiskers vibrating. Great. This is just great.

"Excuse me? I said what?" I reply, trying to dodge, just like Albert.

"Specifically 'no dragon, not okay,'" he replies. Uh-oh.

Now I've done it. The old man snaps his fingers. Ali goes instantly quiet, sitting back on her haunches and cleaning her face as if the cat circus never happened. She doesn't even glance at Albert. What? Ali is a *trained* cat? How does that even work? The old man takes in our ragtag group. Me, Mom, Miss Asher, Slack, and Joe.

"Now is the time you tell what you are up to," he suggests. "Because I don't think it is for book shopping."

"It's a long story," I squeak.

"I have time," he says. "All the time in the world, actually. I have *forever*. You shall begin."

This sounds suspiciously like an order. I glance at my crew. Mom shrugs. It's her "what do we have to lose" shrug. We have come all this way to find the symbol, and now we have. So what happens next? What does it mean? One thing is becoming clear, and that is bringing the old man into our story might be the only way to find out.

Sensing my hesitancy, he gestures toward the old sofa and the chairs. "Please. Sit. I have cookies. Ali, if you would be so kind." Without missing a beat, Ali leaps from the top shelf to the ground and settles in right at the old man's feet. Albert peers down at her, his ears pressed forward in confusion. He was just having a very fine war and now his adversary bailed out! Not fair. But I'm relieved to see his eyes melt back to their mossy-green color.

I clear my throat. "Albert, come down, please." Not being a trained cat, he turns his back on me and commences cleaning his tail. How embarrassing. The old man raises a single eyebrow in my direction. I feel judged.

The old man slips off to the back of the store, returning moments later with a pot of tea and a tray of cookies. There are mint Milanos, my favorite. I help myself to two right away because they are also Joe's favorite, and he can eat a whole bag in a hot minute. The old man pours tea, and everyone waits for someone else to start the conversation. Ali purrs loudly in the old man's lap. He does not eat any cookies, but he watches me shove one in my mouth, and his eyebrow twitches up yet again. More judging. Jeez. This guy.

"Dragons," he says finally. "They are all the rage here in Midhurst, as you can see. People claim they used to inhabit these mountains, and perhaps still do, rising from the volcanos at night to decimate the local sheep herds. The dragon mythology is so strong, in fact, that we are subject to this ridiculous festival every year. It is very loud. And messy. And does not include many folks who collect old books. They see the name of the store and come in, believing I have dragon *swag*. Madness! Shall we discuss?"

"We know nothing about dragons," Joe blurts, spraying cookie crumbs all over the place. "We are on an educational trip to Midhurst to learn about . . . volcanos." He smiles, pleased with his answer. It's pretty good, but the old man is not buying it. He moves Ali to the space beside him and crosses his legs, resting one bunny-slippered foot on his knee.

"Like I said, we can do this forever, because I have the time, but I suspect a certain member of your party is impatient." He glances over his left shoulder to where Albert now perches at the edge of the high bookshelf, peering down at us. His eyes are latched on to the old man. It's true that Albert is impatient, but he is about everything. He goes positively out of his mind when it's meal time. But I take the old man's meaning. Albert has been urging us forward since his unexpected arrival. He's on a mission. We just don't know the details.

"You're right about that," I say quietly, glancing around the small circle. The man looks only at me. Something in his expression makes it clear I have to tell him the truth, that maybe the reason we are here at all is to do just *that*.

He can *help* us. "Go ahead, Cassie," Joe urges. "Tell him."

I gesture to Albert, still on the top shelf. "That's Albert," I say. "He's a dragon. A real one."

Chapter 25

IMPOSSIBLE!

I THINK ALBERT GRINS when I say he's a dragon. Can cats smile? Or maybe he's grimacing? Or maybe one of his whiskers caught some dust? But I take his face to mean I should go on, even if it's really only dust.

"A dragon," I repeat. "He can turn into one, although we don't totally understand the ins and outs of that yet."

"There's always smoke and wild weather, too," Joe adds. "Storms and stuff. We think Albert makes it happen when he turns from a cat to a dragon or when he comes through the rip. That's a doorway to another dimension, just FYI."

"We found him in a dumpster," I continue.

"Boy, did that dumpster stink."

"It really did. I know because I was in it. Anyway, we took Albert home."

"I named him."

"He did," I concur. "Joe named him."

Oddly, the old man does not seem upset by our wild tale. He does not seem worried that his store is full of potentially dangerously confused people. In fact, he waves off the dragon tale entirely.

"This is all interesting," he says. "But actually not. Dragons are not that unusual. What I would dearly like to see is the golden blaze on Albert's chest. If I may?"

Wait a minute. Did he not hear me? Does he think I said "golden retriever" or something?

Slack holds up a hand. "Can we rewind briefly to the part where you said dragons are *not* unusual?"

"We will come back to that," the old man says dismissively. "The golden blaze?"

"Albert?" I say calmly. "Would you mind coming down here?" He's not going to listen. He only listens when I'm saying something he wants to hear. Heat rises on my face. I'm pretty sure Ali is judging me now too. "Albert? Please?"

Finally, my cat takes pity on me and leaps directly from his perch to my lap, landing with a grunt—his or mine, I can't be sure. "Delightful creature," the old man says, but I don't think he means it. Very gently, I pull Albert's chin up, exposing the golden blaze that takes up most of his chest. For the first time, the old man's eyes register an emotion. I can't tell if it is excitement or fear or some combination of both.

"So the marked dragon *finally* shows up," he murmurs. "We've been waiting. We've been waiting a *long* time."

And this is the moment that Mom gets sick of the vagueness of this situation. She's a scientist. Clarity is her main objective in almost every situation, and this one, while really different, is not actually that different.

She gets to her feet. "Okay. We need some answers. What is this place? How do you know about the blaze? And Albert? Is Ali a dragon too? And most importantly, who are *you*?"

Miss Asher snorts. "Cut to the chase, why don't you?"

The old man chuckles. His smile, making its debut, is warm and wide. "These are all valid questions. Please, allow me to introduce myself. My name is Edward Tenbrook. And I know a thing or two about dragons."

I feel his words in the pit of my stomach, like a physical blow. Did he just say his name is *Edward Tenbrook*?

Miss Asher clutches Slack's arm. I'm not even sure she's aware she is doing it. "As in Edward Tenbrook was a distant relative you are named after? Like, maybe your great-great-great-grandfather? Is that what you mean?"

But even as she asks the question, I already know the answer. "I wish," Edward says. "But there have been no others. Only me. Still me."

At my side, Joe starts to do that shallow breathing thing he does when what he *thought* was true about the world suddenly does a sharp left turn away from what *is* true about the world. It can be quite jarring. Believe me, I know. He jumps to his feet and gets into tree pose, a yoga position where your hands are above your head and your left foot tucks gently against your right leg above the knee. It's the pose I put him in after he saw Albert turn into a dragon for the first time. It is very calming. The great thing about this group is leaping from your chair into tree pose is not nearly the strangest part of our day. We barely notice. We can't look away from Edward Tenbrook.

"How?" I whisper. "How are you still here?"

"Dragon's blood. It is a remarkable substance. Just a drop or two can cure human ailments. I can't imagine what *more* of it would do. Perhaps make a human invincible? Or grow him wings and scales and allow him to breathe fire? Anyway, I suspect you know some of this already. You found the diary?"

"We did," Miss Asher says, clearing her throat. "In the old library. After a flood. When we were kids, back when we were friends."

Edward Tenbrook does not ask her to explain that comment. "There was a lot of good information in that diary," he says thoughtfully. "I always wondered what happened to it. I lost it somehow along the way."

"It was in Lewiston," she explains. "That's where we live."

At the name of our city, Edward cringes. "Not my favorite place," he says with a grimace. "Bad memories." But he doesn't stay in those memories for long. He gestures at Albert, partially snoozing in my lap. "So this creature appeared in Lewiston? Out of the blue? During a storm?"

"He did," I reply. "He wanted to go home, so we sent him home, but then we figured out from your diary that was a really terrible idea because marked dragons were in danger, so we were going to open a rip and go and save him, but then he came *back*. He's on some kind of mission. Although we aren't completely sure what that is."

"When he turns into a dragon, does he retain the golden blaze?" Edward asks with an edge of urgency.

I glance down at my hands, resting on top of Albert. "Yes. He does."

Edward leans back in his chair with a sharp exhale. "Then the prophecy is *true*. After all these years, I was beginning to think it was wrong, that no dragon with a golden blaze would ever come."

Joe relaxes his yoga pose, putting both feet on the ground. His breathing has returned to something close to normal. "So how old *are* you?" he asks Edward.

"Very," Edward replies.

"I'd like an exact number, please," Joe says.

Edward counts to himself, using his fingers, and finally says, "One hundred and eighty. Give or take a few years. At a certain point, one just stops counting."

Joe resumes tree pose. "I'm going to faint," he says flatly.

"You sure look good for your age," Mom offers.

"Thank you," Edward says with a sly grin. "I have good company."

Ali jumps into his lap and pushes her fluffy head into his chest until he scratches her behind the ears. She purrs contentedly.

And that's when I connect the dots. Big crazy dots. "Ali?" I whisper. "As in *Alvina*?" At the sound of this name, the cat turns on me, her eyes glowing bright.

"As in *Alvina*," Edward confirms, his fingers deep in her fur.

Okay. Now *I* might faint. What is happening here?

"But . . . *how*?" Joe asks, lowering out of his yoga pose. "The diary said that she *died*, that your family killed her. And Vayne came seeking revenge and burned down Lewiston. Did any of that happen?"

"Oh, all of it happened," Edward says. "Except Alvina didn't die. She *transformed*. For reasons I don't fully understand, and I've had much time to think on it, dragons and cats are similar enough that here in our atmospheric composition, a dragon can *become* a cat. They are unable to become other animals. Or humans. And after she became a cat, we escaped."

Sweat blooms across my forehead. My heart pounds. "Did you ever take her *home*?" I whisper. "Through the rip? To the other side?"

Edward regards me for a moment that seems to go on forever.

"I did not," he says finally. "It was unsafe for Ali, and for me. Would you like to hear the story?"

Would we *like* to hear the story? What kind of question is that? What do you *think*?

Chapter 26

EDWARD'S STORY

EDWARD SETTLES into his chair. "Vayne arrived to find Alvina's lifeless body imprisoned in the cage where my family held her. Terrified, my spineless brothers fled the scene. Vayne tried to revive Alvina. He showered her in golden glitter. He tried to breathe his own life into her. But it didn't work. In a rage, Vayne flew off after my brothers, torching the grand house where they now lived and everyone in it. It was quite a raging fire, consumed the whole city before too long. It wasn't like they had fancy fire trucks in those days, and a bunch of townsfolk with buckets did little good."

"Where were you during all of this?" I ask.

"They had imprisoned me as well, fearful I would try to free Alvina, their cash cow. Or dragon, as it was. But in the chaos of the fire, I managed to get away. I made my way to Alvina in the woods." Edward closes his eyes as if he is still in the moment from so long ago. "I could smell the fire. I didn't know what was happening. When I found Alvina, she was in terrible shape. Just like Vayne, I thought she must be dead. This golden glitter covered her head to tail, like a pulsing electric blanket. I had never seen anything like it. Heartbroken to see my best friend like this, I wrapped my arms around her and pulled her onto my lap. And I just held her, telling her I loved her, telling her how sorry I was, that this was all my fault. And I didn't know how I was going to carry on without her."

Edward gazes into the past. "We stayed like that for some time. I could see the flames of Lewiston in the distance, and I thought, 'Good riddance' to that place. I never wanted to see it again. I never wanted to see my family again. I wanted to get as far away as I could. And just as I was thinking about my escape, Alvina stirred in my arms."

At this point, Alvina the cat stretches, yawns, spins a few circles, and plops back down in her bed, her tail draped over her wet nose. She has clearly heard this tale before and is bored by it. But the rest of us are breathless, hanging on Edward's every word. He was there when Lewiston burned to the ground!

"*And?*" Slack asks impatiently, expressing out loud what all of us are thinking.

"She moved," Slack says. "And opened one big round green eye and huffed a billowy cloud of smoke right in my face, clearing her lungs. And after a few days, she seemed stronger, and we began a journey that landed us here in Midhurst, in the shadow of the volcano. There were no people here at the time, and we lived quite nicely off the land, fishing for our dinner. She made it clear she would not return to the Land of Dragons. She did not want to participate in Vayne's reign of terror and felt she could do little to change it."

"Is that its name?" Joe interrupts. "The place on the other side of the rip?"

"It *does* have a proper name," Edward replies. "But it is not something I could ever pronounce. My best translation was Land of Dragons. Not very original, I know, but it was the best I could do."

Edward smiles and scoops a snoozing Alvina into his arms. He snuggles her close. She raises one eyelid long enough to register her general annoyance at this disruption of her nap but soon settles down. Edward pets her methodically, absent-mindedly.

"All was well until people began to come to this area. I remembered so vividly what happened in Lewiston and was terrified it would happen again. But how to hide a dragon? As a cat, of course," he says. "No one pays attention to a cat. They are more or less invisible. And so, we were free to move about without harassment or unwanted attention, although it was quite a shock the first time I saw her as a cat. But it has been a good life. We built this store when Midhurst was still just a dusty old dirt street in the mountains."

"When did you realize you weren't aging?" Mom asks quietly.

"Oh, I age," Edward says, waving away the question. "Just very slowly. And to keep Alvina safe, that meant I could not have many friends. The fewer people who knew, the better. And something was happening to Alvina, too. There were less and less opportunities for her to regain her dragon form, fewer and fewer nights flying across the starlit sky. And then one day, she could not do it anymore. She had *become* her disguise. She was fully a cat."

Edward scratches her behind the ears, and she purrs

with delight. But I'm confused. If Alvina is no longer capable of being a dragon, then who is Albert's plus-one? Isn't she supposed to fly off to the Land of Dragons as part of the team that dethrones Vayne? And if that is not the case, what are we doing here? Slack must be thinking the same thing.

"Is my interpretation of the prophecy correct?" Slack asks. "Are there meant to be *two* dragons who defeat the Silvers? Now I am starting to have doubts. Actually, I'm pretty much doubting everything I think I know in general, so this is not surprising. It does not help that I had my memory wiped recently. Overall, I'd say I'm very confused." His shoulders sag.

"The prophecy was never an exact translation. The parts I experienced firsthand are, of course, accurate, but some of it was my translation of the information that Alvina imparted to me. We did not speak the same language, but she had a way of showing me things when she was a dragon. A mind trick, of sorts, where she penetrated my thoughts. I'm not sure I always understood exactly what she meant, but it was amazing, like walking through an animated conversation with her. Sadly, that ability seems lost in her cat form. A great loss, as there is really nothing that compares with it."

"Like virtual reality?" Joe asks.

"I don't know what that is, young man," Edward replies. "But if it is like being transported to another world, then yes. Keep in mind, however, humans can never be objective about information. We always see it through our own experience, even when we try not to. Over the years, I have thought of many different ways to interpret the prophecy, some vastly different from the way I thought of it originally when I learned of it. Which is to say it is entirely possible that the marked dragon does not act alone."

"Is Alvina meant to help him?" I ask.

"She never said as much," replies Edward. "But it has been so many years since she has taken dragon form, I don't know if she would even remember. Oh, she was mighty and fierce once, a sight to behold." Edward looks wistful. While he loves his cat, he misses his dragon.

I've been so absorbed with Edward's tale that I fail to notice that Albert has wiggled up next to Alvina. He sits beside her, gently licking her ears with his rough tongue, and she does not mind. The cat who chased him all over the store has been replaced by one content to be on the receiving end of an ear bath. It's *so* cute. It's adorable. It's sweet. It's . . . on fire? Uh-oh. Tendrils of smoke rise from Albert's nostrils. His tail twitches.

"Here it comes!" Joe yells, just as thunder shakes the very walls.

"This is marvelous!" shouts Edward, throwing his hands in the air with delight.

Albert's eyes glow red. "Stand back!" I holler. Everyone leaps out of the way.

Crack!

The little shop billows with smoke. Alvina leaps into the air, puffed up like a Halloween cat, claws extended, ready to do battle. Stacks of books tumble. The cloud engulfs us. My eyes sting and my throat burns.

And there is Albert, emerging, long tail thumping the ground, fire leaking from between his lips.

"Sorry," I mutter. "He kind of made a mess."

But Edward doesn't hear me. He stares at Albert in awe. "He's so beautiful."

"He is," I say proudly, as if I can somehow take credit. "But I'm not sure Alvina thinks so."

Alvina's ears are flat as she faces down the suddenly giant beast that is Albert. He stays very still, watching her closely. After a moment, she stops hissing, turning instead to a steady low growl. Albert closes his eyes. He takes a deep rumbling inhale. The flames vanish. I've seen him concentrate like this before, back in Mercy Grove.

"What is he up to?" Joe whispers.

"The *mist*," I whisper back. And sure enough, a stream of golden mist begins to rise from the blaze on his chest, moving out and filling the space between him and Alvina, wrapping itself around her, seeping into her silver fur coat.

"Is he doing what I think he's doing?" Joe asks.

"That depends on what you think he is doing," I reply.

No one moves. Alvina, no longer hissing or puffed up, locks eyes with Albert. The mist grows thicker until they practically disappear into it. My heart pounds in my ears.

Instinctively, Edward steps forward, acute fear in his eyes, but I grab his arm.

"It's okay. He won't hurt her. I think he . . ." But I don't have time to finish my sentence before another clap of thunder rocks the room. The large display window cracks in a spiderweb.

"Alvina?" Edward yelps. "Where are you?"

And that is when Alvina emerges from the cloud, a blindingly bright silver, as if her scales are made from a thousand tiny mirrors. Long eyelashes curl over stunning amethyst eyes. She is like a fantasy.

"My dear friend!" Edward rushes forward and throws his arms around Alvina. She sighs, her wings flexing under his embrace. "Oh, how I have missed seeing you like this!"

Albert rumbles. It's a sound I've never heard before, with different octaves and notes in a broad range. Alvina, Edward still clinging to her neck, replies with a set of her own sounds. Albert cocks his head, like he is thinking. Another round of rumbles and grunts follows.

"They are *speaking dragon*," Miss Asher says with a gasp.

"Can you understand them?" Slack asks Edward, who shakes his head.

"I was never able to figure it out. But it sounds magnificent, doesn't it?"

He's right. Their language has a musical quality, like drumbeats and flutes in harmony. I cannot pull my eyes from Alvina's brilliance. Albert notices and nudges me with a sharp claw. His eyes flicker with sparks of red.

"I think he's jealous," Joe says with a grin.

"I don't know what you are smiling about," I reply. "A jealous dragon cannot be a good thing."

Joe's smile fades. "That is true."

I pat Albert on his leathery snoot. "You are the best dragon," I say. "You are the smartest, fastest, cleverest, most beautiful dragon in the whole world." This does the trick. He huffs a contented plume of smoke.

"Come, my new friends," Edward says. He keeps a hand on Alvina, gesturing to the door at the back end of the store. "Let us get out of sight before any of these dragon-obsessed revelers spot these real live dragons. My house is just there. No one will see us."

It occurs to me as we follow Edward to his house that the reason there is a dragon festival at all is because people used to see Alvina flying across the night sky. The mythology of dragons emerging from the volcanos grew up around those rumors, which were, in fact, not rumors at all but the truth.

How stunned they would all be to know that.

Chapter 27

FOX AND DANA DO SOME SPYING

FOX AND DANA WAIT a long time at the corner, staring at the entrance of the Dragon Tales bookshop. It is boring work, trying to look casual while watching a door. At one point a mob of dancing dragons plows down the blocked-off street, and they have no choice but to go with the flow. Sometimes to not stand out, you literally must dance in the street. It's actually kind of fun, and Fox is sad when the crowd rolls on, forcing them to go back to staring at the door.

An hour goes by, and another, and still no one comes out of the bookstore. Fox decides they should move closer, despite the risk of getting caught. They walk straight down the middle of the alley not because they are confident but because there is nowhere to hide, no shadows or dark corners or recycle bins or anything.

They approach the store and peer inside. It is quiet and empty. A "Closed" sign hangs in the window, strange in the middle of the day, especially when so many people are visiting Midhurst. Fox tries the door. It's locked.

"Can't see anyone," Dana whispers. "Let's go around the back."

A narrow pathway leads down the side of the store to a closed gate, about eight feet high. The slates are so close together that Fox can't see through them, and the gate's lock is no joke. The owner of Dragon Tales does *not* want anyone back here.

"Boost me up," Fox whispers.

"Huh?"

Fox gestures to a confused Dana to form a sling with her hands so Fox may step on it and gain a foot of height and possibly peer over the gate. Dana does not appear pleased by this idea but does it anyway. Her face turns a funny shade of red as soon as Fox puts her full weight on Dana's laced-together hands.

"Ugh," Dana grunts.

"Don't drop me," Fox warns.

"I'll try not to. What do you see?"

"Trees. Lots of trees. And maybe a house in the back. But wait, something is *glowing*."

"Glowing? Like, on-fire glowing or just shiny?" Dana asks, breathless.

"Shiny. Really bright. *Silver*."

And that is when Fox catches the hazy outline of a shiny silver dragon through the dense trees.

Chapter 28

A DIFFERENT KIND OF VIRTUAL REALITY

EDWARD'S HOUSE IS WARM and rustic, with a lot of wood floors and paneling. The windows are up high and there are skylights. "Prying eyes," Edward says by way of explanation.

Alvina preens under Edward's attention. As a cat, she seemed neutral about his adoration. Mom once told me about how people who speak multiple languages often act differently when they are speaking each language. It's called code-switching. And I think the same thing applies to dragon cats. Alvina acted one way with Edward when she was a cat and a different way now that she is in dragon form. Or maybe dragons are just hopelessly vain. That could be it, too. Either way, whenever Edward tells her how beautiful and smart she is, which is every three seconds, she grows brighter, which barely seems possible, considering she is like a dragon-sized disco ball to begin with.

And right now, the dragon disco ball and Albert are having a very animated conversation. Albert's tail sweeps the length of the living room, and I take a moment to be thankful it is not full of breakable objects. There is practically no furniture save for a tattered love seat and a recliner. Honestly, if I were one hundred and eighty-whatever years old, I'd have a more comfortable place to sit.

The dragon dialogue crescendos, loud enough that we cannot talk over them, and then, just as suddenly, it ceases. Albert looks pleased. Alvina less so, and her eyes are on me. Something was decided, I just have no idea what. I glance at the other humans in the room, and none of them seem to have any idea either.

But I don't have to wait long. On very rare occasions, like maybe once or twice, Albert has beamed a message right into my thoughts. It just showed up there, fully formed, and somehow, I knew that I did not generate it. The message that shows up now, however, is *not* from Albert. There are entirely too many words for it to be Albert. He only has three or four words.

Cassie, I will show you something?

And before I can respond yes or no . . . *SNAP!* My stomach turns over like I'm on the downward plunge of a wild roller coaster. *Oh boy.* To counter the dizziness, I extend my arms, airplane-style. Otherwise, I seriously think I might topple over.

What the heck is going on?

There is no sign of Edward's dark paneling or Joe or Mom or Miss Asher or Slack or ancient Edward or *anyone*. It is just me and Alvina surrounded by towering trees. The light is so bright, I shield my eyes. In our redwood forests, no flowers can grow because the tree canopies shade everything below. But here, the forest floor is littered with bright purple and red blooms. The flowers sparkle in faint sunlight as if they are made of glass. I catch the sweet distinct smell of vanilla hovering in the air, and a breeze blows my hair.

This must be what Edward described, the way Alvina showed him things she wanted him to understand. It should be frightening, but it's not. I can sense Albert's physical presence still beside me. He won't let anything bad happen. I try to relax, loosening my shoulders, looking around. I take a tentative step. Can I move in this vision world? The ground beneath my feet feels solid enough. I take another step.

Alvina appears beside me. Here, she is just normal bright instead of blindingly so. It might be because everything else is dialed up a notch, so she just doesn't stand out as much. Either way, my eyes begin to adjust. There are enormous green dragonflies, the size of pigeons, hovering before me. When I reach out, I brush one's wings with my fingers and he darts away.

Wow! Joe would love this. It's like virtual reality that works with all the senses. Alvina is obviously way better than Albert at this brain-messaging thing. Although, I guess it's not really fair because Alvina is really old and Albert is basically clueless. She's had a lot more time to figure out how it's done. Regardless, there has to be a *reason* Alvina is crawling around in my head. I wait for the reveal.

Alvina indicates I should follow her along a narrow path carved out among the trees. Soon we come to a clearing, a patch of forest where there are no trees. Huddled in the middle are two dragons: a large one who shields most of the smaller one from view. The larger one is a brilliant silver, just like Alvina, but her eyes blaze red. She talks to the smaller one, holding him close so all I can see is a black tail.

Alvina nudges me forward gently so I can get a better look. As my vision grows used to this environment, I can make out more detail as the scene before me continues to unfold. The black dragon wiggles out from under the protective wings of the Silver. I can see all of him now, the golden blaze glowing fiercely on his chest.

Albert.

The Silver looks skyward, concentrating, and a cloud of gold rises up from her. She is so beautiful, like something out of a fairy tale, something unknowable. I can't pull my eyes from her. The golden cloud begins a dance I have seen before, bending and morphing into a long jagged line. It sparks and hisses as it pulls apart, creating an opening, a rip. There is noise in the background, the sound of enormous flapping wings, many of them. The sky fills with gray outlines of enormous dragons, and I understand, as she does, that they are coming for her.

The Silver moves urgently now, placing Albert in the cloud. She closes her eyes. The mist thickens. I take a step forward. Albert is no longer visible. The wild flapping grows louder. The rip sizzles.

The Silver blows away a patch of the mist, revealing

Albert. But he's Albert the kitten I found in the dumpster. In one swift move, the Silver sweeps him up and pushes him through the crackling rip. As soon as he passes through, it seals shut and evaporates into the air. The Silver stumbles and slumps forward. The keening that rises from her is the sound of pure heartbreak.

And I know suddenly that this is the story Albert relayed to Alvina about what happened, just before I found him. I am looking at his mother saving him.

My knees tremble. The sound bounces off the trees. But Alvina is not done with the show. I cannot look away.

The Silver shakes with grief, her forehead flush to the forest floor. Four gray dragons come down through the trees, landing in a circle around the Silver, who does not rise from the ground or even lift her head. It is as if all her energy has left her. While one dragon stands over her ominously, the others search the area.

They are looking for Albert. They don't understand where he has gone. Finally, the dragons circle up, surrounding her, like predators. There is no way she could escape even if she wanted to. And if the dragons explain why they have come, I do not understand it. Two of them sink their sharp claws into her skin, but she doesn't cry out. Once they have her in a secure grip, they take to the air, back up through the trees. I watch until there is nothing left to see.

And then, as if we are turning the page to a new chapter, we jump to another location entirely. It is a damp, dark place where the sunlight cannot penetrate. This must be the catacombs, deep underground, that Slack mentioned. A long corridor of stone is interrupted by cells in which dragons are held. We move down the corridor, coming eventually to the last cell on the block. Inside is the Silver from the forest, but her brilliant scales are dull and lusterless. She is slumped in a corner, her face hidden under a wing. On the wall is a timer counting down to zero. My heart lurches. I know what happens when it runs out. I charge toward the locked cell, but I just pass right through it like a cloud. Alvina gently shakes her head. This is not real. There is nothing we can do.

When Alvina releases her hold on me and the vision evaporates, I feel spent, like I just ran a marathon into the wind. I'm back in Edward's house, and everyone stares at me like I have Milano cookie smeared on my face.

"What just happened?" Mom asks.

"Alvina showed me something," I say quietly, my hand resting protectively on Albert.

"What did she show you?" Mom asks.

As I relate to everyone the details, something occurs to me. If Alvina showed Albert what she showed me, his mother in the cell with the timer ticking down, we might have everything wrong. "This isn't about any prophecy or getting rid of Vayne, is it?" I ask. "Alvina showed you how to rescue your mother. It's why you are here, right? Is that what you need to do?"

Albert cocks his head to the left and gives me a curious look. And then he blinks once.

Chapter 29

ALBERT'S QUEST

DESPITE ALBERT'S BEST EFFORTS, the golden-mist effect wears off and Alvina returns to her cat form, unable to retain her dragon self any longer. Albert also returns to being a kitten and snuggles in with Alvina. It is so cute, I want to just keel over.

Edward is quite sure that if Albert is *not* here because of the prophecy, then he must be seeking critical *information* from Alvina needed to continue the quest to free his mother. "In addition to showing him the cellblock, perhaps she provided the dungeon's location," he suggests. "Or a secret password to get in. Or some other insider information that Alvina would have from years of living in the royal lair."

When I ask Albert directly if this is the case, he gives me a solid blink. *Yes.*

But Miss Asher wisely suggests the two might be related. "It's possible that with the information Alvina has provided, Albert can go and successfully rescue his mother. And by doing this, he sets in motion the actions that will end Vayne's reign."

Edward concurs and reminds us that prophecies, while real, are imprecise. He says this with authority, so none of us question how he knows such things.

Edward, Slack, Mom, and Miss Asher, heads bent together, tear into these ideas like a bear with a fresh salmon. Their eyes glisten and their animated voices rise and fall. Joe and I eat cookies and slurp cold tea. I don't know what Joe is thinking, but, in my mind, an uneasy thought begins to form.

As we leave Edward's cozy home, the dragon festival continues to roar with life.

"I wonder what it must have been like a hundred years ago to see Alvina fly across the night sky, a giant silver beast brighter than any star," Joe muses. "It must have been magical. And scary. But the myth that grew up around these sightings, that dragons hailed from the volcanos themselves, is pretty much perfect. Don't you think? I wish these dancing, twirling, spinning festival-goers could know the truth, even if I know that is not possible. Cassie? Are you listening?"

Huh? No. "Yes."

"No, you aren't. What is going on? Did Alvina fry your head somehow?"

Oh, that is a terrible thought. But not as bad as the one I am actually having.

"Tell me," Joe demands.

"There is something I don't like about this," I say. I glance up at Mom, Miss Asher, and Slack, who walk about twenty paces ahead of us. They talk among themselves. Miss Asher even laughs at something Slack says. A minor miracle right there. They feel as if we have done our part. We've helped Albert do what he needed to do. I squeeze the warm round lump of fur riding along in my pocket but not so hard that I wake him up.

"Specifics," Joe orders.

How do I put this uneasy feeling into words? "I'm not sure how to explain this," I begin.

At the heart of my unease is the terrifying idea of Albert going off on the quest to save his mother *alone*. I thought I lost him once, and that was hard enough. When I believed he'd have a partner, someone to help him, I could almost get my head around it. But now . . . I just don't know.

If Joe had to go on a mission to save, I don't know, one of his fabulous brothers from some nightmare beast who is known for eating brothers and who resides in a cave in a treacherous forest, full of other nightmare beasts and stinging plants and things, I would never let him go alone. The very idea is preposterous. He's my best friend, which means *his* problems are *my* problems, even if helping him puts me at some level of risk.

And the same is true of Albert. He's also my best friend, not in the same way as Joe, but different doesn't mean less. He means the world to me. Of course, this leads to an idea. It's not a good one. It's a terrible one, actually. Which means I have to tell Joe right away.

"I don't want to let him go alone," I whisper finally. "I don't want to let Albert go back and face whatever lies in the way of rescuing his mother by himself."

Joe stops dead on the sidewalk. I can tell he's thinking hard because his eyebrows meet in the middle of his forehead. Up ahead, the others don't even notice. They are wrapped up in the cocoon of shared experience, in this case meeting the world's oldest man and his famous pet dragon-cat. "How do we know he will be by himself?" Joe counters. "We don't know that. Dragons are mighty and fierce and brave and all that other stuff. He probably does not need help and definitely not our help. Besides, what sort of help could we even offer?"

Specifically? Probably none. Those big dragons I saw in the vision could turn us into kindling in an instant. But that is not the point. I *want* to be there. With him. In the Land of Dragons. Just in case.

There is a long pause, during which Joe tilts his gaze skyward and watches the night sky. "So, are we really going to do this?" Joe asks. Joe is the best *best* friend a person could ask for. You could not *invent* a better best friend.

"Yes," I reply without giving it a second thought. "We are going with him. Through the rip."

"Well, I guess our backpacks are all ready to go," he says. "I mean, it *was* the original plan, which somehow makes it less crazy."

It's still plenty bananas, but just making the decision not to let Albert do this alone makes me feel better. We will be there if he needs us. It is what friends do.

And while it is true that this could go sideways very quickly, I am keenly aware that Dad was just crossing the street when he died. He was doing the most ordinary thing possible and now he's gone.

Safety is an illusion. You just never know what is going to happen.

Chapter 30

A RETURN TO LEWISTON

WE ARE BACK in Lewiston by midday. Joe goes home to his grandmother. Slack accepts Miss Asher's invitation to hide in her spare bedroom, and Mom, Albert, and I return to our slightly singed kitchen and living room. The plan is that tomorrow we will drive to Mercy Grove and say a final goodbye and good luck to Albert. Armed with the information provided by Alvina, he will save his mother from certain death. However, my plan is a little different.

Over dinner, Mom asks how I will feel when Albert leaves again. *Oh, that's easy, Mom. The world will be flat and colorless and sad. That's how I will feel. But, um, I'm going with him, so who knows how that turns out?* I don't say any of this aloud. Instead, I stuff my face with pasta and compliment her on making a really good salad, the kind that is mostly croutons, which is how I like it. She tries a few times more. She reminds me that bottling up my feelings is not good or healthy. I should express myself, even if what I'm expressing is sadness. There is nothing wrong with sadness. It's normal as long as it doesn't stay around too long. It's a good thing to be able to feel. I love Albert, so saying goodbye to him tomorrow will be hard, even if I've done it before, even if I know he has to go. She says I can tell her anything. And that is probably true, except for this. I cannot tell her this. I also mention how much I like the salad dressing.

My plan is that Albert flies Joe and me to Mercy Grove tonight, under cover of darkness, and we three go through the rip together. Although Mom and Miss Asher were game to follow us to the Land of Dragons when we were staging a rescue of Albert, the stakes have changed. She would not allow me to go with him to save his mother from Vayne's royal lair, protected by murderous gray dragons. It is too dangerous.

Albert, on the other hand, seems pleased we plan to come along. I just wish he could explain in more detail, or any detail, what we are getting ourselves into. When I asked him to put images in my head like Alvina did, he gave me a blank stare, the kitty equivalent of "Huh?"

Joe has valid concerns about our journey. What if the Land of Dragons is like a gas giant planet and we fall right through it? Or it is so cold, we immediately freeze to death. Or we aren't able to breathe. Or there is no gravity. Or our molecules don't reassemble in the correct manner and our arms end up attached to our foreheads or something equally awful. From what Alvina showed me, I don't think any of these scenarios are likely. But of course I can't be 100 percent sure. Instead, I told Joe to quit worrying. I also told him to be ready when we come to get him at three o'clock in the morning. I suggested setting two alarms, just to make sure.

Not that I am sleeping. I feel guilty about how Mom will feel. But it's entirely possible that time does not pass in any absolute way while we are gone. Remember how time does not exist beyond the event horizon of a black hole? Well, maybe this is the same. Maybe Mom will have no idea that I am even gone, because for her it will be only like five minutes or something.

I try counting sheep, but they turn into dragons. It's hopeless. I give up and let my mind drift to what it will feel like to actually pass into *another* dimension. Has it been done before? It's possible that Joe and I will be the first humans, which seems like a big deal but not something we can share with anyone.

And finally, my mind wanders into the territory of a question I have not wanted to consider up close. Will we be able to *return*? Is this a one-way trip? If I knew it was, would I go anyway?

No, Cassie! Not now! Don't go there!

Okay! Okay! I'll try the stupid sheep again. Albert, on the other hand, sleeps soundly, lying on my chest with both paws resting on my face. It is midnight. Three more hours of counting dragon sheep is so *not* appealing.

Slowly and gently, I prop myself up on my pillow and nestle Albert in against my thigh. Placing my palms together in prayer position, I think, *Rain, snow, sleet, hail; clouds, twister, wind; come on, weather, do it right; blow me up a storm tonight.*

I don't know why exactly I do this. Probably because I'm going bananas counting dragon sheep. I pull my hands apart. The room glows golden with rising mist. I say the words again, but this time I envision the golden mist twirling into a funnel.

And the mist responds! It whirls around, forming a perfect little twister that dances on my outstretched hand. This tiny tornado feels within my control, much more than the one I made in the Starlight. That one definitely had a mind of its own.

"Bigger," I whisper. The tornado obeys my command, growing wider and taller. A heady power fills my senses. "Now smaller." It returns to its original size. "Wow." After gazing at its compact beauty for a minute, I return my hands to prayer position, squishing the little twister flatter and flatter until it disappears entirely. The mist floats up, dispersed, shapeless.

"How about a cloud?" I hold my palms upward and wait. Nothing happens. I repeat the mantra and tighten my focus. "Cloud?" I repeat. It takes longer, but a small dark cloud finally appears in the golden mist, hovering before me. It appears ready to burst, quivering and wavering. Am I going to get rain all over my bed? Before I can squash the cloud, a miniature bolt of lightning shoots out of it, like a laser, and hits me in the knee.

"Ouch!" I roll sideways, waking Albert. What am I doing? I just zapped myself. "Go away, cloud!" The cloud hesitates, and I recognize the sense I had in the Starlight, when my tornado got well and truly away from me. "Cloud," I say sternly. Am I really about to reprimand a bit of weather? "Please go away." As I place my palms together, the cloud dissipates just like the tornado did. That was pretty good, right? I smile at myself in the darkness before noticing that Albert's watching me, his gaze intent.

"What?" I ask. "I can make clouds and tornadoes. It's kind of fun, actually." He climbs up on my chest and taps my nose a few times with a soft paw. And I get the sudden feeling that he is proud of me. I've done something good. Or necessary? But figuring out which will have to wait. The bedside clock reads 2:50. It's time to saddle up and ride.

I'm nervous as I quietly slip on my clothes and shrug on my backpack. And I should be. I'm headed to the Land of Dragons.

Chapter 31

CROSSING DIMENSIONS

I WOULD BE LYING if I said flying wasn't scary. But it's also exhilarating, like the huge adrenaline rush you get from scoring a winning goal (not that I have ever done that) or finishing some superhard school project. My heart races and my palms are damp. But within a few seconds, Albert launches us off the windowsill and into the cool, dark night. As we take flight, my stomach drops, just like on a roller coaster.

"I love flying!" I yell as the wind tangles my hair in my lashes. "Aaaaaah!" It is a feeling like no other, a level of freedom I can't quite describe. We bank left, gliding low along the rooftops, passing houses I have only ever seen at sidewalk level. They look different up here, smaller and more ordinary somehow. Beneath my feet, I recognize the park that lies between my house and Joe's. The last time Albert took us for a ride, I had to practically pry Joe's eyes open, he was so scared. But the second time feels different for me, and I hope it does for him too.

We hover in midair just in front of Joe's house. The windows are dark. The whole neighborhood is asleep. The nighttime sound of crickets is drowned out by the gentle whooshing of Albert's wings. We sink on the upbeat of each wing flap and rise on the downbeat. The rhythm is calming. I could do it all night. But we are not here to just chill in front of Joe's house. He had better be awake.

"It's that one," I tell Albert, pointing to Joe's window on the second floor. Thankfully, Joe's family is not home yet, which means his brother is not in there either. And Joe's grandmother is in the guest room that I happen to know is on the first floor of the house. Albert moves in close and positions me so I can knock on the window.

He appears immediately, lips drawn into a tight line. "Ready?" I ask.

"Ready," he replies.

"Hurry up before someone sees us."

"No one would believe it."

"I know, but still, hurry up!"

Joe waves me off and disappears into the darkness of his room. He is gone *forever*. "Where are you?" I hiss. Does he not recognize I am dangling from a dragon's claws out here?

"I'm getting my alternate-dimension backpack," he growls from the depths of his shadowy room.

"Fine."

"Good." He appears in the window, hat on, backpack bulging. He sets his face. I know that look. He is preparing to do something that freaks him out. I get it.

"Come out on the ledge," I instruct. "Albert will grab you."

"You're kidding, right? Why can't I just go out the front door?"

"Because we have a greater chance of being seen on the ground," I explain.

"It's the middle of the night!" Joe yelps. "Everyone is sleeping!"

"They are going to wake up if you keep yelling."

"I'm not yelling!"

"Albert is not going to drop you. Right, Albert?" In response, Albert exhales a puff of steamy air. "See? That's a yes."

"Says who?" Joe demands.

"Me," I reply. "Now climb out on the ledge. And remember how boring your life was before we met."

"Boring, yes. Safe, yes. Okay, here I come."

The maneuver to scoop up Joe is not elegant, but Albert gets a strong grip on Joe's hoodie and we alight into the sky. Joe screams. A few lights in the nearby houses flicker on. But by the time they look outside to see what the fuss is about, we will be long gone. They will think, "Oh, a raccoon or a cat fight" and go back to bed. There is much we don't see because we talk ourselves out of it.

Joe continues to scream. I'd say his bellowing goes on about fifteen seconds total, which is not a lot of time, but when the screaming is in your ear, it sure does feel like it. We rise higher into the night, plowing into a fogbank where the ground disappears. Without a way to orient ourselves, we have no idea if we are gaining altitude or just cruising. It is disconcerting, and Joe tightens his grip on my arm. My heart speeds up a little bit. I hope there is nothing else here in the fog with us. You know, like a cliff or a helicopter or something.

A few minutes later, we burst out of the fog. Below is an endless expanse of forest lit only by the pale moonlight.

"Mercy Grove, here we come!" I yell.

"Land of Dragons, here we come!" Joe adds. He's right, of course. Suddenly, this is all getting very real.

↓

As our feet touch solid ground, Joe exhales sharply. "Flying is not bad, but I'm always a little surprised I'm still alive at the end," he says.

Me, I could soar through the skies forever. I could circle the globe and then do it again. I would trade my power to make mini tornadoes for flying any day of the week.

Albert stalks around the grove, making a terrible ruckus, like he is trying to sniff out the best place to open a rip. "You did it over there the last time," I point out. He gives me a condescending glance, implying he does not need nor want my advice when it comes to opening rips. Jeez. *Fine.*

Joe nudges me to get my attention. "I know I said this before," he whispers, "but are we sure this is a good idea? Us going through the rip, I mean."

Well, that really depends on the definition of "good idea." "It will be okay," I say.

"I believe you," Joe replies. That's good. I wish *I* believed me.

In sixth-grade science class, the teacher asked if we were given the opportunity to go on the first trip to Mars, would we do it? "Yes" erupted from my mouth before I could even think it through. Of course, space travel is dangerous. The rest of the universe doesn't have any, you know, *oxygen,* so the chance of it ending badly is not zero. But that didn't matter to me. The idea of exploring the unknown is worth the risk.

Going through the rip is like going to Mars, except I really hope there *is* oxygen on the other side, or this is going to be the shortest interdimensional trip *ever*. Albert trundles over and herds us closer to one of the massive trees encircling the space. He makes some motion that I think means to stay put, but I'm also very bad at charades.

"Now what?" Joe asks.

"I think this is a wait-and-see kind of situation," I reply.

"Right." Joe is quivering next to me, maybe with anticipation, probably with fear. "I'm ninety percent sure I might puke."

"You don't have to do this," I say. "I can go alone."

"Are you crazy? No way. And stop offering me an out. We are in this together. We have been since the beginning. That is the way it is. Even if I barf." Joe's words clear away my last bits of sticky anxiety. This does not mean I've stopped freaking out. It just means I'm ready. *We* are ready. Let's get this show on the road.

Albert faces us. He huffs a few times, as if warming up. The sky cracks with thunder and rain begins to fall as golden mist rises from the golden blaze on his chest. It pours out, thick and vibrant, creating a dense cloud around us in no time at all. We are swallowed up. Joe grabs my hand. Our fingers interlace.

"Don't let go," I whisper. "No matter *what* happens."

"Oh, there is no way I'm letting go. Forget that."

Joe's grip tightens. I try to steady my breathing. What will it be like over there? Will I feel weird?

Don't think about it, Cassie! Just breathe!

Boy, Mom and Miss Asher would kill us right now if they knew what we were doing.

The telltale hiss of the rip fills the air. It's a sound that cannot be mistaken for any other, hot and sizzling, like a megawatt sparkler gone berserk. It starts small, the size of a tennis ball, but gathers strength from the surrounding cloud of golden mist and steadily grows larger. It elongates and warps just as I remember. Soon it is the size of a door, the edges rippling and snapping.

Albert's eyes blaze red with determination. He gets behind Joe and me and nudges us forward. Our hands are still firmly clasped.

"Ready?" I ask.

"Sure," Joe replies with mock casualness. "No big deal."

"Barely worth even noticing, right?"

"Right."

We are right at the edge of the rip now. A pool of sweat forms at the base of my spine. "One. Two. Three. Go!"

Together, at the exact same moment, we step over the edge and into the dragon dimension.

Chapter 32

THE LAND OF DRAGONS

IT'S SO DARK HERE, black like the deepest night. Oh. Wait. That's only because my eyes are squeezed shut. I open them just a tiny bit. It's not so dark after all. There is a faint orange cast to a pale blue sky, like we arrived just in time for sunrise. The air is crisp and cool and smells of freshly mowed grass. More importantly, I can breathe. I take a big inhale just to be sure. In the distance, there is loud squawking, as if a bunch of grumpy parrots were rudely awakened before their alarm went off. The ground appears to be solid beneath my feet. My hand is still firmly attached to Joe's. I squeeze his fingers.

"You can open your eyes," I say. "Not a gas giant.

And there appears to be gravity. We aren't, like, floating around."

"Well, that's a relief," he says. His eyes pop open and he drops his solid grip on my hand. He sniffs the air and scans the scene. We are in a forest clearing, but the trees are easily twice the size of the huge redwoods in Mercy Grove. From our position on the ground, we cannot even begin to see their tops. And everything seems to shimmer. Even the tree bark appears infused with some incandescent light whose source is not apparent. Up high in the branches is a spider's web but spun from golden thread. And dead center is less of a spider and more of a translucent guinea pig with six legs. It is not very cute.

I nudge Joe and point. He grimaces. Just at that moment, a dinner plate–sized, buggy-eyed green worm with multiple sets of rainbow-colored wings drifts by. It generates a high-pitched hum, like a fan turned to the highest setting and about to explode. It is cuter than the see-through guinea-pig spider, if we are being honest, despite the noise.

Albert flexes his wings and shoots out a few plumes of fire and smoke, doing a system check to make sure everything dragon is in working order. Joe and I take the pause to figure out if anything about ourselves feels weird.

"I can breathe," Joe says. "That's good. The ground is solid, and I'm not light-headed or anything." He shakes out his arms and legs like we sometimes do in gym class when we are warming up.

Yes, we have oxygen and gravity, but we are not in Lewiston anymore. The creatures are odd, and the forest is bright and sparkling. Even the large boulders strewn around the forest floor seem to pulsate with inner light. It's like someone took our dimension and colored it in with a box of fluorescent markers. It smells intensely of pine, tinged with a whiff of distant campfire. The animals create a soundtrack of unfamiliar pops and whistles and crackles.

And while I agree with Joe that my body feels normal, there is definitely something strange going on with my hands. "Joe, look." I hold my palms upright. They look as if they have been tattooed with gold filigree, images of clouds and lightning bolts, all in motion, like a golden cartoon playing out on my hands. It is *bizarre*.

"Wow, Cassie," Joe says, examining them. "Does it hurt?"

"It feels like I'm petting Albert," I say. "Or maybe a bunch of ants are crawling around on me."

"I like the first one better."

"Yeah. Me too." We watch the swirls for a bit. Golden

clouds form, lightning zaps, rain falls, and the cycle repeats. This part is *not* normal. I'm about to show Albert, but suddenly, he herds us out of the clearing and into the woods, urging us forward. We move through the forest at a deliberate pace, hopping and skipping away from where we came through, the rip still sizzling as it slowly collapses closed behind us. I assume we aren't flying because he doesn't want to be seen. He is, after all, a marked dragon and not welcome here. And I can't imagine the dragons here would be happy to see *us*, either.

I notice things as we go. Flower petals have a hint of iridescence. The air smells like the lilies someone left at our house after my dad died. The wind seems to whistle a tune. I swear, it's perfectly musical. And every time it rises, I feel the swirling, weird cartoons on my hands quickening.

Joe is sure he feels eyes on him. "There are creatures here," he whispers as we hustle along. "I'm just hoping they don't want to eat us."

"You are too skinny to be tasty," I reply.

"Not what I wanted to hear, thank you very much."

"I think you are just tired from interdimensional travel and are stressing out," I say.

"If we get eaten," he responds, "don't say I didn't warn you."

"If we get eaten," I say, "you won't have time to say 'I told you so.' You will be eaten."

"Details," Joe says, waving me off.

Albert picks up the pace. "Hey, Albert?" I say, swatting at his tail to get his attention. "Where are we headed?"

"Not a yes-or-no question, Cassie," Joe reminds me.

I was kind of hoping that in the Land of Dragons, Albert would be able to talk to me, but I guess that only happens in fantasy stories. I rephrase my question. "Are we headed somewhere in particular?" He blinks once and gets right back to hustling through the forest.

Okay, then.

How long we keep this up is anyone's guess. Time here has a strange quality I can't quite put into words, as in I know it's passing because it *must* be, but it also is a little like I am moving through a static environment where nothing around me is changing. I want to ask Joe his thoughts, but we are moving too quickly now for me to spare the air. Just when I am about to beg for mercy, we pull to a halt. Ahead of us lies a village that is *alive* with activity.

"Oh. Wow." Joe takes off his hat and runs his hands over his head a few times. There are *so* many dragons. Some are green or pale rose or yellowish. Others are blotchy with different colors like a calico cat. I catch a glimpse of a purple one. Big. Small. Medium. But none are silver and none are black with golden blazes. I think I might hyperventilate.

"Yeah, wow," I gasp.

Slack was right about dragons having no use for houses like we think of them. Instead, staggered platforms are built into the tree branches, suspended high above the ground. On the platforms are nests lined with straw and leaves and the soft indentations of the dragons who most recently slept there. Smoke billows from torches posted at the village's border. There is also a lookout perched in the highest tree, occupied by a turquoise dragon who scans the horizon. She's looking for something. But what?

Nestled into the forest is a crystal-blue lake. A dozen dragons are at the water's edge, splashing each other and shaking out their wings just like the sparrows do in puddles back in Lewiston. The ground around them is muddy and slick. A din floats up toward us. The dragons are chattering away. The ones splashing look to be young, smaller than some of the older ones that stand back from the water.

"Is this your village?" I ask softly. Albert blinks twice. No.

I'm trying to figure out another question to ask, to understand why we are here, when an alarm sounds, a blast so loud, I jump. But it's not an alarm. It is the turquoise dragon perched in the canopy, *howling*. Albert grabs Joe and me in his claws and, flying so low to the ground our feet drag, bolts for cover on the far side of a fallen tree.

"What's happening?" I yell, wiggling out from under Albert so I can see. Moving rapidly toward us is a dark cloud. Or a flock of crows flying in a tight formation. The ground trembles. A deep angry hiss fills the air.

It's *dragons*, thundering across the sky.

The villagers scatter. Some run for the woods, others take to the air. The fear is palpable. There is no doubt they are under attack.

As the approaching dragons draw near, they begin to take shape. Large matte gray with enormous wingspans, each wing section ending in a sharp, daggerlike point. Around their necks are gold medallions adhered to purple rope. These dragons do not sparkle but rather seem to suck the sunlight right out of the air. The Grays spit fire and roar with fury. Albert bristles beside us, anger coming off him in waves.

We can do nothing but watch. The Grays crash down through the platforms, tearing them from the trees, the straw and leaves fluttering to the ground. Those that they don't destroy, they torch with a single hot plume of fire. I watch, aghast, as a Gray encounters a small green dragon in his path. With a powerful wing, the Gray sweeps the green dragon aside, sending him sailing through the air only to hit hard into a nearby fallen platform, where the green dragon lies without moving. The Gray does not even glance in the direction of the fallen dragon. He flexes his impressive wings and, along with his squad, begins to bellow. The sound is like nails on a chalkboard, and instinctively, I cover my ears.

I count twelve Grays in total. The one who battered the green dragon is clearly the leader. His medallion is bigger than that of the others'. He bares his serrated teeth and howls. Soon a multicolored dragon limps before them. I can't tell if he is old or injured, only that he is broken. He leads the Grays to a mossy rise in the forest floor. Shoving him aside, the Grays begin to tear away the small hill. Beside me, Joe catches his breath.

The mossy hill hides a cache of treasure. As the Grays rip the camouflage to shreds, out spills a shower of gold and silver coins.

The Grays bag up the treasure as they howl and flap their wings either in an act of intimidation or glee, I cannot tell which. Clutching the sacks in clawed feet, they set off into the sky, morphing into a V formation, much like a flock of birds, following their leader as the ruined village smokes beneath them.

Chapter 33

FOX AND DANA GET SEPARATED

AFTER EXPLAINING to the bosses about the silver dragon, they received orders to put eyes on everyone and *get* the dragon. Assistance was on the way but was not going to get here fast enough to watch Slack, the kids, and the librarian. Fox and Dana had to divide and conquer and hope for the best. Fox started her surveillance at Cassie's house, and Dana watched Slack. When Fox called Dana from the car to tell her that Cassie had just flown away into the night on a dragon, Dana told her to quit kidding around. It took Fox a minute to convince Dana this was no joke.

And now Fox, having followed the dragon to Mercy

Grove, waits in the relentless drizzle in the dark. She's cold and her nose runs. Sitting on a stump hidden behind the skinny but plentiful branches of a young redwood tree, her butt soaked through, she watches the black dragon with the golden blaze, the one from the library rooftop, and the kids. They stomp around, dragon included, as if looking for something. But what?

Before long, something begins to happen. Now, Fox has heard about portals to other dimensions, but she has never seen one. It makes her dizzy to watch this one widen, giving her a glimpse of a different world on the other side. She clutches the tree branches to keep steady.

The kids look tentative about crossing over, which makes Fox think it is the first time for them. Can a person who goes through to the other side ever return? Is it even possible?

The impatient dragon nudges the kids through the rip. And just like that, they disappear. He follows closely behind. The rip in the fabric of reality sizzles and snaps. Fox knows she should stay where she is, that she should at least wait for Dana to arrive.

But the kids and the dragon are *gone*. Fox wonders what will happen if she follows them.

"Don't be an idiot," she whispers to herself. *Just sit tight.*

She chews a thumbnail and counts to one hundred. The rip begins to fade, its circumference shrinking. The dragon is *getting away*.

Without thinking, Fox leaps from her hiding place and charges toward the rip. The air grows warmer as she approaches, but she has momentum and is not stopping. She is moving so fast, she can't even slow down to step over the threshold. Instead, she dives through the rip, hands extended in front of her, feet in the air. Her right calf bumps something solid. *It's the lip*, she thinks. *I just kicked the edge of the rip.* Her body snaps with electricity, like she just got a shock but to every cell she possesses, and she is sure she is weightless. And in the next moment, *burning*.

The pain in her calf is bright and intense, as if she held the leg over an open fire. She hits the ground hard on the other side, her shoulder absorbing the shock, but that pain is eclipsed by her leg. Scrambling to a seated position, she examines the damage. The fabric of her pants is melted, and the wound beneath it, the size of her palm, oozes and glistens. She bites her lip to keep from yelping.

What was she thinking? What has she done? This was a very bad idea.

"What a fool you are," she whispers.

As Fox glances around, everything is too bright. She shields her eyes as she reaches for the sunglasses in her jacket pocket, but they are crushed, ruined when she landed on them during entry. The kids and the dragon are a little ways off. Fox limps quietly behind a tree to hide. It's a *massive* tree. Completely, abnormally huge.

But now the dragon urges on the kids. They move through the forest, away from Fox. Panic rises in her throat. Fortunately, the dragon doesn't take flight with the kids, but even on foot, hopping and leaping like dragons do, it is almost impossible for Fox to keep up. She is drenched in sweat and panting hard after just a few minutes. Her leg throbs with every step. There is no way she can keep this up for very long. Her lungs will explode like overfilled balloons, and no one will ever find her. Finally, she stops, gasping, fear creeping in.

It occurs to her that she has no idea how to get back. And if she loses the kids and the dragon, she is basically doomed. This thought provides a nice surge of adrenaline, which cancels out the pain. She *must* keep up.

But just as Fox is about to set off at a newly invigorated sprint, a whoosh coming from behind captures her attention. At first she sees nothing more than a broad shadow, spread wide across the forest floor. And by the time she thinks, *Oh, that shadow is in the shape of . . . dragon wings*, it is too late. A great purple-and-orange dragon grabs her by her suit jacket and lifts her straight into the sky. In no time at all, they are much too high up for her to shrug off the jacket and drop back down.

Fox has seen many weird and unusual things in her job. Sometimes those things are downright scary. But she has never screamed.

Until now.

Chapter 34

A PICTURE IS WORTH A THOUSAND WORDS

IT HAS BEEN ALL OF five minutes since we witnessed the attack on the dragon village. I cannot pull my eyes from the little green dragon. He still does not move. My stomach clenches. My thoughts reel. Beside us, Albert growls. He grabs us by our hoods and takes off flying low and fast, darting around trees and banking hard to avoid obstacles. In a word, it is terrifying, like an out-of-control roller coaster that keeps gaining speed.

"Cassie! We are going to die!" Joe howls.

I would love to comfort him and say we are going to be fine, but I am afraid he might be right. Albert cuts through the forest with abandon, as if he has completely forgotten he is carrying fragile human passengers. And I'm pretty sure there is no emergency room around here that will put us back together if we collide with a tree.

"Close your eyes!" I yell back.

"They *are* closed!"

Well, there you go. I'm out of suggestions. At some point, we have to stop, right? *Please don't crash, Albert. Please don't drop us.* I feel a little like Dorothy. There were many beautiful things about her visit to the Land of Oz, but a lot of it, like the angry witch and the mean old apple trees, was just plain *scary*.

We finally touch down beside a massive roaring river, twenty feet wide and so loud, it is like standing before a jet engine. The river snakes through rolling hills. Behind us is a cave entrance, almost completely obscured from view. Albert tucks his wings in tight and enters. We follow close behind. Inside, it is cold and dark and damp. Not exactly homey. Maybe some kind of hideout.

"So far, I'm not a fan of the Land of Dragons," Joe whispers. "I give it two stars."

I can't argue with that. The ground is littered with silver scales. Is this where Albert's mother hid with him from Vayne before she sent him through the rip? Before she was taken? Albert breathes a plume of fire onto a stone pit, which immediately erupts in a full-blown blaze, brightening the interior of the cave enough to reveal the images carved in the walls. The pictures are dragons engaging in all sorts of what must be typical dragon behavior. Playing, eating, flying, burning up things. It's a record of normal dragon life rendered in beautifully detailed panels of art, like a series of comic strips but without any words.

We study them up close while Albert watches us. And I understand suddenly what is at stake. How can the dragons do all these normal dragon things while living in fear of what we witnessed today? I think of the green dragon from the village and my skin goes cold.

"Hey, Cassie," Joe says, drawing my attention to a series of images to my left. "Look." What I see takes my breath away. It's where the tracing Albert brought through the rip originated, a rising sun behind a dragon shadow, the dragon's tail displayed predominately in the foreground. All around it are volcanic mountains, just like in Midhurst.

"The tracing," I whisper.

"And the *volcanos*," Joe adds.

"Do you think Albert's mother left these clues so he could find Alvina when he needed to?" I ask. "To ask her for help?"

"Maybe. Or maybe Alvina left them herself." We glance at the silver scales littering the ground. Joe might be right. Whoever was here was sending a message to the future.

"Mind . . . blown," I whisper.

"My mind was blown the first time you said the word 'dragon' to me," Joe replies. Well, yes, there *is* that. "And I will never get my head around predicting the future. Do you know what I mean?"

The idea of time ceasing to exist in black holes is hard enough to understand. But the notion that events can ripple back and forth, like a wave hitting the beach and rolling out again, and send echoes of themselves forward is just impossible. But the prophecy and these drawings suggest otherwise.

Albert, however, doesn't intend for us to just stand here contemplating time and the funny way it can behave in the greater universe. With a sharp claw, he begins to etch new images into the stone. It's like standing at the shoulder of a cartoonist and watching the panels come to life.

Joe and I sit back. Joe pulls a Milky Way candy bar from his backpack. The candy bar seems so normal and our circumstances so *not*, I giggle. Joe breaks me off a piece and says, "You keep doing that."

"What? Laughing?"

"No. *That*." He points at my hands, upturned in my lap. A tiny golden twister dances a few inches above my palms. It is more elegant than the Starlight one. The problem is I did not know I was *making* it. "It's a nice tornado."

"Thanks," I reply, feeling my eyebrows knit together. I clasp my hands tight, and the funnel disappears. We return our attention to Albert's frantic scratching.

The first bit of art I ever saw Albert create was a crude drawing of a symbol on my closet door, which turned out to be a map to the locations of the rips. What he is doing now is much more sophisticated. The first panel is of me and Joe standing on a riverbank while Albert soars over it. We wave to him, as if saying goodbye. The second panel is Alvina, in her dragon form, whispering in Albert's ear. Next, Albert comes upon a tree shaped exactly like an umbrella. At the base of the tree is an entrance to a series of underground tunnels. After racing through the tunnels, this way and that, he pops out of the tunnel system near a grand lair at the base of an enormous cliff.

At this point, Albert pauses, checking in to make sure we get it. "Alvina told you where to find a tunnel that leads to where your mom is?" Joe asks. Albert blinks. *Yes.*

"And we are going to storm the castle?" I add. "Or lair?"

"Cassie, you make it sound really dramatic when you say it that way," Joe chides.

"It *is* dramatic," I counter. But I have it wrong. Albert blinks twice and taps his claw on the image of him flying over the river. I glance at Joe.

"Thoughts?" I ask.

"I think he means that we stay here," Joe says. Albert blinks once, stamps the ground, and quickly returns to the cave wall. The new image is him in the castle, or more like under it, in what looks like the prison Alvina showed me. The dungeon is guarded by medallion-wearing Grays, the same ones that destroyed the village. Above, in the lair, a mighty dragon, wings spread wide, roars. The image leaves my mouth dry.

"Vayne?" I squeak. Albert blinks once. "And those are his protectors? His soldiers?"

Blink.

Joe grabs my arm. "Does he think he's going to defeat all those Grays by himself?"

Albert blinks again. Once. Yes, he does believe he's going to defeat all those terrifying dragons by himself. My pulse quickens. Albert continues to etch out the plan.

In the dungeon, Albert finds his mother. Even rendered with great haste in stone, she is beautiful. Albert busts open her prison cell and they escape. There is no sign of the Grays. There is no pursuit.

And that's it. That's the end of the story.

"But, Albert," I say, "the prophecy? Vayne? What about that stuff?"

Albert shakes his head. His tail snaps against the ground. A plume of fire erupts from his mouth. He huffs. His last panel is the four of us, me, Joe, Albert, and his mom dancing around a firepit, happy and safe and together.

And I understand that what has been foreseen by some ancient dragon long ago does not matter. Albert is here to save his mother. And that is all.

Chapter 35

NO WAY

IT IS CLEAR FROM the panels that our role in this is to wait for Albert and celebrate with him and his mom when they return. I would like to find the words to convince Albert that, at the very least, he should take us along. I understand that we are human middle school students and therefore not exactly useful in the Land of Dragons, but anything is better than trying to do this by himself.

In the end, though, I just end up blurting, "Albert, no!"

He slams his tail into the cave wall in response. I translate this to mean *Be quiet, Cassie, and don't tell me what I can or cannot do.*

"Please," I beg. "You don't have to do this alone. Let us help you!"

"It's why we are here," Joe adds.

But Albert will not be swayed. He turns his back on me just as he does when he's a kitten. Finally, Albert pushes his forehead to mine. I feel the heat radiate off him. He's not consenting to us coming along; rather, he is saying goodbye.

And just like that, he is gone. Joe and I run out of the cave in time to see him rise into the sky and disappear.

Joe tugs on my jacket. "What do we do?" he yells above the roaring river.

There are so many things I don't know, questions I can't and may never be able to answer. But I know the answer to this one. We go after him, of course.

I shove Joe back into the cave. "Grab your backpack," I instruct.

"Wait a minute. Albert wanted us to stay here."

"Since when do we do what we are told?"

"Never?"

"You got that right. Backpack. Hurry up. We need to find a way across that river." That thundering, massive, swirling, nasty river. No big deal. Standing on the bank, up close, it confirms itself to be all of those things and more. The spray rising up is freezing cold, too.

"I'm pretty sure dragons don't need bridges," Joe comments, eyes fixed on the water.

"Not necessary when you can fly," I reply.

We stare at the river some more. "Can we swim it?" I ask.

"Only if we want to die," Joe says flatly.

"We don't." A touch of despair prickles my skin. Is this it? Are we stuck?

"I might have an idea," Joe says, digging into his backpack.

"What are you looking for?"

"The rope. I always have it in my backpack. Just in case."

In case of what? A herd of cattle invade school and you have to round them up?

"I figure if we can find a way to string it across, we have a chance to make it to the other side," Joe explains.

"You are a genius," I say.

"And I thought for sure you'd make fun of me for carrying around a rope."

"Never. No way."

Joe pulls out his World Geography textbook, a bag of snacks, a small tool kit, and finally, a yellow-and-blue coil

of rope. "It would be good if we could fly," he says offhand. "Then we wouldn't have this problem. Here's the rope."

Being able to fly would solve lots of problems, but at least we have a rope. Be grateful for the small things. I stoop down and pick up the textbook. Why Joe thought he'd bring it along to the Land of Dragons is anyone's guess. Maybe he planned to do homework in his downtime. No matter. I hold up the book. "How bad would it be if this got wet?" I ask.

Joe is aghast. "Mr. Williams will freak out if I ruin his book!"

"What if I promise to take the blame? That Mr. Williams can yell at *me*?"

"Oh, well, in that case, I guess it's okay."

"Wow. You barely even had to think about that!"

"I was being honest!"

"Anyway, this is what we're going to do." I point to two boulders on the far shore. They are nestled right next to each other with about three inches of space in between. "If we tie the book to the rope and can wedge the book between the two rocks, we can pull ourselves across."

Joe furrows his brow. "In addition to flying, I wish we could walk a slack line. You know, like a tightrope. And not get wet. Because I'm feeling less excited now about the getting-wet part."

"We will only be in for a minute, maybe even less. And remember those dryer things at Walter's Wild West?" I'm referring to this run-down, but also fun, amusement park right over the mountains from Lewiston, with a bunch of water rides where the goal is to get soaked. Scattered around the exit of the best water ride, Splash Down, are these little cubicles about the size of a small bathroom. Plug in a few quarters and step inside, and it's like a hundred hair dryers are aimed at you all at once. In about three minutes, you are dry and your hair is standing straight up in the air.

"Yeah?" Joe replies skeptically.

"I can make a mini tornado and dry us off on the other side," I explain.

He eyes me. I can't tell what he's thinking. But I do recognize that was one of the weirdest sentences I've ever uttered. "All things considered," he says finally, "I suppose that makes sense."

"Great. Hold the book."

Joe does not approve of my knot-tying, so I end up holding the book and he ends up doing the knots. I will admit they are good knots. I was just going to tie them like a shoelace, which would probably lead to us being swept away down the river. I pull on the rope. Nice and sturdy.

We practice twirling it like a lasso, building up the momentum to carry it across the river. It takes us a few tries—okay, *many* tries—to get the book lodged properly between the two rocks, by which time the book is well and truly ruined. Joe reminds me that I am to take the blame when he tells Mr. Williams he will not be getting his textbook back. I remind him back that I already *know* that. Really, we'd like to continue arguing because that means we can put off plunging into the icy river with the giant waves and pulling ourselves across on a skinny rope attached, just barely, to a soggy old book.

But the truth is, someone has to go first, and that someone is going to be me, and I might as well get on with it. The river is not getting any less angry or any warmer while we stand around arguing.

I cinch my backpack up so it sits on top of my shoulders rather than hanging down my back. It still might act like a giant anchor and drag me down the river, but leaving it here seems just as bad. Besides, Joe is very clear that asking him to part with his backpack is basically like asking him to cut off a finger.

"You are being dramatic," I reply.

"I don't think I am."

"I'm going now."

"Into the river?"

"Yes! Where else?"

"I don't know," he says, wringing his hands, "but I was hoping maybe you'd suddenly come up with another idea of how to get across."

"We don't fly," I remind him.

"I know," he says forlornly.

The rope on our side of the river is tied to a large tree. I tug on it a few times. It's secure. I've double-checked everything. Time to get going. I take a step toward the edge, about five feet above the churning water. The minute I step over, I will plummet into the water. There is no purchase to be had on the muddy, steep banks.

Stop panicking, Cassie! Get it together! It's just a little water!

Yeah, right. I clutch the rope in my left hand and fan my opposite arm out beside me to slow my descent when I hit the water.

"Remember, it's going to be really cold, and you will probably feel like you can't breathe when you hit," Joe offers.

"Thanks," I reply. "That makes it so much better."

You can be brave, Cassie. You can do hard things. You just need to try.

Oh boy. I tighten my grip on the rope and step off into the river.

Chapter 36

INTO THE DRINK

FOR A TERRIFYING FLASH, I cannot tell which way is up. It is as if I stepped off into a blender. I am a human smoothie! The water rushes over me, filling my mouth and nose. My backpack slips down and acts just like a sea anchor. I clutch the rope so hard, my fingers cramp, but I will not let go. I pull on the rope, hard, and break through to the surface, the air instantly freezing the droplets on my eyelashes. So. Cold.

Move, Cassie! Swim!

My limbs are concrete, but I kick hard as I slide my hands along on the rope. The water grabs at my legs, pulling them downriver. It's as if a tractor beam is dragging me in and I'm powerless to stop it. If I were to let go, I'd disappear into the froth in an instant. Twenty feet is not very far, but it might as well be a million miles. My vision narrows as my body slowly goes numb. Kick. Kick. Slide. Slide. I let my legs go limp. Fighting the current is like trying to wrestle a riptide: pointless and exhausting. My breath comes in short, hard gasps.

And right when I think I might not make it, my feet connect with the muddy riverbank on the far side. Clutching the rope, I scramble up the side, slipping and sliding, mud clumping in my hair and smearing on my face.

Solid ground. I'm so grateful, I don't even care that the cold actually hurts. I wave to Joe, beckoning him to come on. "No big deal!" I yell.

I can't see his expression, but if I had to guess, I'd say it was abject fear. Did I look that desperate struggling to get across? "Just hold on tight!" I add. Okay. Maybe that wasn't super helpful. "It will be fine! It's not even that cold!" Now I'm just flat-out lying, because my teeth are chattering aggressively enough that I might bite off my own tongue. Honestly, I would only ever do this for Albert or Joe. I have gone from human smoothie to human Popsicle.

Joe takes a step forward and peers over the edge of

the bank. The rope vibrates in the wind, whistling a high, sharp tune. Slowly, he reaches up and grasps the rope in one hand while cinching his backpack tight. I think about the tractor-beam current and how I struggled, and my mouth goes dry. My heart, already pounding from the exertion and the cold, ratchets up a notch. Joe puts his arm out just like I did and steps forward. But with his eyes squeezed shut, his first step is awkward. His feet skid out on the mud, and he plunges on his butt into the water.

"The rope!" I cry. "Don't let go!"

But being fully submerged with the current pulling at him and the waves swamping him is all too much. He flails with his free arm to make it to the surface. Finally, his face breaks through, and he sucks in a big gulp of air, only to have a wave flatten him. Choking and gasping, he lets go of the rope. The water takes him, tumbling him over and back like he's in a clothes dryer and whipping him away down the river.

Panic. Raw fear closes my throat. Time slows down the way it does sometimes when things are bad or scary. Joe's sneakers pop up through a wave and then disappear again. At a turn in the river, in the direction Joe is headed, is a tree with wide, full branches that begin at its base, just like a Christmas tree. Perched on the bank, it is pitched at a precarious angle toward the water. A hard push and it will fall in.

And once in the water, it will stop Joe from going any farther. But he's moving so fast, I will never get to it in time and probably won't be strong enough to push it over even if I do. My mind races, jumping and leaping from idea to idea, desperation clouding any sense.

And then I think of the tornado jumping from my palm. *Wind!* If I can create a small tornado, I can knock the tree into the water. Joe breaks the surface long enough to scream. My heart pounds in my ears. I hold my hands out, palms up, and I say the words.

"Rain, snow, sleet, hail; clouds, twister, wind; come on, weather, do it right; blow me up a storm tonight." Take down that tree. Hit it hard. Do it *now*.

The mist begins to rise, curling and twisting into a funnel. I can't even see Joe now. I squeeze my eyes shut, imagining the small storm tearing at the tree roots, loosening its grip on the ground, toppling it into the water. Without opening my eyes, I sense the mist moving, taking shape at my command, lashing at the base of the tree.

CRACK! SNAP!

The twister hits the tree with a tremendous wallop.

The trunk snaps. And the tree tumbles into the river just in time to arrest Joe's wild ride in a tangle of branches.

Wow! I did that?

Joe pulls himself up just enough and hangs limp over the top. He looks like a puppy left out in the rain. "Joe!" I race down the riverbank. "Say something! Are you okay?"

He gives me a halfhearted thumbs-up without raising his head. His feet still dangle in the river, and his backpack sags from his shoulders. The tree stretches halfway across the river. Gingerly, I climb down the bank into the thick branches, keeping my feet carefully balanced on the trunk, not too excited to take another dip in the water. When I reach Joe, I grab him under the armpits and drag him forward.

"Ow," he mutters. "That hurts."

"You could get up," I reply.

"I'm busy recovering from almost drowning," he shoots back. At least this confirms that he is okay.

"In that case, stop complaining." I yank harder until I have him at the bank. The silver lining is I'm not cold anymore. Between tornado-making and pulling Joe, I'm sweating buckets.

I nudge Joe close to the muddy incline and give him a shove over the lip. He lands with a grunt, wiggling out of

his backpack and lying flat, arms and legs spread-eagle on the ground.

I crawl up beside him. "Good thing that tree was there," he says, spitting out some river water.

"Yes." I nod. "Good thing." Joe's lips are bluish. "Let's go. Moving will make you warmer."

It's not enthusiastic, but he does get up and trudge after me.

Finding a hidden tunnel entrance when all you have to go on is an image scratched into a cave wall is no easy thing. The forest here is thick and dark, with shady pockets and shadows that make us jump. The trees themselves menace, reaching down and pulling at our hair and clothes. And it feels like we are being watched, as if we should whisper so as not to be overheard. Plus, Joe's near-drowning experience in the raging river has put him in a bad mood. We pause so he can rifle through his backpack for a flashlight. This makes him even madder because everything inside is drenched and at least a little bit ruined.

"My favorite pen!" he cries mournfully, laying it gently on the ground. "My notebook! My hat! The granola bars!"

"The hat will dry," I offer.

"Not helpful, Cassie."

"Sorry."

"At least the flashlight is waterproof," he says with a sigh. "So I've got that going for me, anyway." He flips it on, and the forest brightens. We are in a thicket, the canopy above us so dense, no light filters through. I back up a few steps and a few more so I can get a look at the tree overhead.

It's a perfect umbrella. "Joe! This is the tree. Shine the light at the base!"

The beam illuminates the dark entrance to the tunnels, just like in Albert's drawing. The darkness is ominous and foreboding, but we are going in anyway.

Chapter 37

TUNNELS AND LAIRS

THE GROUND DROPS AWAY at a sharp angle the moment we enter the tunnel system. We are headed deep underground, the walls thick with roots and rocks, the ceiling low, the ground uneven. How did Albert even *fit* in here? It seems physically impossible. I trip over my feet repeatedly, grabbing Joe's backpack to save myself until he admonishes me to be more careful. Jeez. I'll *try*. The tunnel journey is all well and good until we come to a fork in the road.

"Left or right?" Joe asks.

"I have no idea," I reply, panic gripping me. It's not like I have a map. Or a clue. We are in a dark underground tunnel system that may or may not lead to the castle we need to reach. Fabulous.

"Left," Joe says finally. And he sounds confident enough that I don't question him, even though I know he has no idea either. We trudge on, slow and deliberate, hoping for a sign that we have gone the right way. It does not help that strange sounds seem to emanate from the tunnel walls themselves, small squeaks and shrill whistles. But upon inspection, there is nothing there. Whatever creatures are making noise, they are good at disguising themselves.

"Maybe the background noise is just different here," Joe suggests. "You know how we don't hear traffic because we are used to it? Or bugs and stuff?"

"Or they are plotting our demise," I counter.

"Great," Joe mutters. I know. Not helpful. We keep going.

Just when I start to wonder if we will *ever* get out of this maze, light appears in the distance. It shimmers around the edges of a crude hole carved in the wall, covered by a wooden panel.

"Joe." I tug on his sleeve. "I think this must be it. The way to the castle."

He nods, pushing gently on the edges of the panel.

"What's a dragon going to do with a doorknob, anyway?" Joe comments as he leans his shoulder into the wooden panel. It gives just an inch, so we can peer at what lies behind it. The images Albert drew made it seem like the tunnels would put us outside the castle. But from this vantage point, it appears we are already *in* the castle.

It's a sprawling, cavernous space, lit by torches secured high up on the heavy stone walls. Mountains of treasure are piled everywhere. Gold, silver, gems, coins, jewelry, medallions, and shiny objects. I know dragons like bling, but this is *ridiculous*. "Why did they have to take everything from that village when they already have *this*?" I hiss.

"I think they want it *all*," Joe replies.

I push the panel open an inch more. There are no dragons in sight. The coast is clear. "Ready?" I whisper.

Joe's face tells me all I need to know. You can *never* be ready to sneak into the castle of a dragon king with a warehouse full of stolen booty.

But we do it anyway, because that is how we roll.

The inside of the treasure room smells like kale that has been in the vegetable bin of the refrigerator maybe a day too long: a deep, rich, and kind of rotten odor that makes my eyes water. Joe crinkles his nose in disgust. I agree. It's gross. And I'd be happy to let them know they need to freshen it up a little if we were not trespassing on dragon royalty in a major way.

On the far side of the treasure trove is a grand marble archway that leads to a throne room, the place where the king and his court gather to relish their power, count their riches, and compliment one another's awesomeness. Instead of an actual throne, because that is about as useful to a dragon as a doorknob, there are golden platforms that seem to hover midair. The biggest, most elaborately decorated one is positioned at the front and is empty. Before it is a sea of silver and gray dragons gathered around in a circle. I can't see what is happening on the inside of the circle, but a high-pitched wail of agony that I feel deep in my core rises from its center.

Albert.

I freeze. Joe pulls me up the side of the massive room, hidden in the shadows. And now I see the dragon at the center of the circle. He's the largest I have ever seen, with a wingspan like a jet plane and a body like a truck. His silver scales are so bright, they hurt my eyes. But it is his furious roar that makes me tremble. It echoes off the walls, rocking the very ground beneath our feet. The Grays, at his back, hiss and spit as Albert, pinned down beneath

Vayne's heavy clawed foot, flails and howls. Two dragons hold his wings so he cannot escape. This is *not* a fair fight.

"Oh, Cassie!" Joe yelps beside me. "Oh no!"

A feeling washes over me, the familiar sense of helplessness I felt when the police came to tell us that my father was dead. I could do nothing. I could not save him. I could not reverse time. I had no *power*.

But now I *do*. I promised to keep Albert safe, no matter what, and even though we are here in his world, in the Land of Dragons, that is still the truth. The prophecy said a storm would aid the marked dragon on his journey. A storm would shield him from harm and protect him from malevolent forces. And I think the prophecy meant *me*.

Be the storm, Cassie.

But can I possibly create something big and strong enough? I hear Dad's voice, clear as a bell in my mind. *Just try.*

I close my eyes and say the words. Once. Twice. Again. "*Rain, snow, sleet, hail; clouds, twister, wind; come on, weather, do it right; blow me up a storm tonight.*" The mist begins to rise from my hands, swirling and looping.

A twister, I think. At the very least, it will give Albert a chance to break free. The energy in me rises. The funnel grows.

Big. Bad. Strong.

"Cassie, you're doing it!" Joe yells. But I dare not open my eyes. I continue to feed the storm power, focused only on its strength.

Now go, tornado! Go and create chaos!

In my mind, I send the swirling cloud right at Vayne. I open my eyes to see the dragons in attendance begin to scatter, howling and shrieking. The storm swirls violently, lifting some of the dragons clear off their feet. Joe and I are blown backward into the wall, pressed hard into the cold marble.

It is quite a storm. It moves deliberately, cutting a path through the dragons, tossing them aside, heading for Vayne, who continues to hold Albert. It encircles him, twisting and whirling. The dragons holding Albert's wings are swept away, and I wait to see Albert freed.

But he is not. Mighty Vayne doubles down, pressing Albert to the ground so there is no way he can move. Albert's screams reach my ears despite the tornado's noise. My storm is no match for Vayne's strength. It is the biggest, nastiest storm I can conjure, and it is *not* working.

Chapter 38

VAYNE, KING OF THE DRAGONS

I WOULD LIKE TO TAKE a moment and full-out panic. If my worst storm is not enough, then what happens? The problem is panic takes energy and mine is low, having given it all to the storm. And I don't have a plan B.

But Joe does. "Cassie, the storm needs more power. Use *mine*. Take power from me." His words dance around in my head, searching for purchase, for a place to land. Is this possible? Joe doesn't possess golden mist, but can I use his energy anyway? Will I hurt him if I do? Albert's screaming leaves me no choice but to try.

I take Joe's hand in mine. "Let go if you feel bad," I

instruct. He nods in a way that I know he won't do as I've asked. My stomach churns. Everything is on the line here. I close my eyes, I say the words, the mantra, and a moment later, my depleted stores of energy begin to fill. The power meter rises out of the red. Mist appears, thick and stretchy.

Go to the tornado! Make lightning! Stop Vayne!

The mist takes off, lengthening like a snake in the grass, headed for the funnel cloud. Joe, beside me, staggers. I let go of his hand and catch him before he falls. "Joe!"

He gives me a feeble thumbs-up. "Is it working?"

CRACK!

The tornado, raging stronger now, explodes with a burst of hot lightning. The bolt hits Vayne dead center in the chest. And the mighty king collapses to the ground.

Joe and I are frozen in place. Did that just happen? An instant later, Albert bursts through the edge of the tornado and crashes into us. He's alive! I throw my arms around his neck. "Albert!" Joe leans into him, too, as Albert wraps his wings protectively around us. "Are you okay? Did he hurt you?"

In response, he snorts and stomps his foot. I can't tell if he's mad we are here when he told us to stay put or grateful for the rescue. Whatever it is, he is not going to take the time right now to explain. Holding us tight, he launches into the air, cruising just above the ground.

Behind us, it is pandemonium. The gray and silver dragons squawk and growl and yip in horror and dismay. And when I glance back, I see Vayne raising his head, injured but not dead.

I know where we are going. To the dungeons, to get Albert's mother. The tunnels leading there are narrow, but Albert does not slow down. Joe presses his palms to his eyes. I get it. It has been a rough day. To end it by crashing into a wall would be a total drag.

The underground prison cells are cramped and damp, with stone walls and bars made from an unfamiliar metal, probably something resistant to fire. The dungeon is full of beautiful colorful dragons, wings wrapped around themselves, huddled in corners against the chill. Albert releases us with a thud as a Gray guard launches himself in our direction. Joe and I hit the dirt, covering our heads, but this dragon is no match for Albert. Much as he did with Slack, he hisses out a stream of poison that knocks the Gray flat before he can even get off one angry fireball.

"Take that!" Joe cries. I guess he is feeling better. We scramble to our feet to follow Albert, gingerly stepping over the unconscious Gray. Near where the guard was stationed is a control panel. Albert hits the buttons and simultaneously the bars on all the cells rise. For good measure, Albert breathes a plume of fire on the panel, instantly melting it to goo.

The imprisoned dragons begin to tentatively emerge. Some of them start to talk. Soon the dungeon is a cacophony of sound as they all speak at once. Albert doesn't answer any of them but strides to a cell at the end of the row. Once there, he leans down at the open cell and bows his head. A dragon emerges. Imagine a million Christmas tree lights sparkling at once. She takes my breath away. This dazzling Silver wraps Albert in her brilliant wings much in the way he just did with us. Her embrace is so complete, Albert disappears.

"His *mom*," Joe whispers. I nod, a lump in my throat the size of a grapefruit. She's alive and safe and *here*. I sense the rest of the prisoners watching us with curiosity from behind. After a long moment, the Silver spreads her wings, and Albert emerges, a dopey look on his face. He gets the same look on his cat face when I give him treats *and* scratch his ears at the same time. I understand that Albert does not belong to me, but right now that knowledge is a sharp stitch in my side.

The Silver's eyes pass over us and I swear they narrow. And the curiosity that I felt behind us, is it tinged with hostility? Albert must sense this too. He leaves his mother's side and stands in front of us. What follows is a lot of dragon yelling and barking and hissing and howling. My eardrums ache from the noise. And I just know they are debating whether or not Albert should allow them to eat us.

"I hope he explains how we helped," Joe says out of the side of his mouth. We are both too afraid to move an inch.

"Yeah," I reply. "And fast."

It feels like this goes on for a long time, but it is probably only two minutes—a really long two minutes—and in the end, Albert seems to have convinced them that we are not the enemy and that their common enemy, Vayne, is on the defensive. Finally, the Silver waves a wing over the other dragons, silencing them. She says something to Albert, who bows graciously in response and pats us on the head like we are dogs. He really does! But at least the volume has dropped considerably now that our allegiance is no longer in question.

What happens next is the prisoner dragons gather around the Silver. They wait for her to speak, leaning toward her in anticipation. And I realize that *she* is the leader here, not Albert. Is she telling them now that while Vayne is injured they need to make their move? Gather their resources and take back what is rightfully theirs?

Whatever the plan, they better do it fast. A thunderous roar echoes from the tunnels leading to the dungeon. Vayne and his troops have regrouped, and they are coming for us.

Chapter 39

FOX CAUGHT

IT'S THE THUNDEROUS NOISE that wakes Fox. She finds herself in a small cell tucked in a corner of this dark, wet dungeon, with a vague memory of being surrounded by terrifying gray dragons. These are not interdimensional-species-loving dragons who want to be friends. They are something else entirely.

And they wanted something from her, she is quite sure, but her mind is fuzzy. Did they do something to her brain? Quickly, she runs through the details of her life—her name, birthday, favorite food, best-loved song. Relieved she can remember those, she tries to stretch her limbs in the small space and clear her thoughts. What did the dragons *want* from her? They showed her pictures, images like cartoon panels. They made terrible noise, not unlike the noise she hears now, coming from a place somewhere not too far away in this labyrinth. There was wing-flapping and foot-stomping, and she was *terrified*.

But the thing they wanted? Now Fox remembers. They wanted to know *how* she got here. And they wanted to know exactly *where*. Yes. That last part got them agitated. Was it her fault she didn't speak dragon and could not sketch much more than a stick figure? How on earth was she to explain to them about the rip and where it was in the forest when she barely understood these things herself? But she did try, didn't she?

Yes. Fox remembers now. She *did* tell them something. Worse than that, she told them *everything*. She even acted it out, like some twisted game of charades with dragons. Her cheeks flame hot with shame at how quickly she gave up the goods. Had anyone asked if she was the type to share secrets at the first bit of discomfort she would have said, *No way!* But, faced with scary dragons, fear won out, and she told all. Of course, she has no idea if the dragons understood what she was saying. But what if they did? What if she gave them enough that they can find the rip and go *through* it?

What if she just released a horde of angry dragons on her world?

Her job, one that she had dedicated her life to, is all about saving the humans from what they don't know and can't understand, and now she has potentially just gone and created a situation much more epic in scale than anything she has ever dealt with.

Shivering in the damp, Fox wraps her arms around her knees to keep warm. She's tucked into a tight ball when the grim silence is interrupted by a terrible racket. Should she scream for help? Can she somehow escape? She can backtrack to the rip. But even if she can get out of this place and backtrack to the rip, she has no idea how to open it.

Suddenly, Fox is overwhelmed by how much she misses Dana. She should have waited for her partner in Mercy Grove. Why didn't she just wait?

Exhausted and hungry, Fox hangs her head. This is hopeless, and hopeless is not a feeling she is familiar with. It's not fun.

"I wish I could get out of here," Fox whispers to no one.

And just like that, the iron bars on her cell slide up into the ceiling.

Chapter 40

ESCAPE

THE NOISE OF THE ANGRY dragon posse headed toward us crescendos. The escaped dragons and the Silver form a tight line at the mouth of the tunnel down which the enemy comes. But when the Silver gestures for Albert to take his position, he refuses. This leads to another round of howling, clearly laced with heightened emotions. Albert gestures to us, where we stand quaking in our still soggy shoes, multiple times.

"She wants him to stay," I whisper to Joe.

"And he wants to save us," Joe replies. Yes. He's right. The enemy is nearly upon us. With a final deep hiss at the

Silver, Albert scoops us up in his claws and bolts for the tunnel on the opposite side of the dungeon. I see shock in the Silver's eyes. That he would be gone almost as soon as he came is not something she anticipated. But here we are, racing out of the dungeon and leaving them behind.

Eventually, we burst out into a forest, not unlike the one where Joe and I originally went in, but there is no sign of the umbrella tree, so we must be somewhere else. Albert does not rest. He flaps his wings, pushing us skyward, soaring high above everything now. It's dark out and impossible to see where we are headed, but as soon as we land, I know. We are back at the rip.

Albert wastes no time. We are surrounded by golden mist, and the ragged edges of the rip appear, popping and crackling before us. "You aren't coming, are you?" I ask quietly even as I know the answer.

Albert huffs and pulses his wings. He blinks twice. *No.*

I knew this. Not only does he not belong to me; he doesn't belong in my world. While an image of Albert at his mother's side in the palace fills me with pride, it also makes me sad. My sweet, fuzzy kitten will not return to me. But we came to help and we *did*. And now that is done.

The rip grows wide enough for us to step through. I throw my arms around Albert and squeeze him tight, trying to imprint the sound and smell and feel of him before we leave.

When we get back home, we will go back to being boring old middle school students, suffering through bad cafeteria lunches and homework. Eventually, this adventure will seem like a distant dream.

Of course, we might not survive my mother and Miss Asher, so maybe worrying about these things is premature.

In *The Wizard of Oz*, when Dorothy finally makes it home, she is so relieved and happy to be there. While she enjoyed parts of her adventure, mostly she just wanted to leave. I don't feel quite so excited. Will my powers fade? Will my ability to create weather disappear? Will I ever see Albert again?

"Cassie," Joe says gently. "It's time to go."

He's right. Mercy Grove is visible on the other side. The rip stretches and elongates, and soon it will destabilize. Joe and I clasp hands. "Goodbye, Albert," I say, barely able to make the words come out.

But Albert is not looking at us, about to step through the rip and out of his dimension. His gaze is fixed on the sky above and on the Grays rapidly descending on our position. Joe is through the rip, I am posed on the lip, and Albert is under attack.

The rip crackles. Joe yanks me so my feet are planted firmly back on the soil of Mercy Grove. The rip is collapsing. Soon I will be on one side and Albert will be on the other, surrounded by a swarm of dragons who intend him harm. He does not want to be back on our side. He has a battle to fight in the Land of Dragons. But he's of no use if he's dead.

I make the choice. Leaping back through the shrinking rip, I throw myself between Albert and the Grays, creating enough confusion that I can shove Albert toward Joe and safety. It takes all my strength. Albert bellows. The Grays flail. Albert reaches back toward me with a sharp claw. It sinks into my flesh as he hauls me toward him. My skin burns as the rip closes around me.

As I fall to the ground on our side, I smell singed hair and burned fabric. Joe is screaming. I want to ask if Albert is okay, but my lips won't move. And *oh*, everything hurts. Everything hurts a lot. There is something wrong with my vision, too. It's wavy and out of focus. I hope my mom knows I love her. And Miss Asher. I start to have the sense I won't see them again. Does Joe know he's my best friend? Have I told him that enough?

And Albert. How I love Albert. How lucky I am that I found him. My wish for the world is that everyone gets to love something as much as I love Albert. My breathing echoes raspy and uneven in my ears. Joe is crying. I don't think I've ever seen him cry.

And there is Albert, hovering above me. There's dampness on my skin. But it feels foreign, as if water is pouring over my body.

Not water. Blood. *Albert's blood.*

I feel funny, like everything is tingling. It smells funny too, earthy, like freshly cut grass. My senses are overwhelmed. There is too much happening, and none of it makes sense. I see myself flying across the sky. But I am not me, not exactly.

The blackness expands like spilled oil and everything goes dark.

Chapter 41

DANA ENCOUNTERS THE UNEXPECTED

IN THE CAR on the way to Mercy Grove, Dana plays the music as loud as it will go. It keeps her awake. She calls Fox a few times, but her partner doesn't pick up. The service up here is terrible. That is probably the reason.

The road is curvy, and it takes a long time to get there. Fox's car is in the parking lot for the Mercy Grove hiking trail. At least they didn't miss each other. After changing into proper footwear and a better coat, Dana makes good time down the trail. Maybe Fox somehow already caught the dragon and they can go home. Dana is a little tired of the rain.

She is wondering how this case will ultimately wrap up when the forest quiet is disrupted by a thunderous roar, as if she is suddenly standing beneath a raging waterfall. The ground vibrates with it.

What is happening? There are no animals here that can make this sort of sound, no cars or trucks or airplanes or people or anything. She picks up her pace, instinctively running toward the uproar, her palms instantly sweaty.

There is an elbow-shaped bend in the trail, around which the circle of trees that comprise the grove come into view. As Dana makes the turn, she is met with a sight she doesn't quite understand. Enormous gray dragons, a dozen of them at least, stream through a sizzling, sparking hole in the fabric of reality. Their wings beat aggressively, and it sounds like an orchestra where the musicians all play random notes. Plumes of fire burst forth from their mouths, torching the ancient trees and setting them ablaze. They race skyward, red eyes scanning the surroundings, a small army of furious dragons headed north over a million acres of forest.

Stunned, Dana ducks out of view. Her knees shake. Everything has gone horribly sideways. *Where* is Fox? As she watches the dragons darken the sky above, all she can think is, *They're here.*

Chapter 42

HOME

I OPEN MY EYES to see Mom, Joe, and Miss Asher standing around me. Even Slack is bedside, eyebrows anxiously knitted together. They loom in a way that makes me think they have reason for concern. I blink a few times, waiting for the terrible pain of the burns to hit me. But it doesn't. I wiggle my toes. All good. I clench my hands into fists. That seems to work okay too, even if my skin feels tight across my bones.

"What happened?" I croak. "Where's Albert?"

Joe, cheeks still stained with tears, grins at me and points. Albert, it turns out, is tucked into my armpit, sleeping soundly. I pull him in tighter and wait for them to answer my first question. Clearly, I'm in my bedroom. I'm alive and not injured. But I don't remember anything beyond Albert's blood on me. Mom pushes my hair back off my forehead, just like when I'm sick. And yet, I feel . . . really *good*. Strong.

"It worked," Joe says with a touch of awe. He describes how my burned skin seemed to absorb Albert's blood like a sponge and regenerate. "You said it itched. And stung."

"I did?" I ask. "I don't remember that part."

"That's how I knew you would be okay," Joe explains. "You got stuck between dimensions when the rip closed. But Albert saved you. You know, with his blood. Really gross, but, man, it *works*. You look normal. Or as normal as you can look, anyway."

"Not funny," I reply.

"Sorta funny," Joe says.

"Did I . . . hurt Albert?" I ask quietly.

Miss Asher takes my hand. "Albert is fine," she says. "Very tired, like after an illness, but he will be okay."

Something in my chest releases. I don't ever want to leave these people. I love them all so much. Slack is even growing on me, with his arm loosely draped over Miss Asher's shoulders, giving her support and comfort. Tears leak from the corners of my eyes.

"It's okay, Cassie," Mom whispers. "You need to rest. Let's go. All of us, out." She very efficiently herds everyone out of my room, but thirty seconds later, Joe tiptoes back in.

"She'll figure out I'm back here soon enough," he whispers, sitting gingerly on the edge of my bed.

"What happens now?" I ask. And what I mean is, on the other side of the rip, the Silver is free. Is she gathering her resources, figuring out a way to end Vayne's rule for good? And what about Albert? Will he go back? I stare at my skin. There is no sign that Albert used his blood to save me. I have soaked it all up.

"I don't know," Joe says. "But we are definitely in trouble. On account of going to the Land of Dragons without telling anyone, in the middle of the night, and you almost dying and stuff. They are just waiting until you are better to tell you. It would be more convenient if interdimensional travel had some impact on time. If it acted like time does over the event horizon of a black hole, you know, not passing so we came back exactly to the moment when we left. Kind of like flying from Hong Kong to San Francisco, arriving before you left. You get to do the day over again. Then we wouldn't be in trouble. Or we'd be in less trouble? I don't know."

"But I *am* better," I point out. I actually feel like I could do the running pacers for PE class without even getting winded. I feel like I could *crush* them. It is very weird. "I feel fine." An understatement if ever there was one.

Joe shrugs. "I don't think it matters. We are still in trouble."

"Were you scared?" I ask quietly.

"Yeah," Joe says, casting his gaze beyond me. "But I think it means I can be brave even when I have only myself to rely on. It was good Albert's blood started working right away because I was not sure how *long* I could be brave without you. If you know what I mean."

I nod. Yes. "Is Albert really okay?"

Joe tilts his head, lost in thought. He doesn't know how much to tell me, and that tells me enough. Albert was in danger because he saved me. I squeeze him gently, not wanting to disturb his restorative sleep.

I love you, Albert. And I would do it all again. Exactly the same.

But, in response, there is nothing but silence.

Chapter 43

THE UNEXPECTED

I AM GROUNDED for life. My mother says I may petition for release sometime in my twenties, but she doesn't guarantee the outcome. I can see in her eyes how terrified she was by what happened, and I can't seem to explain that I didn't do it *to* her. It was only about Albert.

On day two of confinement, I wake up to find my pillow singed and new burn marks on the carpet. "Albert," I reprimand. "You have to get control of that. Mom is mad enough at me already. Torching my room will not win me my freedom."

Worse, I've finished all the books in the house and must figure out a way to secure a quick trip to the library before my brain turns to mush. I will become a puddle of despair. I will go bananas. How can Mom say no to *reading*? Albert sits on my lap, watching me curiously.

"What do you think, Albert?" I ask. "If Mom doesn't let me go to the library, I can always just carry the house there on a tornado, right? Drop it into the parking lot, dash in for a book, and tornado the house home again." I glance down at my palms. The golden residue remains, so maybe that really is an option. Albert's whiskers twitch, and his tail swishes back and forth, sweeping across my comforter. He seems recovered from saving me and back to normal Albert. As for me, I keep feeling . . . well . . . *stronger*. And the sensation grows with each passing hour.

For example, the idea that I could just up and fly off to the library is not that weird. Like flying around the sky might not be so *hard*. I want to talk to Joe about these new feelings and try to untangle them, but he can't leave the house either, so it's down to carrier pigeons or smoke signals. If I'm stuck in this house for much longer, I will definitely consider the smoke signals.

Albert stretches across my lap. I rub the smooth spot on his nose. He purrs, kneading my leg with his sharp little claws. I have yet to ask him about when he will go back. I know he won't stay much longer, now that he is feeling strong again, but if I put off asking, I can pretend that he might. I can't imagine being here without him. It's just too terrible.

"I wish you'd stay forever, Albert," I whisper, nuzzling my face into his fur.

Cassie, I will show you something?

I pick my head up. What was that? I remember those words. It is exactly what Alvina said before she showed me the scene of Albert coming through the rip and ending up in the dumpster.

"Albert? Was that you?"

He cocks his head to the left, eyes focused on me. A small shiver runs down my spine. But why it does, I can't say. My pulse quickens. I bring Albert up to eye level. If he can show me things like Alvina did, I have a million questions I want to ask! I want to understand about his mother. Is she the benevolent ruler the prophecy predicted? What happens when he goes back? Will he be okay? Will I ever see him again? Are there other dragons hiding here in this dimension as cats? Can they go home now, or is it too late, like Alvina?

Oh boy. *SNAP!* Here it comes, that wave of motion sickness, like I might barf on my shoes. My vision goes wavy and my stomach rolls over. The room disappears, just like it did with Alvina in Midhurst. We are back in the forest at the edge of a crystal-clear lake. I know we are in the Land of Dragons because a dinner plate–sized butterfly flits by my nose and the trees sparkle in a way that just does not happen on our side. Albert is with me, in full dragon form. Smoke leaks from his nostrils, and his wings pulse up and down. The golden blaze on his chest glows as if it is infused with glitter. But I realize that no matter what, his eyes are always pure Albert, the essence of him. He can show up in different packaging, but who he *is* remains absolute. My friend. My protector. My cat-dragon. And I love him forever and ever.

This does not make him any more patient, however. He paws the ground and thumps his tail, shoving me toward the water. "Slow down!" I holler. "Is this really the time for swimming?"

But he does not want to go swimming. No. He wants to show me something, my reflection in the water. And when I look down, I see something I don't expect, something I could *never* expect, not in a million lifetimes. Two dragons look back.

Two dragons. And one of them is *me*.

Acknowledgments

I started writing children's books when my kids were little, and I spent hours and hours reading with them. I would dream of Gruffalos and llamas in red pajamas. Eventually, we moved on to thrilling adventure stories that I couldn't get out of my head. One day, I sat down and wrote one. It was not planned. I didn't know what I was doing. Most days, I still don't.

That first middle grade book, Mrs. Smith's Spy School for Girls, was dedicated to Max and Katie. They have changed so much since then, as has the world. The challenges of the future are significant. I decided to dedicate Land of Dragons to them as well, to bookend to my time spent in this space but also to remind my children, and young people everywhere, you can do amazing things. You have the power to change the world. And when the going gets tough, remember I am here on the sidelines, cheering for you all the way.

Happy reading, friends.